Symbol	*Meaning*	*Section*
$\gamma_{\bar{\sigma}}$	list search greater	1.5
$\bar{\gamma}$	list search less	1.5
γ_{σ}	list search less or equal	1.5
δ_J	rearrangement operator	10.5
Δ_J	rearrangement operator class	B.5
λ	least	1.4
λ_2	lesser	1.4
Λ	circular permutation operator	10.3
Λ	null set	1.3
μ	greatest	1.4
μ	interchange operator	B.7
μ_2	greater	1.4
ν	number of entries in list	1.2
π	assignment permutation operator	10.4
ρ	retard	4.6
σ	list search equal	1.5
Σ	stage operator	10.3
ϕ_i	fence number	4.4
Φ_i	fence item	4.4
χ	exchange	1.4
ω	address calculator	6.1
$\lceil \quad \rceil$	search partition, upper	1.5
$\lfloor \quad \rfloor$	search partition, lower	1.5
$[\quad]$	integral	4.3
[a]	location of	1.1
$\rightarrow$	is placed in	1.1
$\prec$	precedes	1.1
$\smile$	is strung on to	1.1
$<$	less than	1.2
$\leq$	less than or equal to	1.2
$>$	greater than	1.2
$\geq$	greater than or equal to	1.2
$=$	equal to	1.2
$\neq$	unequal to	1.2
$(\quad)$	contents of	1.1
$\subset$	included in	1.3
$\cap$	intersection	1.3
$\cup$	union	1.3
&	and	1.3
$\vee$	or (inclusive)	1.3
$\supset$	implies	1.2
$\rightarrow$	new value of	1.3
$\longrightarrow$	transfer	1.4
$\in$	element of	1.3

Computer Sorting

PRENTICE-HALL INTERNATIONAL, INC., *London*
PRENTICE-HALL OF AUSTRALIA, PTY. LTD., *Sydney*
PRENTICE-HALL OF CANADA, LTD., *Toronto*
PRENTICE-HALL OF INDIA PRIVATE LTD., *New Delhi*
PRENTICE-HALL OF JAPAN, INC., *Tokyo*

Computer Sorting

IVAN FLORES

Computer Consultant

Professor of Statistics
Bernard Baruch School of Business
City College of New York

PRENTICE-HALL, INC., Englewood Cliffs, N. J.

Current printing (last digit):

10 9 8 7 6 5 4 3 2

Library of Congress Catalog Card Number 69-14804

Printed in the United States of America

PREFACE

The importance of sorting is well known. It has a great many applications:

- commercial problems
- compiler and assembler design
- scientific problems
- operating systems
- list processing

This book offers an extensive explanation and analysis of all popular sorting techniques, including those

- confined to internal memory
- using magnetic tapes
- with disk or drum auxiliary memories

The text is aimed at the student of computer science who has acquired a basic knowledge of programming such as that offered by *Computer Programming*.† He should also have some facility with symbol manipulation, although specific mathematical knowledge is not required. The book is provided as a text for curricula in computer science, engineering, or mathematics at the senior or graduate level. It is also suitable for computer engineers, problem programmers, or systems programmers.

Sorting involves extensive list manipulation. A language like LISP or IPL-V might suffice. But the complication involved in learning it might deter the reader. Instead, a notation especially expressive of sort operations is developed in Chapter 1. Introduced during the exposition about list manipulations, it is easily absorbed; its meaning and relation to those operations is immediately apparent.

Chapter 2 provides a bridge between the notation and assembly languages used: FLAP (very much like FAP) and 360AL. This is the basis for later quantitative contrast of different sort techniques.

† Ivan Flores, *Computer Programming* (Englewood Cliffs, N.J.: Prentice-Hall, Inc., 1966).

In Chapter 3 we examine sort by selection and counting. Search techniques are presented in Chapter 4. Sublist sorting in Chapter 5 includes quadratic and tournament sorts.

Address calculation, a specialized sort, is scrutinized in Chapter 6.

Merging can be done with only two or with several lists. The alternatives are analyzed in Chapter 7.

Replacement sorting makes longer initial sorted strings, using a fixed length sorting area. This is examined in Chapter 8 and applied to two earlier methods.

Tape sorts are introduced in Chapter 9. The polyphase sort is detailed in Chapter 10. A thorough contrast of tape sorts is presented in Chapter 11. Disk and drum problems are touched on in Chapter 12.

Chapter 13 translates some of the FLAP programs into 360AL, showing the simplicity of the process.

I. F.

CONTENTS

Computer Sorting

1 LISTS, THEORETICAL CONSIDERATIONS

1.1 NOTATION

Introduction

This book draws heavily on programming principles established previously in my earlier book, *Computer Programming*. The approach here, however, is to develop a universal notation for sorting problems. It appears to be a simple matter to translate from this notation to almost any assembly language and certainly to any procedure-oriented language such as FORTRAN or ALGOL.

It is possible to write sorting procedures in a procedure-oriented language.† However, the most efficient sorting programs are not generated by compilation. Since sorting routines are used so frequently for EDP problems, it is better to write them in an assembly language. Translation from operational notation to assembly language is demonstrated with both FLAP and and IBM 360 Basic Assembly Language (BAL) examples.

Importance

We are concerned with the manipulation of complex strings of information. To place them in order, these strings go through many gyrations. It is easier to keep track of what happens to such packages when we specifically devise a notation to do so.

†See my sorting algorithms published in *Comm. ACM* for January, 1962, Vol. 5, No. 1, pp. 48–50.

Units

As explained in *Computer Programming*, information can be manipulated in packages which are either machine- or use-oriented. The words we use for machine-oriented data division, going from the smallest to the largest, are: **bit, word, block, reel.**

Use-directed data division presented in the same format comprises: **character, field, record, file.**

Logical symbols

Frequently we will state conditions that prevail in a given problem using the logical connectives AND, OR, and IMPLIES. For these we use, respectively: &, V, $\supset$.

Cell versus content

We shall carefully distinguish between a memory or a machine cell and its contents. A **cell** is where a piece of information is stored. For word-oriented machines, a memory cell contains a single word. However, a record may consist of several words and is contained in a cell. The **cell label** or **name** applies to the series of words which comprise the complete record. Since the technique for manipulation of information is fairly independent of whether that information consists of one or several words, a single label suffices. Thus A is a symbolic name for an address of a cell or set of cells.

CELL LOCATION

A given machine might use a set of digits or a combination of digits and letters to distinguish a cell. It is my policy to use a single capital letter (which may be subscripted) to name a cell, a series of words where a record is found. Thus A, B, etc. represent cells.

DATA

The data to be manipulated can be completely alphabetic information such as "HARRY," or numeric such as "037 . . . 81," or mixed, called **alphanumeric.** The computer manipulates these as bit sets regardless; it may use, for instance, "00110 . . . 01." Information is replaced or named in our discussion by a single lowercase symbol such as a, b, c, etc.

An item is a record, or fraction thereof, or a substitue therefor. It occupies a cell, too.

Transformation

CONTENTS

We distinguish the contents of a cell by placing parentheses about a cell label. To make an equivalence between an item and the contents of a cell, we use an equals sign. Thus

$$(\mathrm{A}) = \mathrm{a} \tag{1.1.1}$$

conveys that *A* contains a datum previously labelled *a*.

LOCATION

Square brackets indicate the location where an item is stored. Thus

$$[\mathrm{a}] = \mathrm{A} \tag{1.1.2}$$

indicates that *a* is stored at the location *A*.

TRANSFER

To move informtation from one place to another, we use the single arrow. We place an item *a* in the location *B* thus

$$\mathrm{a} \longrightarrow \mathrm{B} \tag{1.1.3}$$

and then we have

$$(\mathrm{B}) = \mathrm{a} \tag{1.1.4}$$

To place *a* at the cell previously occupied by *b*, we note

$$\mathrm{a} \longrightarrow [\mathrm{b}] \tag{1.1.5}$$

Class notation

In defining operators and notations of various sorts, we use class notation. **Operators** operate on or modify class members. A **unary** operator works on only one class. The **binary** operator, such as the arrow, operates on two classes, items and cells. We redefine the three operators defined in (1.1.1), (1.1.2), and (1.1.3) in class terms below,

$$(\text{cell}) = \text{item} \tag{1.1.6}$$

$$[\text{item}] = \text{cell} \tag{1.1.7}$$

$$\text{item} \longrightarrow \text{cell} \tag{1.1.8}$$

In these definitions, class names were substituted for the class members for which the relation may hold.

Cell

Cell as used here may contain one or several words of memory in the word-oriented machine, or one or many characters of memory in the character-oriented machine. We shall deal with lists of cell names. To indicate that one cell address or set of cell addresses **precedes** another in memory (the former address is *smaller* than the latter), we use an order relation which prevails for the cell labels. The precedence notation introduced in Chapter 2 of *Computer Programming* is used. In class notation,

$$\text{cell} \prec \text{cell} \tag{1.1.9}$$

To state that cell A precedes B (or $[a]$ precedes $[b]$) we say

$$\mathrm{A} \prec \mathrm{B} \qquad (\text{or } [\mathrm{a}] \prec [\mathrm{b}]) \tag{1.1.10}$$

This statement is the same as saying that B follows A. If (1.1.10) holds, then we may write,

$$\mathrm{B} \succ \mathrm{A} \tag{1.1.11}$$

which defines the **follow** operator, $\succ$. The precedence relation is not reflexive nor symmetrical, but it is transitive: A may not precede itself; if A precedes B, B may not precede A; if A precedes B and B precedes C, then A precedes C.

Items

A cell holds just one item; the item contains several fields. One of these fields is an identifier or key indicated by the subscript K. Thus the key field of record a is indicated a_K. Many other fields may exist in the item. We might refer to all data fields (excluding the key) simply as a_D.

Then the entire item a consists of stringing out the key field a_K and the data field a_D, indicated by the **concatenating operator,** a little saucer. We have

$$\mathrm{a} = \mathrm{a_K} \smile \mathrm{a_D} \tag{1.1.12}$$

Order

There is an order relation imposed upon the keys to permit us to sort our list. When we relate the keys by this ordering relation, we usually drop the subscript K. The following relations are defined elsewhere in mathematics for real, integral or natural numbers:

$$< \quad \leq \quad = \quad \geq \quad > \quad \neq \quad \cup \quad \cap$$

The rules for manipulating these relations and their characteristics are familiar to the reader. For sorting it is the key which determines the order relation. Hence we have

$$a < b \equiv a_K < b_K \tag{1.1.13}$$

where $\equiv$ means "is the same as." An *item* is said to be greater than another if its key is greater than that of the other.

1.2 LISTS

Cell lists

All lists are written in boldface type. Cell name lists are in uppercase boldface type. Cells in the cell list are text type of the same character but subscripted. Hence a list **A**, consisting of cells A_1, A_2, etc., is indicated thus:

$$\mathbf{A} = A_1, A_2, \ldots, A_n \tag{1.2.1}$$

Notice that to enumerate the cells in the cell list we have to know the number of cells, n, in the list. To determine the number of cells in the cell list, we apply the number operator, ν. Operators (introduced a little later) generally are Greek letters with some mnemonic quality. For the number operator, we use ν (pronounced "noo," which sounds a little like our n, and so suggests the word "number"). Above we have

$$\nu\,\mathbf{A} = n \tag{1.2.2}$$

and, in general,

$$\nu \text{ list} = \text{number} \tag{1.2.3}$$

Precedence

In general, the names in a cell list name have the precedence relation indicated by the symbol subscripts, so that A_1 precedes A_2 and so forth, indicated as

$$\mathbf{A}:\quad A_1 \prec A_2 \prec \cdots \prec A_n \tag{1.2.4}$$

Another way to write this is

$$A_i \prec A_j \supset i \prec j \tag{1.2.5}$$

In other words, the addresses for which the symbols A_1, A_2, etc., stand are in the same order as the symbol subscripts.

Item lists

Item names are written in lowercase letters and **a** is a list of items; we have

$$\mathbf{a} \equiv a_1, a_2, \ldots, a_n \tag{1.2.6}$$

The number operator, as you might expect, can be applied to an item list to determine its number,

$$\nu \mathbf{a} = \mathrm{n} \tag{1.2.7}$$

Whereas the precedence relation applies to all cell lists, we cannot say anything about the order relation with regard to the item list. In fact, it would be restrictive if we expected an item list to be ordered. Further, although the precedence relation applies to the cell list, the order relation does not apply to their contents, except in sorted lists.

Sorted lists

An item list is said to be sorted if the same order relation applies to any two adjacent members of the list. To indicate that a list is ordered, we place a small *o* at the upper left hand corner of the list symbol. We have as an example of a sorted list

$$^{o}\mathbf{a}\colon \quad \mathrm{a}_1 \leq \mathrm{a}_2 \leq \cdots \leq \mathrm{a}_n \tag{1.2.8}$$

We say that a cell name list **A** is sorted in ascending order if the item list composed of the contents of each cell is in ascending order thus:

$$\mathrm{A}_i \prec \mathrm{A}_j \supset (\mathrm{A}_i) \leq (\mathrm{A}_j) \tag{1.2.9}$$

and that it is sorted in descending order if

$$\mathrm{A}_i \prec \mathrm{A}_j \supset (\mathrm{A}_i) \geq (\mathrm{A}_j) \tag{1.2.10}$$

1.3 MEMBERSHIP, INCLUSION

Membership

Inclusion for a cell list is indicated as

$$\mathrm{A}_i \in \mathbf{A} \tag{1.3.1}$$

An item is included in an item list thus:

$$\mathrm{a}_i \in \mathbf{a} \tag{1.3.2}$$

In general, we have

$$\text{member} \in \text{class} \tag{1.3.3}$$

With bracket and parenthesis notation, we can indicate cross membership. For instance, to show that an item is stored in one cell of a list, we write

$$[\mathrm{a}_i] \in \mathbf{A} \tag{1.3.4}$$

Similarly, to show that a cell contains an item of a known item list, we write

$$(A_i) \in \mathbf{a} \tag{1.3.5}$$

List identity

To indicate that the item list formed by taking the contents of the cells on a given cell list, and making a list out of them, is identical to a given item list, we write

$$(\mathbf{A}) = \mathbf{a} \supset (A_i) = a_i \tag{1.3.6}$$

Similarly, to indicate that the list formed by the set of locations where a given item list is stored is identical to a given cell list, we write

$$[\mathbf{a}] = \mathbf{A} \supset [A_i] = A_i \tag{1.3.7}$$

Sublists, complements

The **sublist** of a given list is formed by applying a left superscript to the list label thus:

$${}^1\mathbf{A} \text{ is a sublist of } \mathbf{A}$$

The **inclusion relation,** $\subset$, indicates that the sublist is contained in the main list. The precedence relation applies to both the main list and the sublist, so that we have

$$\begin{aligned} {}^1\mathbf{A} \subset \mathbf{A} \;\&\; {}^1A_i, {}^1A_j \in {}^1\mathbf{A} \;\&\; A_{k_i}, A_{k_j} \in \mathbf{A} \\ \&\; {}^1A_i = A_{k_i} \;\&\; {}^1A_j = A_{k_j} \;\&\; A_i \prec A_j \supset A_{k_i} \prec A_{k_j} \end{aligned} \tag{1.3.8}$$

Here the right subscript indicates the element of a list whether in the list or the sublist. Thus

$${}^1A_j \text{ is the } j\text{th element of the first sublist of } \mathbf{A}.$$

The statement of (1.3.8) says that two elements of a sublist, ${}^1\mathbf{A}$, of **A** have correspondents in **A** and that the precedence of the elements in the sublist is identical with the precedence of the elements in the main list.

The **complement** of a sublist is always with respect to the original list which contains it, and it is formed by deletion of all of the sublist members from the main list. The complement list is indicated by a right superscript *c*. We have then

$${}^1\mathbf{A} \subset \mathbf{A} \supset {}^1\mathbf{A}^c \subset \mathbf{A} \;\&\; {}^1\mathbf{A}^c \cup {}^1\mathbf{A} = \mathbf{A} \;\&\; {}^1\mathbf{A}^c \cap {}^1\mathbf{A} = \Lambda \tag{1.3.9}$$

This says that the **union** (indicated by $\cup$) of a sublist and its complement is the original list, and that a sublist and its complement share no elements —that the **intersection** (indicated by $\cap$) of a sublist and its complement is the **null** set, Λ (the set which has no members).

ITEM LISTS

The sublist of an item list is indicated by a left-hand superscript as in the case of the cell sublist, and we have

$$ {}^{1}\mathbf{a} \subset \mathbf{a} \tag{1.3.10}$$

The complement of a sublist is defined in a natural manner thus:

$$ {}^{1}\mathbf{a} \cup {}^{1}\mathbf{a}^{c} = \mathbf{a}; \qquad \text{we have} \quad {}^{1}\mathbf{a} \cap {}^{1}\mathbf{a}^{c} = \Lambda \tag{1.3.11}$$

List change

A cell name list might be expected to remain constant throughout the exposition; the contents of these locations may change between operations so that, after a chain of operations, the contents of the cells in the list may change completely. To record the time-varying aspect of a cell name list, we vary the left subscript. Thus we may have,

$$ {}_{1}\mathbf{A} \neq {}_{2}\mathbf{A}; \qquad ({}_{1}\mathbf{A}) \neq ({}_{2}\mathbf{A}) \tag{1.3.12}$$

which says that, although the cell lists are the same, the lists of items derived from the cell lists are not the same.

This notation is continued to sublists. We have for the jth sublist at time i the following relation,

$$ {}^{j}_{i}\mathbf{A} \cup {}^{j}_{i}\mathbf{A}^{c} = {}_{i}\mathbf{A}; \qquad {}^{j}_{i}\mathbf{A} \cap {}^{j}_{i}\mathbf{A}^{c} = \Lambda \tag{1.3.13}$$

Index advance

Since we will be dealing with a lot of subscripts, we need some mechanism for setting and advancing the subscripts. We use the same single arrow to indicate information which alters or sets a subscript. To set index i to 1 and index j to 3, we use

$$ 1 \longrightarrow \mathrm{i}; \qquad 3 \longrightarrow \mathrm{j} \tag{1.3.14}$$

To advance an index, we add 1 to its contents. However, parentheses are omitted since no confusion should arise,

$$ \mathrm{i} + 1 \longrightarrow \mathrm{i} \tag{1.3.15}$$

Similarly, to retreat an index, we have

$$ \mathrm{j} - 1 \longrightarrow \mathrm{j} \tag{1.3.16}$$

Of course we can dream up all kinds of functions with the indexes or subscripts which will be obvious to the reader, such as

$$ \mathrm{i} + 3 - \mathrm{j} \longrightarrow \mathrm{i} \tag{1.3.17}$$

1.4 OPERATIONS

We introduce in this section a number of operators. A list of operators with their meanings and class notations is found in Appendix A.

We have discussed class notation; in the *text* the class name is italicized. Thus it was noted earlier that the transfer operator is defined as

$$\text{item} \longrightarrow \text{cell} \tag{1.4.1}$$

We can refer to either *item* or *cell* as shown in this very sentence.

List transfer

A **list transfer** takes the form

$$\text{item list} \longrightarrow \text{cell list} \tag{1.4.2}$$

where *item list* and *cell list* must be of identically the same size. Otherwise, we would not know into which cell each item goes. If the lists are evenly matched, then we know that the first item goes into the first cell, the second item into the second cell, and so forth. We have these three possibilities:

$$\mathbf{b} \longrightarrow \mathbf{A}; \qquad \nu\,\mathbf{b} = \nu\,\mathbf{A} \tag{1.4.3}$$

$$(\mathbf{B}) \longrightarrow \mathbf{A}; \qquad \nu\,\mathrm{B} = \nu\,\mathbf{A} \tag{1.4.4}$$

$$\mathbf{b} \longrightarrow [\mathbf{a}]; \qquad \nu\,\mathbf{b} = \nu\,\mathbf{a} \tag{1.4.5}$$

In (1.4.5), when we move the contents of item list **b** to where **a** was stored, **a** is of course destroyed.

Advance

The **advance operator, $\boldsymbol{\alpha}$,** moves the contents of a cell to the cell which follows it.

$$\alpha\ \text{cell} \tag{1.4.6}$$

To advance cell *A* we have

$$\alpha\,\mathrm{A}\colon\ \ (\mathrm{A}) \longrightarrow \mathrm{A} + 1 \tag{1.4.7}$$

What is at $A + 1$ is destroyed, of course.

Advancing an item again destroys the contents of the next cell. We present an item advance as

$$\alpha\,\mathrm{a}\colon\ \ \mathrm{a} \longrightarrow [\mathrm{a}] + 1 \tag{1.4.8}$$

ADVANCE LIST

A list is advanced by moving the contents of each cell to the one directly ahead of it. Of course, to make the process nondestructive, we move the *last* cell contents first to the one which follows it. We have

$$\alpha\,\mathbf{A}:\quad (A_i) \longrightarrow A_i + 1, \qquad \text{all } A_i \in \mathbf{A} \tag{1.4.9}$$

We can advance an item list similarly,

$$\alpha\,\mathbf{a}:\quad a_i \longrightarrow [a_i] + 1, \qquad \text{all } a_i \in \mathbf{a} \tag{1.4.10}$$

Exchange

An exchange of the contents of two cells must be done without destroying the contents of either cell. Usually this requires an intermediate storage location. We provide the **exchange operator** with

$$\text{cell}\ \chi\ \text{cell} \tag{1.4.11}$$

We define the exchange of two cells thus

$$A\ \chi\ B:\quad (A) \longrightarrow B; \qquad (B) \longrightarrow A \tag{1.4.12}$$

We may interchange two items thus

$$a\ \chi\ b:\quad a \longrightarrow [b]; \qquad b \longrightarrow [a] \tag{1.4.13}$$

Minimum operator

The minimum operator chooses the least from a list of items. First let us examine the **binary minimum operator, $\boldsymbol{\lambda_2}$.**

We have

$$\lambda_2\ \text{item, item} \tag{1.4.14}$$

This operator selects the minimum of the *two* items. Thus we have

$$\lambda_2\ a, b = \min\{a, b\} \tag{1.4.15}$$

The **minimum operator, $\boldsymbol{\lambda}$,** operates on a list, selecting the minimum of that list,

$$\lambda\ \text{list} = \text{item} \tag{1.4.16}$$

We have

$$\lambda\,\mathbf{a} = \min\{a_i\}, \qquad \text{all } a_i \in \mathbf{a} \tag{1.4.17}$$

It is possible to present all the items to which the operator applies directly in the notation, so that we have

$$\lambda\ a, b, c, d, \ldots, h = \min\{a, b, c, d, \ldots, h\} \tag{1.4.18}$$

The λ operator may be interpreted in terms of the binary operator λ_2. Thus

$$\mathbf{a} = \lambda_2 (\lambda_2 (\lambda_2 (\cdots \lambda_2 (a_1 a_2) \cdots a_{n-2}) a_{n-1}) a_n) \tag{1.4.19}$$

This is useful for programming because most machines do only binary comparisons.

CELL LIST

To find the minimum of the contents of a list of cells, and to keep our results in a form similar to the original lists, we require that the result is a cell location. Hence we have

$$\lambda\, \mathbf{A} = [\lambda\, (A)] = [\min \{(A_1)(A_2) \cdots (A_n)\}] \tag{1.4.20}$$

MAXIMUM OPERATOR

We define a maximum operator, μ, and a binary maximum operator, μ_2, in a similar fashion. We have

$$\mu_2\, a, b = \max \{a, b\} \tag{1.4.21}$$

$$\mu\, \mathbf{a} = \max \{a_i\} \tag{1.4.22}$$

and we have

$$\mu\, \mathbf{A} = [\mu\, (A)] \tag{1.4.23}$$

Logical operations

It is useful at times to provide for certain operations to occur only if a give relation holds. To indicate this, we place the relation within parentheses and assign the value 1 if the relation is **true**; we give this function the value 0 if the relation is **false**. Examples of this are

$$\begin{array}{ll} (0 < 1) = 1 & (3 \neq 3) = 0 \\ (5 < 7) = 1 & (3 \geq 3) = 1 \\ (6 < 3) = 0 & (4 > 5) = 0 \end{array} \tag{1.4.24}$$

Special symbols

In examining the lists of cells, we may wish to remove an item and prevent that cell from registering on the next examination. To do this we present two special symbols:

ƶ is a key larger than any other available;

a is smaller than any other symbol group available.

1.5 LIST OPERATIONS

List search equal

We define a list search equal operator, σ (sigma is a Greek S and abbreviates "same"). This permits us, given an item, to examine a list starting from the beginning, searching for the item. When it is found, its ordinal number within the list is indicated. Thus we have

$$a \, \sigma \, \mathbf{b} = b_i \supset a = b_i \;\&\; a \neq b_j, \qquad j < i \tag{1.5.1}$$

Notice that this operator σ finds the *first* item in the item list **b** which is equal to the search item a; there may be other items later in the list which are equal to a. This may be stated in our notation as

$$a = b_i \;\&\; a = b_k \;\&\; k > i \supset a \, \sigma \, \mathbf{b} = b_i \tag{1.5.2}$$

The operator is used thus

$$\text{item } \sigma \text{ item list} \tag{1.5.3}$$

We may apply the search operator to a cell list to find the cell which contains the first cell which contains an item equal to the given item. The operator is then applied as

$$\text{item } \sigma \text{ cell list} \tag{1.5.4}$$

It is defined as

$$a \, \sigma \, \mathbf{B} = B_i \supset a = (B_i) \;\&\; a \neq (B_j) \;\&\; j < i \tag{1.5.5}$$

Given a cell for which it is necessary to find a cell in a list, the contents of which match up with the contents of this cell, then the operator is in the form

$$\text{cell } \sigma \text{ cell list} \tag{1.5.6}$$

It is then defined as

$$A \, \sigma \, \mathbf{B} = B_i \supset (A) = (B_i) \;\&\; (A) \neq (B_j) \;\&\; j < i \tag{1.5.7}$$

SEARCH DIRECTION

From (1.5.7) it is clear that the search proceeds in the direction of ascending subscription. Thus (A) is *first* compared to (B_1), then to (B_2), etc. To request a search in the opposite direction, why not reverse the order of the symbols, thus,

$$\text{cell list } \sigma \text{ cell} \tag{1.5.8}$$

so that we have

$$\mathbf{B} \, \sigma \, A = B_i \supset (A) = (B_i) \;\&\; (A) \neq (B_j) \;\&\; j > i \tag{1.5.9}$$

NOT FOUND

The foregoing definitions have been given under the permise that the list contained the desired item. If absent, the result is represented by the empty element, Λ. Our search is for nought then, and we indicate it thus

$$\mathrm{a}\,\sigma\,\mathbf{b} = \Lambda \qquad \mathrm{a} \neq \mathrm{b} \qquad \text{all b} \in \mathbf{b} \tag{1.5.10}$$

$$\mathrm{a}\,\sigma\,\mathbf{B} = \Lambda \qquad \mathrm{a} \neq (\mathrm{B}) \qquad \text{all B} \in \mathbf{B} \tag{1.5.11}$$

$$\mathrm{A}\,\sigma\,\mathbf{B} = \Lambda \qquad (\mathrm{A}) \neq (\mathrm{B}) \qquad \text{all B} \in \mathbf{B} \tag{1.5.12}$$

Elements search greater

When searching ordered lists to find where an **element** (same as *item*) greater than or equal to a given element is placed, we use the operator γ. We define this operator for a list ordered increasingly

$$\mathrm{a}\,\gamma\,{}^{0}\mathbf{b} = \mathrm{b}_{\mathrm{i}} \supset \mathrm{b}_1 \leq \mathrm{b}_2 \leq \cdots \leq \mathrm{b}_{\mathrm{i}-1} < \mathrm{a} \leq \mathrm{b}_{\mathrm{i}} \leq \mathrm{b}_{\mathrm{i}+1} \leq \cdots \leq \mathrm{b}_{\nu} \tag{1.5.13}$$

We may find that there is no element in our list which is greater than the given element

$$\mathrm{a}\,\gamma\,\mathbf{b} = \Lambda \supset \mathbf{b} \leq \mathrm{a} \tag{1.5.14}$$

where $\mathbf{b} < a$ means $b_i < a$ for all b_i in $\mathbf{b}$. We have applied the search operator to an *element* list so that it is given in class form thus

$$\text{element } \gamma \text{ ordered element list} \tag{1.5.15}$$

We apply the search greater operator to an ordered *cell* list

$$\text{element } \gamma \text{ ordered cell list} \tag{1.5.16}$$

It is then defined by

$$\mathrm{a}\,\gamma\,\mathbf{B} = \mathrm{B}_{\mathrm{i}} \supset (\mathrm{B}_1) \leq (\mathrm{B}_2) \leq \cdots \leq (\mathrm{B}_{\mathrm{i}-1}) < \mathrm{a} \leq (\mathrm{B}_{\mathrm{i}}) \leq (\mathrm{B}_{\mathrm{i}+1}) \leq \cdots \leq \mathrm{B}_{\nu} \tag{1.5.17}$$

If no cell is found, we have

$$\mathrm{a}\,\gamma\,\mathbf{B} = \Lambda \supset (\mathbf{B}) > \mathrm{a} \tag{1.5.18}$$

Finally we may have the operator in the form

$$\text{cell } \gamma \text{ ordered cell list} \tag{1.5.19}$$

It is then defined by

$$\mathrm{A}\,\gamma\,\mathbf{B} = \mathrm{B}_{\mathrm{i}} \supset (\mathrm{B}_1) \leq (\mathrm{B}_2) \leq \cdots \leq (\mathrm{B}_{\mathrm{i}-1}) < (\mathrm{A}) \leq (\mathrm{B}_{\mathrm{i}}) \leq (\mathrm{B}_{\mathrm{i}+1}) \leq \cdots \leq \mathrm{B}_{\nu} \tag{1.5.20}$$

and

$$\mathrm{A}\,\gamma\,\mathbf{B} = \Lambda \supset (\mathbf{B}) \geq (\mathrm{A}) \tag{1.5.21}$$

DECREASING LIST

If we apply the search greater operator to a decreasing list, there are just two alternatives for what we find. Suppose that c is given by

$$c_1 \geq c_2 \geq c_3 \geq \cdots \geq c_n \tag{1.5.22}$$

Then

$$a \gamma \mathbf{c} = c_1 \vee \Lambda \tag{1.5.23}$$

UNORDERED LIST

Applied to an unordered list, γ finds the first item in that list which is greater than or equal to the given item. Then

$$a \gamma \mathbf{b} = b_i \supset b_i \geq a \;\&\; b_j < a, \qquad j < i \tag{1.5.24}$$

$$a \gamma \mathbf{B} = B_i \supset (B_i) \geq a \;\&\; (B_j) < a, \qquad j < i \tag{1.5.25}$$

$$A \gamma \mathbf{B} = B_i \supset (B_i) \geq (A) \;\&\; (B_j) < (A), \qquad j < i \tag{1.5.26}$$

Search greater

The operator γ looks for an item greater than or equal. Suppose we wish to exclude the "equal to." We do this by defining the operator $\gamma\bar{\sigma}$. It is defined by

$$a \gamma\bar{\sigma}\, \mathbf{b} = b_i \supset b_i > a \;\&\; b_j \leq a, \qquad j < i \tag{1.5.27}$$

$$a \gamma\bar{\sigma}\, \mathbf{B} = B_i \supset (B_i) > a \;\&\; (B_j) \leq a, \qquad j < i \tag{1.5.28}$$

$$A \gamma\bar{\sigma}\, \mathbf{B} = B_i \supset (B_i) > (A) \;\&\; (B_j) \leq (A), \qquad j < i \tag{1.5.29}$$

Search less

We define the operator $\bar{\gamma}$ which looks for an item less than the given item. Note first that the bar inverts the meaning so that, instead of *greater than or equal to*, we have *less than*. Second, note that the usefulness of this operator is mainly in application to ordered lists, where the items are in *descending order*. We have the definitions

$$a \bar{\gamma} \mathbf{b} = b_i \supset b_i < a \;\&\; b_j \geq a, \qquad j < i \tag{1.5.30}$$

$$a \bar{\gamma} \mathbf{B} = B_i \supset (B_i) < a \;\&\; (B_j) \geq a, \qquad j < i \tag{1.5.31}$$

$$A \bar{\gamma} \mathbf{B} = B_i \supset (B_i) < (A) \;\&\; (B_j) \geq (A), \qquad j < i \tag{1.5.32}$$

Search less or equal

We define the operator $\bar{\gamma}\sigma$ as searching for an item which is less than or equal to a given item. We define this operator in only one case, since the rest should be obvious.

$$\mathrm{a}\ \bar{\gamma}\sigma\ \mathbf{b} = \mathrm{b_i} \supset \mathrm{b_i} \leq \mathrm{a}\ \&\ \mathrm{b_j} > \mathrm{a}, \qquad \mathrm{j} < \mathrm{i} \tag{1.5.33}$$

Search direction

All search operators are subject to the direction convention whereby reversing the direction of the symbols reverses the direction of the search. Here is an example of this:

$$\mathbf{B}\ \gamma\ \mathrm{a} = \mathrm{B_i} \supset (\mathrm{B}_\nu) \leq (\mathrm{B}_{\nu-1}) \leq \cdots \leq (\mathrm{B_{i+1}}) < (\mathrm{A}) \leq (\mathrm{B_i}) \leq (\mathrm{B_{i-1}}) \leq \cdots \leq (\mathrm{B_1}) \tag{1.5.34}$$

Search partition

If we apply the search greater equal operator to a list, the element which we find partitions the original ordered list into two parts. We use the pair ⌊ ⌋ for the lower partiton, the one for which the elements are less than the given element. It is defined as

$$\lfloor \mathrm{a}\ \gamma\ \mathbf{b} \rfloor = {}^1\mathbf{b} \supset {}^1\mathbf{b} < \mathrm{a}\ \&\ {}^1\mathbf{b}^c \geq \mathrm{a} \tag{1.5.35}$$

Here as before we have ${}^1\mathbf{b} < a$ means all the elements of ${}^1\mathbf{b}$ are less than a. Then we have

$${}^1\mathbf{b} < \mathrm{a} \supset {}^1\mathrm{b_i} < \mathrm{a} \qquad \text{all } {}^1\mathrm{b_i} \in {}^1\mathbf{b} \tag{1.5.36}$$

We also have

$${}^1\mathbf{b} \cup {}^1\mathbf{b}^c = \mathbf{b}; \qquad {}^1\mathbf{b} \cap {}^1\mathbf{b}^c = \Lambda \tag{1.5.37}$$

The upper partition yields all those elements which are greater than or equal to the given element. For this we use the pair ⌈ ⌉, and we have

$$\lceil \mathrm{a}\ \gamma\ \mathbf{b} \rceil = {}^2\mathbf{b} \supset {}^2\mathbf{b} \geq \mathrm{a}\ \&\ {}^2\mathbf{b}^c < \mathrm{a} \tag{1.5.38}$$

Notice also that

$$\lceil \mathrm{a}\ \gamma\ \mathrm{b} \rceil \cup \lfloor \mathrm{a}\ \gamma\ \mathbf{b} \rfloor = \mathbf{b} \tag{1.5.39}$$

and

$$\lceil \mathrm{a}\ \gamma\ \mathbf{b} \rceil \cap \lfloor \mathrm{a}\ \gamma\ \mathbf{b} \rfloor = \Lambda \tag{1.5.40}$$

The search partition is defined for the element search of a cell list as follows

$$\lceil \mathrm{a}\ \gamma\ \mathbf{B} \rceil = [\lceil \mathrm{a}\ \gamma\ (\mathbf{B}) \rceil]; \qquad \lfloor \mathrm{a}\ \gamma\ \mathbf{B} \rfloor = [\lfloor \mathrm{a}\ \gamma\ (\mathbf{B}) \rfloor] \tag{1.5.41}$$

We search a cell list for the contents of a given cell, making partitions thus

$$\lceil \mathrm{A}\,\gamma\,\mathbf{B} \rceil = [\lceil(\mathrm{A})\,\gamma\,(\mathbf{B})\rceil]; \qquad \lfloor \mathrm{A}\,\gamma\,\mathbf{B} \rfloor = [\lfloor(\mathrm{A})\,\gamma\,(\mathbf{B})\rfloor] \tag{1.5.42}$$

In general, the search partition is confined to ordered lists. However, by natural extension, we may define it with regard to unordered lists.

Notice that if the item searched for is absent from the list, the following partition then prevails

$$\mathrm{a}\,\gamma\,\mathbf{b} = \Lambda \supset \lfloor \mathrm{a}\,\gamma\,\mathbf{b} \rfloor = \mathbf{b}; \qquad \lceil \mathrm{a}\,\gamma\,\mathbf{b} \rceil = \Lambda \tag{1.5.43}$$

Other search partitions

A list may be partitioned by compound operations such as $\gamma\bar{\sigma}$ and $\bar{\gamma}$. These result in the following relations

$$\lceil \mathrm{a}\,\gamma\bar{\sigma}\,\mathbf{b} \rceil = {}^{3}\mathbf{b} \supset {}^{3}\mathbf{b} \leq \mathrm{a} \tag{1.5.44}$$

$$\lfloor \mathrm{a}\,\bar{\gamma}\,\mathbf{b} \rfloor = {}^{5}\mathbf{b} \supset {}^{5}\mathbf{b} < \mathrm{a} \tag{1.5.45}$$

$$\lceil \mathrm{a}\,\bar{\gamma}\,\mathbf{b} \rceil = {}^{4}\mathbf{b} \supset {}^{4}\mathbf{b} \geq \mathrm{a} \tag{1.5.46}$$

$$\lfloor \mathrm{A}\,\bar{\gamma}\,\mathbf{B} \rfloor = {}^{6}\mathbf{B} \supset ({}^{6}\mathbf{B}) < (\mathrm{A}) \tag{1.5.47}$$

etc.

Search backward partitions

When the symbols are written to direct a search from higher subscripted elements to lower ones, partitions are applied as might be expected. For instance

$$\lfloor \mathbf{B}\,\sigma\,\mathrm{a} \rfloor = {}^{7}\mathbf{B} \supset ({}^{7}\mathbf{B}) \geq \mathrm{a}; \qquad {}^{7}\mathbf{B}^{c} \supset ({}^{7}\mathrm{B}_{i}^{c}) < \mathrm{a}, \text{ all i} \tag{1.5.48}$$

$$\lceil \mathbf{B}\,\sigma\,\mathrm{a} \rceil = {}^{8}\mathbf{B} = {}^{7}\mathbf{B}^{c} \tag{1.5.49}$$

Repeat function

The repeat function simulates the DO loop. It allows us to repeat a number of operations with respect to a given subscript variation or condition. We use **R** to indicate that an operation is to be repeated starting with the conditions which are noted beneath **R** and continuing, altering the dummy index until the conditions above **R** are met. We use **R** to define the advance operator, α.

$$\alpha\,\mathbf{A} \equiv \underset{i=n}{\overset{1}{\mathbf{R}}}\,(\mathrm{A}_i) \longrightarrow \mathrm{A}_{i+1} \tag{1.5.50}$$

or alternatively

$$\alpha\,\mathbf{A} \equiv \underset{i=n}{\overset{1}{\mathbf{R}}}\, \alpha\, A_i \tag{1.5.51}$$

The partition operator is defined as

$$\lfloor a\,\gamma\,\mathbf{b} \rfloor = 1 \longrightarrow j; \qquad \underset{i=1}{\overset{n}{\mathbf{R}}}\,(a < b_i)\{b_i \longrightarrow {}^1b_j;\;\; j+1 \longrightarrow j\} \tag{1.5.52}$$

PROBLEMS

1.1 Why do we distinguish between a cell list and an item list in sorting?

1.2 Write an expression for:
- (a) the number of items in list **B** greater than r
- (b) the number of items in list **b** less than r
- (c) the number of items in list **a** less than or equal to r
- (d) the number of items in list **A** less than r and also in **B**
- (e) those items in **C** greater than r and not in **D**

1.3 In sorting, why do we need notation for:
- (a) precedence
- (b) complementation
- (c) inclusion
- (d) subsets
- (e) counting
- (f) least, greatest
- (g) upper and lower subsets
- (h) concatenation
- (i) exchange
- (j) advance
- (k) retard
- (l) repeat
- (m) search

1.4 Write in our notation that:
- (a) **R** and **S** are complements
- (b) **R** and **S** are not complements
- (c) **R** and **S** are identical
- (d) **R** and **S** are the same size but not identical
- (e) **R** is a subset of **S** is a subset of **T**
- (f) **Q** and **P** are overlapping subsets of the same set

1.5 What is the difference between *preceed* as applied to *cells* and *items*?

1.6 For $p < q$ search **A** (in our notation) where (**A**) is in ascending order:
- (a) for all cells with items y where $p < y < q$
- (b) where $p \leq y \leq q$
- (c) where $y < p$ or $q < y$
- (d) where $y \leq p$ or $q \leq y$

1.7 Repeat 1.6 where (**A**) is in descending order.

1.8 Use the repeat functions to define these partitions.
- (a) (1.5.38)
- (b) (1.5.44)
- (c) (1.5.45)
- (d) (1.5.46)
- (e) (1.5.47)
- (f) (1.5.48)
- (g) (1.5.49)

2 OPERATOR IMPLEMENTATION

2.1 PROGRAM CONSIDERATIONS

Types of languages

In designing programs, there are three kinds of languages we can deal with

* problem-oriented languages
* assembly lanugages
* machine languages

COMPILER LANGUAGES

The problem-oriented language is translated by the compiler and is generally oriented toward one of two kinds of applications: scientific or commercial. Scientific languages such as FORTRAN and ALGOL permit us to write the problems of algebra, calculus, and differential equations so that they can be easily translated for the computer. Business languages such as COBOL permit easy prescription of accounting processes. Neither type of language lends itself to list manipulation operation.

MACHINE LANGUAGES

A machine language uses a configuration of bits which the machine recognizes as a command in its repertoire. We can move upward from this level slightly by placing machine language in symbolic form, absolute assembly language. Neither of these alternatives is appealing to the sophisticated programmer.

ASSEMBLY LANGUAGES

A macro assembly language resembles machine language. However, it has been broadened to use mnemonics and symbolic addressing, and it provides for construction and use of macros. Most software is built at the assembly language level.

Choice of languages

Of the three types of languages, the assembly language offers the most universality for our sorting discussion. There is one other alternative: this is a special purpose language for list manipulation such as IPL-V, SLIP, etc. These are limited in use and difficult to learn. As a consequence, it was deemed easiest to translate from operator notation directly into assembly language.

There are many assembly languages which may be chosen. The language depends upon the machine, and again, there are three choices:

* fixed word length
* character-oriented
* byte-oriented

I took a language from the first and last categories since the middle category, the character-oriented machine, works very much like a byte-oriented machine.

For scientific use we have the choice of one-address versus three-address machines. Since there are few three-address machines, a one-address language is chosen. The IBM 7090 series is typical of scientific computers in the one-address category of fixed word length. However, its mnemonics are not user oriented. Hence I have chosen my own version of FAP which I call FLAP, and which has been discussed in detail elsewhere.

For the byte-oriented machines, the IBM 360 Series assembly language will find general use in the future since so many machines are compatible with it.

Aim

In this section we introduce FLAP. Then in succeeding sections we show how operations in operator notation are converted to subroutines or program segments. This will make possible the analysis of the sorting operations. Table 2.1.1 gives in arrow notation the meaning of each FLAP mnemonic.

In later chapters, routines and programs will be written in FLAP to show how sort principles are applied. Some of these will be converted into 360 AL in Chapter 13.

Table 2.1.1 FLORES ASSEMBLY PROGRAM (FLAP) MNEMONICS

Line						*Indexable*
	Transfers					
1	To	XMR	$(M) \rightarrow R$			Yes
2	From	XRM	$(R) \rightarrow M$			Yes
3	Between	XRR'	$(R) \rightarrow R'$			No
4	Special	XOM	$0 \rightarrow M,$	XOR	$0 \rightarrow R$	Yes
	Logic					
5		ANDTA	$(A)\ \&\ (M) \rightarrow A$	ANDTM	$(A)\ \&\ (M) \rightarrow M$	Yes
6		ORTA	$(A) \vee (M) \rightarrow A$	ORTM	$(A) \vee (M) \rightarrow M$	Yes
	Shifts					
7	Out	SRR	$0 \xrightarrow{M} R$	SLR	$R \xleftarrow{M} 0$	No
8	Around	ERR	$(R) \xrightarrow{M} R$	ELR	$R \xleftarrow{M} (R)$	No
9	Long	LSR	$(A) \xrightarrow{M} Q;\ (Q) \xrightarrow{M} A$			No
	Arithmetic					
10		ADD	$(A) + (M) \rightarrow A$	ADA	$(A) + \lvert (M) \rvert \rightarrow A$	Yes
11		SUB	$(A) - (M) \rightarrow A$	SBA	$(A) - \lvert (M) \rvert \rightarrow A$	Yes
12		MLR	$(M) \times (D) \rightarrow A$	MUL	$(M) \times (D) \rightarrow A, Q$	Yes
13		DIV	$(A)\ /\ (M) \rightarrow Q$			
	Decision and action					
14	Unconditional	NOOP	$\Rightarrow I + 1$	STOP	$\not\Rightarrow$	No
15		UCJ	$\Rightarrow M$			Yes
16	Decision	CMP	$(A) > (M)\ 1 \rightarrow G$ $0 \rightarrow E, L$	$(A) = (M)\ 1 \rightarrow E$ $0 \rightarrow G, L$	$(A) < (M)\ 1 \rightarrow L$ $0 \rightarrow G, E$	Yes
17	Conditional	JOG	$G = 1 \Rightarrow M;\ G = 0 \Rightarrow I + 1$			Yes
18		IOE	$E = 1 \Rightarrow M;\ E = 0 \Rightarrow I + 1$			Yes
19		JOL	$L = 1 \Rightarrow M;\ L = 0 \Rightarrow I + 1$			Yes
20		CAS	$(A) > (M) \Rightarrow I + 1$	$(A) = (M) \Rightarrow I + 2$	$(A) < (M) \Rightarrow I + 3$	No

	Index manipulations					
21	Fill	XMN,n	$(M_M) \rightarrow n$	XNM	$(n) \rightarrow M_M$	No
22		XAN,n	$(A_M) \rightarrow n$	XNA	$(n) \rightarrow A_M$	No
23		XPN,n	$M \rightarrow n$			No
24	Increment	NPP,n	$(n) + M \rightarrow n$	NMP,n	$(n) - M \rightarrow n$	No
25	Compare	CMPN,n	$(n) > M\ 1 \rightarrow G$	$(n) = M\ 1 \rightarrow E$	$(n) < M\ 1 \rightarrow L$	No
			$0 \rightarrow E, L$	$0 \rightarrow G, L$	$0 \rightarrow E, G$	
26	Compare and jump	JNP,n	$(n) \geq 0 \Rightarrow M$	$(n) < 0 \Rightarrow I + 1$		No
27		JNNZ,n	$(n) \neq 0 \Rightarrow M$	$(n) = 0 \Rightarrow I + 1$		No
28		JNZ,n	$(n) = 0 \Rightarrow M$	$(n) \neq 0 \Rightarrow I + 1$		
29		JNN,n	$(n) < 0 \Rightarrow M$	$(n) \geq 0 \Rightarrow I + 1$		No
30	Increment, test,	TUN,n	$(n) + 1 \rightarrow n$	$(n) < 0 \Rightarrow M$	$(n) \geq 0 \Rightarrow I + 1$	No
31	and jump	TDN,n	$(n) - 1 \rightarrow n$	$(n) > 0 \Rightarrow M$	$(n) \leq 0 \Rightarrow I + 1$	No
	IO					
32		READ	(Input) $\rightarrow$ M			Yes
33		WRITE	(M) $\rightarrow$ Output			Yes
34		REWIND	rewind device			No
35		JOIE	indication $\Rightarrow$ M	no indication $\Rightarrow I + 1$		Yes
	Subroutine linkage					
36		JAS	$I + 1 \rightarrow M - 1 \Rightarrow M$			Yes
37		JSR	$I \rightarrow RJR; \Rightarrow M$			Yes
38		JRA	$\Rightarrow (RJR) + M$			No
39		JSN,n	$I \rightarrow n; \Rightarrow M$			No
	Others					
40		JOO	Overflow $= 1 \Rightarrow M$;	Overflow $= 0 \Rightarrow I + 1$		Yes
41		EXEC	$\Rightarrow M; \Rightarrow I + 1$			No

2.2 DATA MOVEMENT

Cell transfers

It is not possible to transfer information from one memory cell directly to another memory cell in a single operation, even though a single command may request it. For fixed word length computers, two commands are required to move one word. Transfer uses an intermediate register. A transfer from cell R to cell S may be done in FLAP using the A register as displayed in Fig. 2.2.1.

```
XMA    R
XAM    S
```

Fig. 2.2.1 Routine for $R \longrightarrow S$.

List transfers

To transfer a list from one location to another requires the operations of Fig. 2.2.1 repeated for the entire list. The list may be moved in sequence, taking the contents of the first cell of the donor list and placing it into the first cell of the acceptor list. FLAP lends itself to processing backwards as in Fig. 2.2.1. After an index register has been set up, each cell transfer requires two transfers and an incrementation step.

Advance and retard

To advance a list, it is still convenient to process our list backwards. The subroutine of Fig. 2.2.2 is usable if we make changes so that both ends of the list are properly positioned as in Fig. 2.2.3.

```
XPN,6    N
XMA,6    R - 1
XAM,6    S - 1
TDN,6    * - 2
```

Fig. 2.2.2 Routine for $\mathbf{R} \longrightarrow \mathbf{S}$, where $\nu(\mathbf{R}) = \nu(\mathbf{S}) = \mathrm{N}$.

```
ADV    XPN,3    N
       XMA,3    R - 1
       XAM,3    R
       TDN,3    * - 2
```

Fig. 2.2.3 ADV, SR for $\alpha\,\mathbf{R}$.

To retard a list, we move the contents of each cell backwards. This cannot be accomplished by simply reversing the procedure of Fig. 2.2.3 because we would be wiping out cells as we moved information backwards; at the end of the operation, we would find that all the cells in our list had the same quantity in them. We leave it to the reader to set up a subroutine to do this.

Exchange

To exchange the contents of two lists means to exchange the contents of a cell in one list with the contents of the corresponding cell in the other list, at the same time placing the contents of the cell from the first list into that of the second list. To do this we store the contents of corresponding cells in *two* separate registers. For FLAP the A and D registers are chosen. Since the contents of both cells are preserved, it is a simple matter to switch them around as we reenter them into their lists as shown in Fig. 2.2.4.

```
XCHNG   XPN,4   N
        XMA,4   R − 1
        XMD,4   S − 1
        XDM,4   R − 1
        XAM,4   S − 1
        TDN,4   * − 4
```

Fig. 2.2.4 XCHNG SR for $\mathbf{R}\ \chi\ \mathbf{S}$.

Timing

To determine the time required for subroutines using operators, we make some definitions. We define the time for a transfer as t (e.g. XMA); the time for a housekeeping operation such as setting an index, tallying a counter, or making a jump is n.

The time to do a simple move operation from one cell to another is then given as

$$\mathrm{T}(\mathrm{R} \longrightarrow \mathrm{S}) = 2t \tag{2.2.1}$$

where $T(R \longrightarrow S)$ indicates the time for the move operation. Similarly, the time to move an entire list is given as

$$\mathrm{T}(\mathbf{R} \longrightarrow \mathrm{S}) = \nu\ \mathbf{R} \times (2t + n) \tag{2.2.2}$$

The time to advance a list is determined by inspection of Fig. 2.2.3 as

$$\mathrm{T}(\alpha\ \mathbf{R}) = \nu\ \mathbf{R} \times (2t + n) \tag{2.2.3}$$

The same time is required for a retard operation. From Fig. 2.2.4, the time required to exchange two lists is given as

$$\mathrm{T}(\mathbf{R}\ \chi\ \mathrm{S}) = \nu\ \mathbf{R} \times (4t + n) \tag{2.2.4}$$

An analysis of various internal sorts has been done elsewhere† and the results are presented in Appendix B.

2.3 COMPARE; LIST SEARCHES

Subroutines

Some of the little programs developed here will be set up as subroutines so that they can be used by other routines developed later. In designing a subroutine, we consider two things: linkage and the calling sequence. Linkage conventions are described in *Computer Programming*, Section 4.5. The one which we adopt uses the FLAP command JSN (jump set index), which fills an index with the contents of the instruction counter as a jump is made. This permits the subroutine to access the calling sequence.

As a convention we always link using index 4, thus

JSN,4 name (2.3.1)

Here *name* is the name of the subroutine being called.

The calling sequence consists of a set of cells which follows the call statement. These cells can contain

* data
* integers
* list addresses

The use of this technique is exemplified by

JSN,4 LEAST (2.3.2)

for the subroutine LEAST of Fig. 2.3.1 which is described later. The line labelled CALL is the command which takes us to the subroutine. Following it are the four cells of the calling sequence.

The first cell contains the address of the start of the list which is to be searched. This is a NOOP command using index 1 with, as address, the list starting point. Specifying an index with the list start allows the subroutine to sequence through the list. Here we use index 1 for list sequencing. The second cell in the calling sequence contains an integer specifying the number of items in the list. The third and fourth cells are for the results produced by routine, respectively: the position of the desired item and the item itself.

LEAST

The *least* operator, λ, scans a list to find the smallest item. The subroutine LEAST for doing this is found in Fig. 2.3.1. The first two steps obtain the length of the list from the calling sequence and insert it in index 1. This

†Ivan Flores, "Analysis of Internal Computer Sorting," *JACM*, Vol. 8, No. 1, (January, 1961), pp. 41–80.

```
CALL    JSN,4      LEAST
        NOOP,1     L
        NOOP       N
        NOOP       Position of least
        NOOP       Least
LEAST   XMA,4      2           get length
        XAN,1                  set length into index 1
        NMP,1      1           reduce length by 1
FIX     XNM,1      TEMP        save item number
        XMA,I,4    1           get item
LOOP    NMP,1      1           set pointer to next item
        JNN,1      OVER        jump if all list checked
        CMP,I,4    1           is this item least?
        JOG        FIX         new item least
        UCJ        LOOP        old item least
OVER    XAM,4      4           least item to call sequence
        XMA        TEMP        get pointer
        XAM,4      3           for call sequence
        UCJ,4      5           return
```

Fig. 2.3.1 LEAST, SR for **L.**

quantity is then reduced by 1 so that, when it is added to the list start, L, it yields the list end point, L + N − 1 (we process the list backwards). We set up to start the loop by entering the present item number at TEMP (at FIX). We then get that item and place it in the accumulator.

The last item on our list is now in the accumulator. We retard the list pointer at LOOP, checking next to see if we have examined all the list. If not, we compare this next item with the one in the accumulator. If the result is greater, or equal, the item in the accumulator is the least one so far; if the result is less, the item just compared is the least so far. In this latter case, we jump to FIX to get the item into the accumulator and to store its position in TEMP. Otherwise we continue the loop at LOOP. When the index goes negative at LOOP + 1, it means that we have examined the entire list, and we jump to OVER. There, we enter the item, as well as its ordinal number, into the calling sequence.

Time

Let us examine the time required to perform LEAST in terms of t's and n's. The first three steps of the prgram required two transfers and index manipulation; the three last steps require three transfers.

The section called LOOP is done $N - 1$ times—once for each item of the list except for the first. The time required for it is given by

$$\mathrm{T\,(LOOP)} = t + 3n \qquad (2.3.2)$$

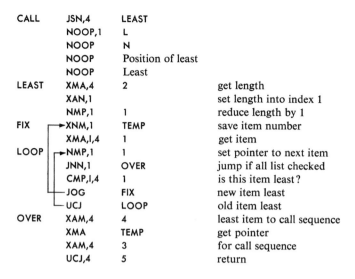

The section FIX is performed only when an item is found which is *less*

than all previous items encountered. Length of time encountered for these two steps is

$$\text{T (FIX)} = 2t + n \tag{2.3.3.}$$

This sequence appears for less than half the items. We can then get an estimate for the entire subroutine as

$$\begin{aligned}\text{T (LEAST)} &= \frac{\text{N} - 1}{2}(2t + 6n + 2t + n) + 5t + n \\ &\doteq \text{N}(2t + 4n)\end{aligned} \tag{2.3.4}$$

Other searches

MOST

MOST is like LEAST; only a slight change is required in the subroutine itself, and no change is required in the calling sequence. When we search a list to find an item which meets a given condition, we use the format shown in Fig. 2.3.2.

CALL	JSN,4	search type	
	NOOP,1	L	list start
	NOOP	N	list length
	NOOP		position of sought item
	NOOP		item sought

Fig. 2.3.2 Call sequences for FLAP SR's for the following searches:

MOST	maximum
LSEQ	equal
LSGR	greater
LSLSEQ	less than or equal
LSLS	less then
LSGREQ	greater or equal

FOR CONDITIONS

This format is the same as for LEAST with one exception. For these searches, the item which is sought is provided in the calling sequence. The SR searches the list to find, for instance, an item which is *less than or equal to* the given item. Its order within the list is then supplied to the calling sequence.

To reiterate, three things are supplied by the calling sequence: the list starting point, the list length, and the item sort. One thing is determined by the SR: the position of the desired item in the list.

PROBLEMS

2.1 Write a FLAP SR for the retard operator ρ and call it **RET**.

2.2 Write **MOST** in FLAP to find the maximum of a list using the calling sequence and method of Fig. 2.3.1.

2.3 Write FLAP SRS for list searches using the call sequence of Fig. 2.3.2. Write them so that only one or so commands need be changed to go from one SR to another. Do:
(a) **LSEQ** for the operator σ
(b) **LSGR** for the operator $\gamma\bar{\sigma}$
(c) **LSLSEQ** for the operator $\bar{\gamma}\sigma$
(d) **LSLS** for the operator $\bar{\gamma}$
(e) **LSGREQ** for the operator γ
Place **O** at **CALL** +3 if item sought is absent.

2.4 Write the SR **LS** with this call sequence:

CALL	JSN, 4	LS
	NOOP, 1	L-1
	NOOP	N
	NOOP	T
P	NOOP	
I	NOOP	
	NOOP	X

where L is the list start; N is the list length; T is a type designator: 1 for *equal*, 2 for *less*, 2 for *less, or equal*, 4 for *greater*, 5 for *greater or equal*; P is the position number; I is the item; **X** is not used.

2.5 Rewrite Problem 2.4 so that **X** is an exit address that is jumped to indirect if relation desired is absent.

2.6 Consider an unordered list starting at **L** of length **N. LEAST** separates it into an upper and lower part. **MOST** can find the greatest of either half. Write a program to find the greatest of the lower set using the aforementioned SRS.

2.7 Rewrite Problem 2.5 for examining a list in the reverse order; call the SR **RLS.**

2.8 Write as FLAP SRS, **MOVE** and **XCHANGE** with these call sequences:

JSN, 4	MOVE (or XCHANGE)	
NOOP	N	number of words
NOOP, 1	S	source start
NOOP, 1	D	destination start

2.9 Convert SRS of 2.8 to macroforce.

2.10 Rewrite **LEAST** (**MOST**) for records of **R** words using the macros developed in Problem 2.9.

2.11 Rewrite 2.4 for:
(a) System/360
(b) the IBM 1401

3 USING SELECTION TO SORT

3.1 SELECTION SORTING

Philosophy

We wish to sort an input list of items **a** which is contained at the cell list **A** and produce an output list which is in ascending order.

$$(\mathbf{A}) = \mathbf{a} \tag{3.1.1}$$

One way to do this is to examine the old list, looking for the minimum item. It is placed in a new list, S, at the first cell, *S*. After placing the first item, we wish to review the original list again, looking for the *next* smallest item. The trouble is that, since the original item is still in **a**, *it* will turn up during the second list examination. To eliminate this difficulty, we remove the *least* item from consideration by placing the maximum key $\mathfrak{z}$ in the cell from which we withdraw the minimum item.

In the second scan of the list, the minimum item is absent, its place being occupied by $\mathfrak{z}$. The minimum selected this time is hence the next-minimum of the original list. When it is placed into S, it, too, is replaced by $\mathfrak{z}$. The third scan of the list then selects the next-to the-next-to the minimum. This continues until the list S is filled.

We next examine an example, and then, in the following section, we describe it in operator notation.

Example

Figure 3.1.1 shows a list of cells **A** and the cell contents (**A**). There is also a destination list, S, which at present is empty or contains trash of no interest to us, but eventually will contain the list (**A**) in order.

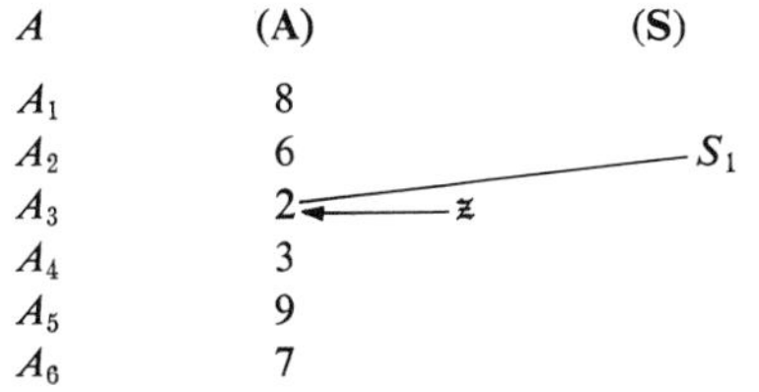

Fig. 3.1.1. Selection of first item from A for S.

The first operation is to examine the contents of A, using λ to select the minimum. We place it in the first cell of **S**, S_1.

In order that the next review of the list does not turn up with the same item key, namely 2, we insert z in the cell which previously contained the minimum, namely A_3. After this, the list **A** is called $_1$A and appears as in Fig. 3.1.2. Reviewing this list, λ will choose A_4 which contains the key 3; this is placed in the second cell of **S**, S_2.

Figure 3.1.3 shows list $_4$A which still contains two items to be sorted. The figure indicates how these items are located and entered.

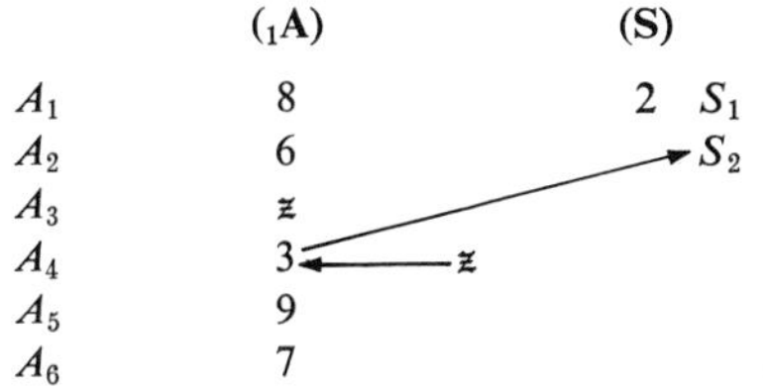

Fig. 3.1.2 Selection of second item from $_1$A for **S**.

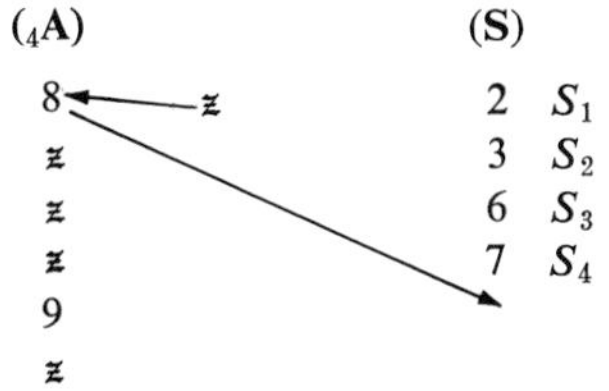

Fig. 3.1.3 Selection of next-to-last and last item for **S**.

($_6$A)	S
z	2
z	3
z	6
z	7
z	8
z	9

Fig. 3.1.4 Lists **A** and **S** after selection sort.

Finally, Fig. 3.1.4 shows ${}_6\mathbf{A}$ which now contains all ƶ's since each time we found an item it was replaced by ƶ. On the right side of the figure, **S** contains the original items in ascending order, as desired.

3.2 SELECTION PROCESSES

To select the minimum from **A**, we apply λ and transfer the result to the first cell of **S**

$$(\lambda\ \mathbf{A}) \longrightarrow \mathbf{S}_1 \tag{3.2.1}$$

To eliminate this item from consideration, place ƶ in that cell

$$\not{z} \longrightarrow \lambda\ \mathbf{A} \tag{3.2.2}$$

After doing this, relabel **A** as ${}_1\mathbf{A}$ thus

$$\not{z} \longrightarrow \lambda\ \mathbf{A}:\quad {}_1\mathbf{A} \tag{3.2.3}$$

Find and place subsequent items in a similar way. For instance, find the ith item from the ith list and place it in S_{i+1} thus

$$(\lambda\ {}_i\mathbf{A}) \longrightarrow \mathbf{S}_{i+1} \tag{3.2.4}$$

After doing this, place a ƶ at this location and relabel the list.

$$\not{z} \longrightarrow \lambda\ {}_i\mathbf{A}:\quad {}_{i+1}\mathbf{A} \tag{3.2.5}$$

We state the entire process in operator notation by appending the repeat operator to (3.2.4) and (3.2.5) with one other simple condition, which is

$${}_0\mathbf{A} = \mathbf{A} \tag{3.2.6}$$

Then we have

$$\underset{i=0}{\overset{n-1}{\mathsf{R}}} \begin{cases} (\lambda\ {}_i\mathbf{A}) \longrightarrow \mathbf{S}_{i+1} \\ \not{z} \longrightarrow \lambda\ {}_i\mathbf{A}:\quad {}_{i+1}\mathbf{A} \end{cases} \tag{3.2.7}$$

3.3 SELECTION ANALYSIS

SELECT

The routine **SELECT** to do a selection sort is found in Fig. 3.3.1.

We use index 2 to point to the output list **S**. Since we create this list in the forward direction, step 1 sets index 2 to 0. **LEAST** which follows determines the least item in the input list **R**.

At step 7, we bring item from **SMALL** and place it in the output list. Steps 9 and 10 determine whether there are more items left. If so, steps 11 through 13 replace the item withdrawn from the input list by ƶ. We then advance the pointer and continue the routine.

```
SELECT   XPN,2    0             set output pointer to 0
         JSN,4    LEAST         find least
         NOOP,1   R             )
         NOOP     N             |
SMALOC   NOOP     —             >call sequence
SMALL    NOOP     —             )
         XMA      SMALL         } put next item into
         XAM,2    S             } output list
         CMPN,2   N-1           for last item
         JOE      CONTINUE      continue program
         XMA      =ƶ            ) place ƶ in
         XMN,1    SMALOC        > input list where last
         XAM,1    R − 1         ) item was removed
         NPP,2    1             advance output pointer
         UCJ      SELECT + 1    get next item
```

Fig. 3.3.1 SELECT, routine for selection sort.

3.4 SELECTION AND EXCHANGE

Objections to selection sorting

The main objection to selection sorting is the amount of space required. The original list is in **L**. A separate output area **S** must be provided. This is, of course, in addition to the program area, **P**. Further, a complete review of the list **L** is required each time an item is selected. There is a need for a sentinel ƶ which must be inserted after each item is selected.

Selection and exchange permits us to use the original input area **L** as the output area, thus eliminating **S**. Further, only a sublist of the original list is reviewed. Hence there is no need for a special character, ƶ.

Procedure

As before, we search the list **L** to find its minimum, $\lambda\,\mathbf{L}$. When it is found, instead of placing it on a new list, we exchange the contents of $\lambda\,\mathbf{L}$ and those of L_1, the first item, in the input area.

$$\mathrm{L}_1\ \chi\ \lambda\ \mathbf{L} \tag{3.4.1}$$

After this exchange, we know that the first item is the least of the original list. We now have a new sublist, but its length is one less than that of the original list.

$${}_1\mathbf{L} = \{\mathrm{L}_2, \mathrm{L}_3, \ldots, \mathrm{L}_n\}; \qquad \nu_1\mathbf{L} = \mathrm{n} - 1 = \nu\,\mathbf{L} - 1 \tag{3.4.2}$$

Our next operation is to review the sublist to find its minimum. When we find it, we perform an exchange as before.

$$\mathrm{L}_2\ \chi\ \lambda\ {}_1\mathbf{L} \tag{3.4.3}$$

We now have a new sublist with one less item on it, given by

$$ {}_2\mathbf{L} \leq \{L_3, L_4, \ldots, L_n\}; \qquad \nu_2\,\mathbf{L} = n - 2 = \nu\,\mathbf{L} - 2 \tag{3.4.4} $$

In general, after i operations, we have a sublist, ${}_i\mathbf{L}$ which contains $n - i$ locations. Its complement, ${}_i\mathbf{L}^c$, contains i items which are in order. We find the minimum of the sublist and exchange it with the top item of the sublist

$$ L_{i+1}\ \chi\ \lambda\ {}_i\mathbf{L} \tag{3.4.5} $$

We then define our new sublist, ${}_{i+1}\mathbf{L}$

$$ {}_{i+1}\mathbf{L} = \{L_{i+2}, L_{i+3}, \ldots, L_n\}; \qquad \begin{aligned} \nu_{i+1}\mathbf{L} &= n - i - 1 \\ &= \nu\,\mathbf{L} - i - 1 \end{aligned} \tag{3.4.6} $$

Example

This technique is demonstrated by the example which begins with Fig. 3.4.1. Our original list, **L**, has six locations, L_1 through L_6. The search for the least element, $\lambda\,\mathbf{L}$, finds that it is located at L_3 and that the item key is 3, as shown at the left of the figure. The item at L_3 is exchanged with the item at L_1, after which the new list appears as at the right of Fig. 3.4.1. Figure 3.4.2 shows subsequent steps in the selection and exchange process.

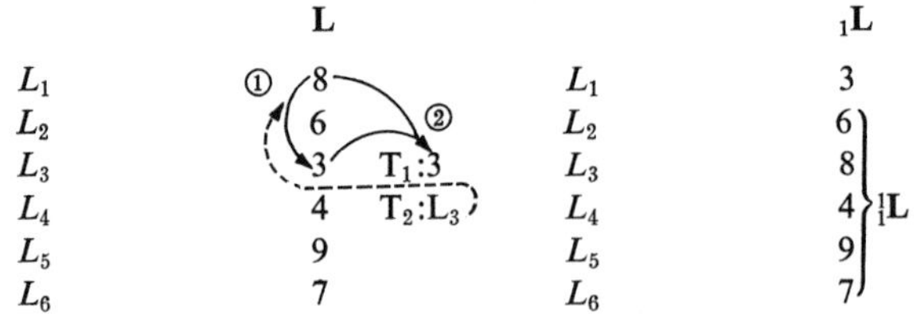

Fig. 3.4.1 First operation for selection and exchange sort.

${}_2\mathbf{L}$	${}_3\mathbf{L}$	${}_4\mathbf{L}$	${}_5\mathbf{L}$
3	3	3	3
4	4	4	4
8 } ${}_2^2\mathbf{L}$	6	6	6
6	8 } ${}_3^3\mathbf{L}$	7	7
9	9	9 } ${}_4^4\mathbf{L}$	8
7	7	8	9

Fig. 3.4.2 Continuation of selection and exchange sort example.

3.5 SELECTION AND EXCHANGE ROUTINE

The difference set

We indicate that we wish to remove elements from a set with a subtraction sign. Thus the set $\mathbf{x} = \mathbf{a} - \mathbf{b}$ means that we keep in the new set $\mathbf{x}$ all elements in $\mathbf{a}$ which are not also members of $\mathbf{b}$. Another way to state this is

$$\mathbf{x} = \mathbf{a} - \mathbf{b} \supset \mathbf{x} \cup \mathbf{b} = \mathbf{a} \;\&\; \mathbf{x} \cap \mathbf{b} = \Lambda \tag{3.5.1}$$

The difference set of interest in selection and exchange is the one that is left after we remove all sorted elements. The first selected element is placed in L_1. The first difference set is then

$$^{0}\mathbf{L} = \mathbf{L}, \qquad ^{1}\mathbf{L} = \mathbf{L} - \mathrm{L}_1 \tag{3.5.2}$$

Subsequent difference sets are given by

$$^{i}\mathbf{L} = \mathbf{L} - \bigcup_{j=1}^{i} \mathrm{L}_j \tag{3.5.3}$$

Routine

The routine for selection and exchange sorting is given completely when the repeat operator is applied to (3.4.5). We state this in terms of our difference sets thus

$$\mathop{\mathbf{R}}_{i=1}^{n-1} \mathrm{L}_i \, \chi \, \lambda^{i-1}\mathbf{L} \tag{3.5.4}$$

Since analysis requires that we know each step in our procedure, we eliminate the transfer operator χ after considering how the transfer operation is performed.

As we examine our difference list $^{i-1}\mathbf{L}$, we place the least element so far in a temporary storage location T_1; furthermore, we place the location of this minimum element so far in another storage location T_2. At the end of our search procedure, we find that the minimum element is at T_1 and its location at T_2. Since the duplicate of one of the elements that takes part in the search procedure is stored at T_1, we may write over that element. We therefore can take the top item in the sublist and place it where we withdrew the minimum item. Since the location of this minimum item is in T_2, we store our non-minimum element at (T_2).

The entire selection and exchange procedure is presented in operator notation, without the exchange operator, as

$$\mathop{\mathbf{R}}_{i=1}^{n-1} \begin{cases} (\lambda\, ^{i-1}\mathbf{L}) \longrightarrow \mathrm{T}_1 \\ \lambda\, ^{i-1}\mathbf{L} \longrightarrow \mathrm{T}_2 \\ \quad (\mathrm{L}_i) \longrightarrow (\mathrm{T}_2) \\ \quad (\mathrm{T}_1) \longrightarrow \mathrm{L}_i \end{cases} \tag{3.5.5}$$

FLAP Program

The FLAP routine for performing a sort by selection and exchange SCLTEX is presented in Fig. 3.5.1. It is very similar to the selection sort SELECT with the exception of the interchange routine.

1.	SLCTEX	XPN,2	R	list start
2.		XPN,3	N	list length
3.	LOOP	XMN,2	LISTART	} set parameters into
4.		XNM,3	LISTLON	} LEAST
5.		JSN,4	LEAST	
6.	LISTART	NOOP,1		
7.	LISTLON	NOOP		} call sequence
8.	SMALOL	NOOP		
9.	SMALL	NOOP		
10.		XMN,1	SMALLOC	
11.		XMA,2	0	bring in present list top
12.		XAM,1	R	put where least item found
13.		XMA	SMALL	} put present least
14.		XAM,2	0	} item at top of list
15.		CMPN,3	2	check for last item
16.		JOE	CONTINUE	continue program
17.		NMP,3	1	unsorted list is shorter
18.		NPP,2	1	it starts at higher call
19.		UCJ	LOOP	find next item

Fig. 3.5.1 SLCTEX, continue for sort log selection and exchange.

3.6 COUNTING

Philosophy

In sorting by counting, there are four lists to be considered:
- **I** is the original input list; it may be the input buffer from a tape read operation.
- **L** is the unsorted list which is made as each item from **I** is examined. It may consist simply of a key word—a key and the address of the record in the buffer.
- **C** is a set of counters which ranks each item in **L**.
- **S** is the sorted output list.

The procedure is to bring in successive items from **I** and place the item or a key word in **L**. As this is done, a new counter records the rank of the new item, and the other counters are adjusted to indicate their new ranks with respect to the item added.

Example

Let us examine the counting example shown in Fig. 3.6.1. To start we clear all the counters, **C**. The first item is brought in to L_1, and no examination or counting is done. It is an 8.

The next item, 3, is placed at L_2. As this is done, all the items in the cells

2		3		4		5		6		7		8
L	C	L	C	L	C	L	C	L	C	L	C	S
8	1	8	2	8	3	8	3	8	4	8	5	2
3	0	3	1	3	1	3	1	3	1	3	1	3
		2	0	2	0	2	0	2	0	2	0	4
				7	2	7	2	7	3	7	4	6
						9	4	9	5	9	6	7
								4	2	4	2	8
										6	3	9

Fig. 3.6.1 Example of sorting by counting.

above L_2 are reviewed. There is only one such time, and it is an 8. We now need a rule for adjusting the counters as we examine the items of **L**.

If a list item examined is larger than the latest item, add 1 to its counter; if the item examined is smaller than the latest item, add 1 to the counter corresponding to the latest item.

Since 8 is larger than 3, we add 1 to C_1. The next item, 2, is entered at L_3. Since it is smaller than both 8 and 3, a 1 is added to the counters corresponding to each of these elements. C_3 remains at 0.

The fourth item entered at L_4 is 7. It is smaller than 8, so we add 1 to C_1, making it 3. It is larger than 3 and 2 which are, respectively, at L_2 and L_3: counters C_2 and C_3 are unaffected; one count for L_2 and L_3 is added to C_4.

The fifth item, 9, entered at L_5, is larger than all previous items. Four counts are therefore added to C_5 and none to any of the other counters.

New items are added to **L** and the counters adjusted accordingly until we have the seven items and their seven counters shown in frame seven of the figure. To make the sorted output list, we transfer each item to a position one greater than that indicated in the counter.

The first item of **L** is 8. C_1 contains 5, indicating that 8 should be placed in the sixth position of **S**. L_3 is 2 and C_3 is 0, showing that 2 is the first item in **S**. The last frame (8) shows the sorted output.

Notice that when indexing or some other form of address modification is used, **C** contains the number which should be added to the starting point of the list to get the desired address where the element should be stored.

Counting procedure

We state the counting procedure in operational terms. First we clear all counters,

$$\underset{i}{\mathrm{R}}\ 0 \longrightarrow C_i \qquad (\text{or } \mathbf{0} \longrightarrow \mathbf{C}) \tag{3.6.1}$$

As each element is brought, it is placed at a successive location in **L**. Suppose that we have placed the latest element in L_i. We must now compare its contents with those of each previous cell L_j. If the latest is larger, we add 1 to the counter, C_i corresponding to the latest item,

$$(L_i) \geq (L_j)\{(C_i) + 1 \longrightarrow C_i\} \tag{3.6.2}$$

If the latest is smaller, we add 1 to the counter for the other item counter, C_j

$$(L_i) < (L_j)\{(C_j) + 1 \longrightarrow C_j\} \tag{3.6.3}$$

We repeat this for all elements which precede L_i.

$$\mathop{\mathbf{R}}_{j=1}^{i-1} \begin{cases} (L_i) \geq (L_j)\{(C_i) + 1 \longrightarrow C_i\} \\ (L_i) < (L_j)\{(C_j) + 1 \longrightarrow C_j\} \end{cases} \tag{3.6.4}$$

The complete sort requires that we perform the operation of (3.6.4) as each new item is brought in. Therefore we have

$$\mathop{\mathbf{R}}_{i=2}^{n} \mathop{\mathbf{R}}_{j=1}^{i-1} \begin{cases} (L_i) \geq (L_j)\{(C_i) + 1 \longrightarrow C_i\} \\ (L_i) < (L_j)\{(C_j) + 1 \longrightarrow C_j\} \end{cases} \tag{3.6.5}$$

Transfer; complete routine

For any given element at, say, L_i its location on the output list is one more than is contained in the corresponding counter. To place it at this position we perform

$$\mathop{\mathbf{R}}_{i=1}^{n} (L_i) \longrightarrow S_{(C_i)+1} \tag{3.6.6}$$

The entire operation for sort by counting is presented in Fig. 3.6.2. Notice here that, if key words are placed in **L**, then we transfer records from the input buffer **I** to the sorted output list **S**, using the source address in **L** and the output address with an adjustment indicated by **C**.

$$\mathop{\mathbf{R}}_{i=1}^{\nu C} 0 \longrightarrow C_i$$

$$\mathop{\mathbf{R}}_{i=2}^{\nu L} \mathop{\mathbf{R}}_{j=1}^{i-1} \begin{cases} (L_i) > (L_j)\{(C_i) + 1 \longrightarrow C_i\} \\ (L_i) < (L_j)\{(C_j) + 1 \longrightarrow C_j\} \end{cases}$$

$$\mathop{\mathbf{R}}_{i=1}^{\nu L} (L_i) \longrightarrow S_{(C_i)+1}$$

Fig. 3.6.2 Sort by count routine.

Program

Figure 3.6.3 shows a routine for a sort by counting.

```
SCOUNT   XPN,1    N          {clear counters
         XOM,1    C-1
         TDN,1    *-1
         XPN,2    1          {initialize pointers
                             {to top of lists
     ┌──→XPN,1    1
LOOP │ ┌→XMA,2    L          get next item
     │ │ CMP,1    L-1        {compare with a
     │ │┌JOL      SMALL      {former item
     │ ││ XMA,2   C          {it's greater, add 1
     │ ││ ADD     =1         {to former item counter
     │ ││ XAM,2   C          {and replace
     │ ││┌UCJ     CHECK
SMALL│ │└┼XMA,1   C-1        {it's smaller, add 1
     │ │ │ADD     =1         {to this item's counter
     │ │ │XAM,1   C-1        {and replace
CHECK│ └─┴TDN,1   LOOP       {is sublist checked
     │                       {against this item?
     │   NPP,2    1          {have all
     │   CMPN,2   N+1        {items been
     └───JOL      LOOP-1     {checked?
OUTPUT   XMA,2    L-1        {
         XAN,1               {places items
         XMA,2    L-1        {from L in key
         XAM,1    S          {order onto S
         TDN,2    OUTPUT     {
```

Figure 3.6.3 Routine for sort by counting with segment for output placement.

PROBLEMS

3.1 Make a flowchart for selection sorting.

3.2 Make a flowchart for a selection sort for descending order.

3.3 Write **SLCTD**, a descending selection sort like **SELECT**.

3.4 Flowchart **SLCTEX**.

3.5 Flowchart and write in FLAP, **SLCTXD**, a descending select and exchange sort.

3.6 Rewrite **SLCTEX** for records of **R** word using these macros, if necessary:

MOVE	number of words, source start, destination start
XCHANGE	number of words, source start, destination start

3.7 Repeat 3.6 for **SLCTXD**.

3.8 Consider an *active* file of records, **I**, each of length *R* brought into main memory (core) to be *posted* onto a master file on desk. As each record is placed into a memory list, **L**, a sort by count using counters, **C**, is done. However, to use **C** advantageously, it should be in order. **C′** is a list of locations in **L** and is in the same order as the records should be to post them in order. Write a two-place program to:

(a) prepare **C**

(b) sort **C** by count and replace the count with the correspondent location in **L** to form **C′**.

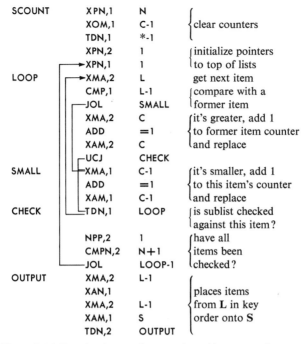

4 SORTING BY SEARCH

4.1 INSERTION SORTING

Philosophy

Here we take items as they arrive and insert them where they belong in an ordered partial list. When we get a new item, we are sure all items so far have been placed in order. We look at the partial sublist, using a search operator to find the place in that list where the new item belongs. This place will probably be occupied unless the item goes at either end. We move the item at that position and all subsequent items ahead exactly one place to make room for the new item which is then inserted. The partial list has grown by one but is still in order.

Example

Figure 4.1.1 is an example of insertion sort. On the left we have the original list, **L**, from which we will take, in order, items as they appear, starting with L_1 and proceeding to L_6. The first sublist, $_1\mathbf{S}$, is easy to form: We take the contents of L_1 and place it at S_1; no search is required.

At L_2 we find 6. The first item in $_1\mathbf{S}$ is greater than 6 and, hence, should be placed at the first position. $_2\mathbf{S}$ consists of 6 and 8, in that order.

We now get the third item, 3. It is less than 6 and again must occupy the first position. The items at S_1 and S_2 must be moved to S_2 and S_3, respectively, and then 3 is placed in S_1.

The fourth item is 4. It is greater than 3 and belongs at S_2. The items at S_2 and S_3 must be moved to S_3 and S_4, respectively, to make room for 4,

	L	${}_1S$	${}_2S$	${}_3S$	${}_4S$	${}_5S$	${}_6S$
L_6	5	$(L_2) \longrightarrow 8$	$(L_3) \longrightarrow 6$	3	$(L_5) \longrightarrow 3$	1	1
L_5	1		8	$(L_4) \longrightarrow 6$	4	3	3
L_4	4			8	6	4	4
L_3	3				8	$(L_6) \longrightarrow 6$	5
L_2	6					8	6
L_1	8						8

Fig. 4.1.1 Sorting a short list by an insertion sort.

which is placed at S_2. Two more operations complete the sort; these are illustrated in the figure.

Operators

To find the location where the next item belongs, we use the search operator γ. The proper position is given by

$$L_{i+1} \gamma {}_iS \tag{4.1.1}$$

The operator forms a partition of the output cells into two groups. The upper group is designated by

$$\lceil L_{i+1} \gamma {}_iS \rceil \tag{4.1.2}$$

The members of this group are advanced, using α, thus

$$\alpha \lceil L_{i+1} \gamma {}_iS \rceil \tag{4.1.3}$$

Finally, we have room in the output list for the new item which is inserted there thus

$$(L_{i+1}) \longrightarrow L_{i+1} \gamma {}_iS \tag{4.1.4}$$

Routine

Steps (4.1.3) and (4.1.4) are repeated for each item of the input list. The insertion routine in operator form is written as

$$\begin{aligned} &(L_1) \longrightarrow S_1 \\ &\underset{i=1}{\overset{n-1}{\mathbf{R}}} \begin{cases} {}_iS = \{S_1, S_2, \ldots, S_i\} \\ \alpha \lceil L_{i+1} \gamma {}_iS \rceil \\ (L_{i+1}) \longrightarrow L_{i+1} \gamma {}_iS \end{cases} \end{aligned} \tag{4.1.5}$$

4.2 PROGRAM FOR SORTING BY INSERTION

The program FLAP for sort by insertion is called SINSRT and is presented in Fig. 4.2.1. We are going to take items from **R** and from a new list **S**. The first item is placed in the first position of list **S** in the first three steps of the program. At LOOP we get the next item. It is placed in the proper position in the calling sequence of the search routine. The present length of the ouput list, which has been stored in index 2, is also placed in the calling sequence. The search subroutine is then called to find where the new item should be squeezed in. This is called PLACE, and it is set into a comparison command so that we know when to stop advancing items. Beginning at MOVE we advance all the items ahead of the place where this one is to go. The command COMP is used to tell us when we are done. After making space for the new item, we simply place it in this space, and if all the items have not been properly placed we return to LOOP.

```
SINSRT   XMA      R        Get first item from R.
         XAM      S        Put it at first space of S.
         XPN,2    1        Set output list size to 1.
LOOP     XMA,2    R        Get next item.
         XAM      ITEM     Place in call sequence.
         XNM,2    SIZE     Set list length in call sequence.
SEARCH   JSN,4    LSGR     )
         NOOP,1   S        |
SIZE     NOOP              >Search subroutine.
PLACE    NOOP              |
ITEM     NOOP              )
         XMN,3    PLACE    }Set stopping places
         XNM,3    COMP     }  for advancing.
         XMN,3    SIZE     Set end of set to be advanced.
MOVE     XMA,3    S - 1    )
         XAM,3    S        |
         NMP,3    1        >Make room for new item.
COMP     CMPN,3   ——       |
         JOG      MOVE     )
         XMA,2    R        Get item.
         XAM,3    S        Place it.
         NPD,2    1        Set for next item.
         CMPN,2   N        Done?
         JOL      LOOP
              return
```

Fig. 4.2.1 SINSRT, routine for sort by insertion from list **R** to list **S** of length N.

4.3 BINARY SEARCH

One fault of sorting by insertion is the length of the search. And in general, serial search is longer than it need be. That is, if we have an ordered list of length n through which we are searching, the expected number of operations is $n/2$ if the population distribution is rectangular.

The items to be sorted have a number of possible keys determined by the permutations of characters which may occupy each position of the key field.

If, for the list being sorted, each key is equally likely—each character can appear in any position with equal probability—the key distribution is said to be **rectangular.** Most lists do *not* have this property. For a list of names, we are much more likely to find surnames beginning with *S* than beginning with *X*!

Binary search

The maximum expected number of comparisons between the sought key and the list items for binary search is $\log_2 n + 1$. The actual number of comparisons may be less than this. Because of the nature of the search, we are able to narrow down the location of the element in much fewer tries.

To make a small-scale comparison, consider a list of 100 items. Serial search requires that we examine 50 items. Binary search requires that we examine 7 items or less.

Philosophy

Consider a list **L** and an item *a*. Binary search prescribes that we split the list in half and determine in which half *a* belongs. Next we take that half and divide it in half. We determine which of the two quarters *a* lies in. We halve that quarter to determine which eighth *a* lies in. We continue thus until we find the exact element corresponding to *a* if it is there.

Beta operator

Now we define a scalar operator, β, which determines the number of the item that divides the original list approximately in half. A scalar operator operates on a number, not on a list or item. The number upon which we operate is ν **L**.

To define β we need the integral operator which takes a real number and finds the integer just smaller than that number. Here we use the brackets as the integral operator and define it as

$$[\mathrm{p}] = \mathrm{k} \supset \mathrm{k} \leq \mathrm{p} < \mathrm{k} + 1 \qquad (4.3.1)$$

where *p* is a real number and *k* is an integer. The brackets are used where no confusion arises because this is the mathematical convention.

We define the beta operator as

$$\beta\, \mathrm{x} = \left[\frac{\mathrm{x} + 1}{2}\right] \qquad (4.3.2)$$

where *x* is an integer and [ ] is the integral operator. Here β chooses an interval of half when possible or a little greater otherwise. This is the step required in our search.

MULTIPLE APPLICATION

It is permissible to apply the beta operator several times successively so that

$$\beta^2 x = \beta(\beta x) = \beta\left[\frac{x+1}{2}\right] = \left[\frac{\left[\frac{x+1}{2}\right]+1}{2}\right] \tag{4.3.3}$$

and

$$\beta^3(x) = \beta(\beta^2 x) = \left[\frac{\left[\frac{\left[\frac{x+1}{2}\right]+1}{2}\right]+1}{2}\right] \tag{4.3.4}$$

and, in general,

$$\beta^k(x) = \beta\beta^{k-1}(x) \tag{4.3.5}$$

A short table of β's appears as Table 4.3.1.

Table 4.3.1 A SHORT TABLE OF β'S.

X	β	β^2	β^3	β^4	β^5
2	1				
3	2	1			
4	2	1			
5	3	2	1		
6	3	2	1		
7	4	2	1		
8	4	2	1		
9	5	3	2	1	
10	5	3	2	1	
11	6	3	2	1	
12	6	3	2	1	
13	7	4	2	1	
14	7	4	2	1	
15	8	4	2	1	
16	8	4	2	1	
17	9	5	3	2	1
18	9	5	3	2	1
19	10	5	3	2	1
20	10	5	3	2	1

SHORTHAND

When we apply β to the number of items in a list, we write simply

$$\beta \mathbf{L} \equiv \beta \nu \mathbf{L} \tag{4.3.6}$$

4.4 FENCE FINDING

Fence number operator

We now establish a fence number operator to establish the *number* of the fence item. This is the item which partitions the list into two halves, a half into two quarters, a quarter into two eighths, and so forth.

$$\phi_1 = \left[\frac{\nu \mathbf{L}}{2}\right] + 1 \tag{4.4.1}$$

Then the location, Φ_1, of the first fence item, is given as

$$\Phi_1 = \mathbf{L}_{\phi_1} \tag{4.4.2}$$

FENCE ITEM OPERATOR

We now wish to examine the fence item. We define a fence item operator which obtains the fence item from the list, **L**, and we also introduce a shorthand for it which is now given for the first fence item

$$\Phi_1 \mathbf{L} = \Phi_1 = (\mathbf{L}_{\phi_1}) \tag{4.4.3}$$

The general fence item is given as

$$\Phi_i \mathbf{L} = \Phi_i = (\mathbf{L}_{\phi_i}) \tag{4.4.4}$$

Second fence

We have found the first fence. We determine the proper half in which to look next by a comparison of a with Φ_1: If the two are equal, the item sought is found; if a is smaller, we confine our search to the upper half of the list; if a is larger, we examine the lower half of the list.

HOW FAR

Having determined the proper half of the list, we next decide how far to look. The beta operator provides us with this knowledge. $\beta\,\phi_1$ is the distance to move from $[\Phi_1]$ to find the second fence.

FENCE

We have enough information to prepare the second fence number ϕ_2,

$$\phi_2 = \phi_1 \pm \beta\,\phi_1 \tag{4.4.5}$$

The use of $+$ or $-$ is determined by whether the item searched for, a, is greater or less, respectively, than the fence item Φ_1. Hence we have

$$\phi_2 = \phi_1 + (\mathrm{a} > \Phi_1)\,\beta\,\phi_1 - (\mathrm{a} < \Phi_1)\,\beta\,\phi_1 \tag{4.4.6}$$

which tells us to do the following things:

1. Take the first fence.
2. *Add* the second fence distance quantity $\beta\,\phi_1$ if the search is to take place in the upper half.
3. *Subtract* the second fence distance $\beta\,\phi_1$ if the search is to proceed in the lower half.

The second fence item, Φ_2 is given by

$$\Phi_2 = (\mathbf{L}_{\phi_1}) \tag{4.4.7}$$

Third fence

The first operation found $[\Phi_1]$, the center of the list. The second operation found the center of the proper sublist, establishing it as $[\Phi_2]$. We needed the number of items in a quarter, which we determined as $\beta\,\phi_1$. For the third fence, we need the number of items in an eighth. Call it n_3; it is given by

$$\mathrm{n}_3 = \beta^2\,\phi_1 \tag{4.4.8}$$

Then the third fence number, ϕ_3, is given as

$$\phi_3 = \phi_2 \pm \beta^2\,\phi_1 \tag{4.4.9}$$

Again, whether we move ahead or behind in our search depends upon the search item size a as compared to the fence item Φ_2; thus

$$\phi_3 = \phi_2 + (\mathrm{a} > \Phi_2)\,\beta^2\,\phi_1 - (\mathrm{a} < \Phi_2)\,\beta^2\,\phi_1 \tag{4.4.10}$$

General fence

Suppose we have just obtained the $(i - 1)$th fence number, ϕ_{i-1}, and the $(i - 1)$th fence item, Φ_{i-1}. We wish to get the next fence number ϕ_i. We need the new distance n_i. The old distance, n_{i-1} is given by

$$\mathrm{n}_{\mathrm{i}-1} = \beta^{\mathrm{i}-2}\,\phi_1 \tag{4.4.11}$$

by an extrapolation of (4.4.8). Hence we may define n_i

$$\mathrm{n}_\mathrm{i} = \beta\,\mathrm{n}_{\mathrm{i}-1} = \beta^{\mathrm{i}-1}\,\phi_1 \tag{4.4.12}$$

This is how far we move from ϕ_{i-1} to get ϕ_i. Thus

$$\phi_\mathrm{i} = \phi_{\mathrm{i}-1} \pm \mathrm{n}_\mathrm{i} \tag{4.4.13}$$

FENCE ITEM NUMBER

The direction of motion depends on the size of the last fence, and we find

$$\phi_i = \phi_{i-1} + (a > \Phi_{i-1})\,\beta^{i-1}\,\phi_1 - (a < \Phi_{i-1})\,\beta^{i-1}\,\phi_1 \qquad (4.4.14)$$

and, of course

$$\Phi_i = (\mathbf{L}_{\phi_i}) \qquad (4.4.15)$$

End of search

Recall that the equations derived earlier, (4.4.6), (4.4.10), and (4.4.14), do not provide for equality of the search item a and the fence item Φ_j. When equality exists, the desired list item is found, and search is terminated.

$$a = \Phi_j \supset a \neq \Phi_i\,(i < j)\ \&\ a\,\sigma\,\mathbf{L} = [\Phi_j] \qquad (4.4.16)$$

a ABSENT

It is obvious from (4.4.14) that if $a = \Phi_j$, then Φ_{j+1} is undefined. Hence if Φ_k is defined, we know a has not been previously found in **L**. We then state

$$a \neq \Phi_k \supset a\,\sigma\,\mathbf{L} = \Lambda \qquad (4.4.17)$$

where k is given by

$$k = [\log_2 \nu\,\mathbf{L} + 1] \qquad (4.4.18)$$

If **L** contains multiple appearances of a, then binary search will not necessarily reveal the *first* appearance of a in **L** but it certainly will unearth *an* appearance of a in **L**.

Other searches

All the search operations may use the binary search technique if caution is observed. For instance, multiple appearances of a in **L** throw off the search.

GREATER, EQUAL

To apply γ to a list **L** with nonduplications of a, we have

$$a = \Phi_j \supset a\,\gamma\,\mathbf{L} = [\Phi_j] \qquad (4.4.19)$$

$$a < \Phi_k \supset a\,\gamma\,\mathbf{L} = [\Phi_k] \qquad (4.4.20)$$

$$a > \Phi_k\ \&\ \phi_k < \nu\,\mathbf{L} \supset a\,\gamma\,\mathbf{L} = [\Phi_k] + 1 \qquad (4.4.21)$$

$$a > \Phi_k\ \&\ \phi_k \geq \nu\,\mathbf{L} \supset a\,\gamma\,\mathbf{L} = \Lambda \qquad (4.4.22)$$

Notice that the only time that a γ search can come up with an answer in less than k looks is when a is equal to some Φ_j, $j \leq k$, (4.4.19). Otherwise the $(k - 1)$th look localizes the spot. The kth look tells us if Φ_k *is* the item (4.4.20). If not, from previous looks, we know that although $a > \Phi_k$, it must be that $a < ([\Phi_k] + 1)$, which is hence the desired item (4.4.21). Finally, if a is greater than all the items in **L**, then $a \, \gamma \, \mathbf{L}$ is missing (4.4.22).

OTHER

It is left as an exercise for the reader to determine a set of equations similar to (4.4.19–22) which apply to all the other search operators.

Examples

To illustrate the technique of binary search for equality, the example of Fig. 4.4.1 is presented. Another example for the operator γ is presented in Fig. 4.4.2.

$$\nu \, \mathbf{L} = 7$$

$$\phi_1 \, \mathbf{L} = \left[\frac{7}{2}\right] + 1 = 3 + 1 = 4$$

$$\Phi_1 = (L_4) = 6$$

$$6 < 8$$

$$\beta\phi_1 = \left[\frac{4+1}{2}\right] = 2$$

$$\phi_2 = \phi_1 + \beta \, \phi_1 = 4 + 2 = 6$$

$$\Phi_2 = 8$$

$$8 \, \sigma \, \mathbf{L} = L_6$$

L	
1	L_1
3	L_2
4	L_3
6	L_4
7	L_5
8	L_6
9	L_7

Fig. 4.4.1 Binary *search equal* example, find $8 \, \sigma \, \mathbf{L}$.

$$\phi_1 = \left[\frac{7}{2}\right] + 1 = 4$$

$$\Phi_1 = (L_4) = 6$$

$$5 < 6$$

$$\beta \, \phi_1 = \left[\frac{4+1}{2}\right] = 2$$

$$\phi_2 = \phi_1 - \beta \, \phi_1 = 4 - 2 = 2$$

$$\Phi_2 = (L_2) = 3$$

$$5 > 3$$

$$\beta^2 \, \phi_1 = \left[\frac{2+1}{2}\right] = 1$$

$$\phi_3 = \phi_2 + \beta^2 \, \phi_1 = 2 + 1 = 3$$

$$\Phi_3 = (L_3) = 4$$

$$5 > 4$$

$$5 \, \gamma \, \mathbf{L} = [\Phi_3] + 1 = L_4$$

$$(5 \, \gamma \, \mathbf{L}) = (L_4) = 6$$

(L)	**L**
1	L_1
3	L_2
4	L_3
6	L_4
7	L_5
8	L_6
9	L_7

Fig. 4.4.2 Binary *search greater* example, find $5 \, \gamma \, \mathbf{L}$.

4.5 SEARCH AND INSERTION IMPROVEMENT

Retard function

We have defined an advance function, α, and used it for moving items forward when a search has indicated where the new item belongs. If the new item must be put early in the sublist ${}_i\mathbf{S}$, then all the succeeding items must be advanced. We can gain an advantage if, instead of advancing items, we retard them. The retard operator is defined thus

$$\rho\, \mathbf{A}: \quad (\mathrm{A}_i) \longrightarrow \mathrm{A}_{i-1} \tag{4.5.1}$$

We use the retard or advance operator according to whether the new item belongs in the lower or upper half of the sorted sublist ${}_i\mathbf{S}$.

Binary search using retard or advance

Figure 4.5.1 shows operator notation for binary search using the improvement just discussed. Figure 4.5.2 shows a rather small list by this technique. Notice that whether we use the advance or retard operator depends only on the first fence item Φ_1: for $a \geq \Phi_1$ use α; for $a < \Phi_1$ use ρ.

$$\begin{aligned}
&(L_1) \longrightarrow S_I \\
&I \longrightarrow j, k \\
&{}_1\mathbf{S} = \{S_I\} \\
&{}_i\mathbf{S} = \{S_j, S_{j+1}, \ldots, S_I, \ldots, S_{k-1}, S_k\}
\end{aligned}$$

$$\underset{i=n}{\overset{\nu L-1}{\mathbf{R}}} \begin{cases} (L_{i+1}) < \Phi_1\, {}_i\mathbf{S}\{\rho\lfloor L_{i+1}\, \gamma\, {}_i\mathbf{S}\rfloor; & j-1 \longrightarrow j\} \\ (L_{i+1}) \geq \Phi_1\, {}_i\mathbf{S}\{\alpha\lceil L_{i+1}\, \gamma\, {}_i\mathbf{S}\rceil; & k+1 \longrightarrow k\} \\ \qquad (L_{i+1}) \longrightarrow L_{i+1}\, \gamma\, {}_i\mathbf{S} \end{cases}$$

Fig. 4.5.1 Routine for sort by binary search with insertion word advance or retard.

	L	${}_1\mathbf{S}$	${}_2\mathbf{S}$	${}_3\mathbf{S}$	${}_4\mathbf{S}$		${}_5\mathbf{S}$	${}_6\mathbf{S}$	
					→		1	1	1
L_6	5			↑	3	3	3	3	3
L_5	1			→ 3	3	4	4	4	4
L_4	4		→ 6	6	6	6	→ 6	6	5
L_3	3	S_I(Start) 8	8	8	8	8	8	6	6
L_2	6							8	8
L_1	8								

Fig. 4.5.2 A small list sorted by the routine of Fig. 4.5.1.

4.6 BINARY SEARCH PROGRAM

Searching as a graph

Let us represent the search process using a graph and particularly a directed tree, as shown in Fig. 4.6.1. The nodes of the tree represent the number of the item under examination; the branches indicate the calculations required to determine which node to examine next. Further, in the graphs that are illustrated, the horizontal position also corresponds to the approximate position of the element in the list.

As an example, examine Fig. 4.6.1. We start with seven elements in the list. But we do not look at the seventh element. Instead, we apply ϕ_1 to find that the fourth element should be examined first. The element next examined depends upon the result of the comparison between element four and the item searched for: if the item searched for is less than the fourth element, we look at element two next; if the item searched for is greater than element four, we look at element six next.

Notice that three levels or three looks are required to examine seven elements completely in Fig. 4.6.1.

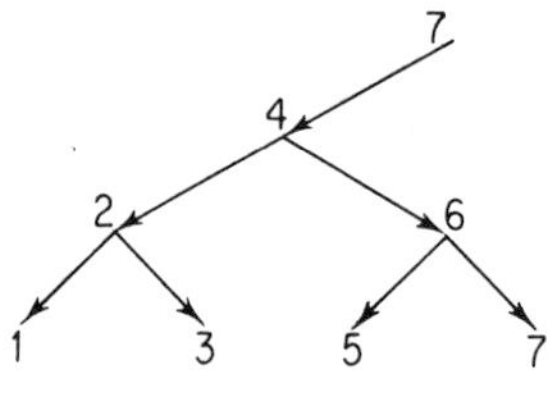

Fig. 4.6.1 A graph of a binary search of seven items.

Non-hit cells

Sometimes it may not be necessary to examine the designated as the one sought. This decision occurs at the final level where we have reduced the possible candidates for equality with the given item to two. In this case, if we eliminate one member of the pair and we know that the equality relation prevails for at least one member of the list, then it is the other member of the pair for which we search.

Alien cells

To simplify the programming and the search procedure, we permit cells outside the list proper to be referenced. The cells may be actually examined or the program may contain means for detecting that we are looking outside the list proper and return the proper indications. From this we can decide what the next element examined will be. This is best shown with an example.

EXAMPLES

Figure 4.6.2 contains four examples of binary search procedures. Let us just look at the first in Fig. 4.6.2a. We have a list of eight items. We first look at item five. Next we look at either item two or item eight. According to the comparison at item two, we either look at item four or item zero next. The request to examine item zero can cause the program to ignore a look at this level and look instead at item one on the next level. Or the program may actually look at the cell numbered zero. For this instance we require that the cell zero contain a key smaller than any conceivable key, which we indicate

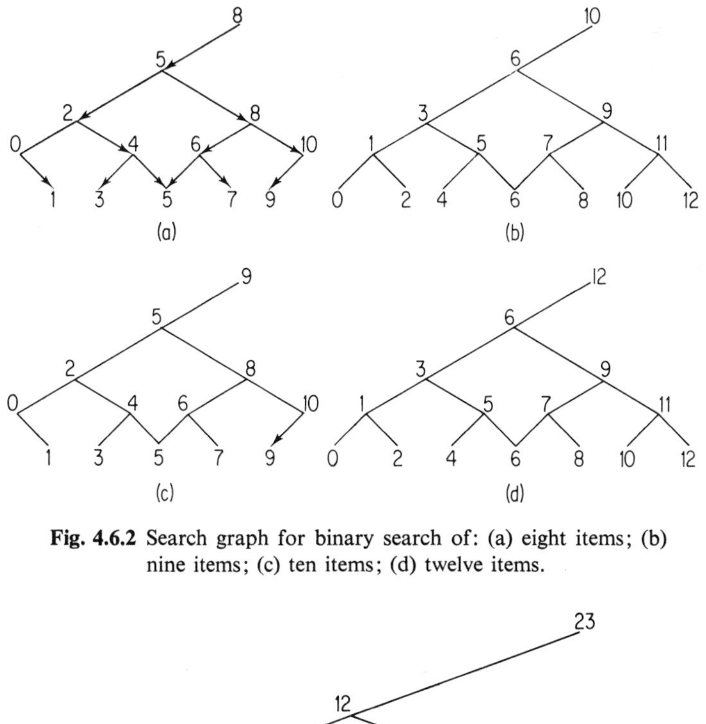

Fig. 4.6.2 Search graph for binary search of: (a) eight items; (b) nine items; (c) ten items; (d) twelve items.

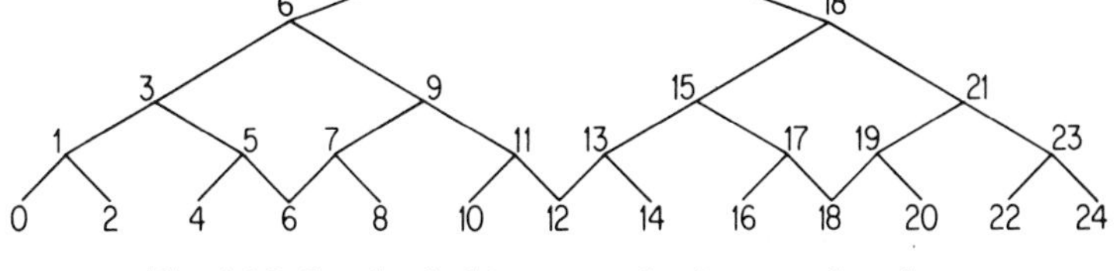

Fig. 4.6.3 Graph of a binary search of twenty-three items.

as **a**. A similar case arises after looking at the eighth element. This requires us to look at the tenth element for which none is recorded. The program may protect us here, or else we must fill the tenth element with a key larger than any conceivable element, viz., z.

The reader may examine the other examples in Fig. 4.6.2 and 4.6.3 to complete the explanation.

Search termination

Whether the search goes to completion is determined by the relationship dictated in the search description. When a search is for *equal*, *equal or greater*, or *equal or less*, it can terminate before the final level. This is illustrated by Fig. 4.6.4, where a list of eight items is used. The first item examined is the fifth element. If it is identical with the item searched for, our search terminates immediately. If equality is not part of the relationship specification, then generally the search will continue to the final level. Let us look at the final decision in Fig. 4.6.4. Suppose that the final item examined is element three. Equality means that element three is the desired item. If the item searched for is less than item three, then we have the following relationship

$$(L_2) < X < (L_3) \tag{4.6.2}$$

and X belongs at L_3. On the other hand, if the item searched for is greater than the one in the third position, the following relationship prevails

$$(L_3) < X < (L_4) \tag{4.6.3}$$

and X belongs at L_4. As soon as we have reached the bottom level, we have completely determined the position in the list at which the search for item belongs.

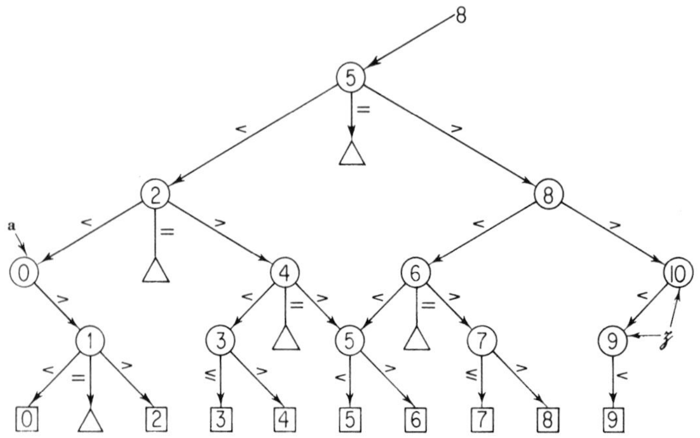

Fig. 4.6.4 Final placement of an item for a binary search of eight items.

Binary search program

The binary search subroutine is presented in Fig. 4.6.5. At the top of that figure, we find the calling sequence, which contains six entries. The first entry contains the location which precedes the starting point on the list and an index specification of a first index. This permits the routine to index automatically through the list. The second item contains the list length. Into the third item in the calling sequence, ITEM, will be placed the actual item searched for if found by the routine. The key is in the first three digits. The routine places in the fourth item in the calling sequence, a pointer indicating the ordinal number corresponding to the position in the original list where the searched-for item belongs. When the routine is completed, it returns to the calling sequence: It returns to the fifth position if the items in the original list should be moved backward to make room for the new item; it returns to the sixth position if the items in the original list should be moved forward to make room for the new item.

USE

The subroutine BISRCH may be used for a σ (equal only) or γ (greater or equal) search, depending upon the call sequence and its interpretation. For the σ search, a routine is placed at either ITEM or POINT or both. If these are not effected by BISRCH, the item has *not* been found.

For a sort, a γ search is required. It is always successful. Even when $a \gamma \mathbf{L}$ lies outside of **L**, this means that a goes at the end of **L**. Anyway, POINT shows where the item should be entered, and the return tells us whether to use α or ρ to make space.

START

To start the routine, we bring the number of items from the call squence into the accumulator and multiply this by $\frac{1}{2}$, using MUL to round down and achieve the *integral* function. We add 1 to this to form ϕ_1. We store this result in a cell called B and also in index 1. We also store it in a cell called PHI, the fence cell, and also in a cell called HALF, to distinguish in which half of the list the item belongs.

COMPARISON

At COMPAR we compare the given item with the fence item and jump to HIT if they should be equal. The sequence which follows inserts either ADD or SUB into the location, CMND.

Next at COMPAR+5 we check if there are more items in our list and,

```
                        Call
            JSN,4       BISRCH
            NOOP,1      L-1           sorted list
LENGTH      NOOP        N             length
ITEM                                  item
POINT                   POINTER       position to replace
RRTRN                   return        to retard list
ARTRN                   return        to advance list
-----------------------------------------------------------------
BISRCH      XMA,4       2             get length, N, from call sequence
                                      now find φ1:
BETA        XAD
            MUL         = 0.5         {= [N/2] + 1
            ADD         = 1           {
            XAM         B             and save in B
            XMN,1       B             and in index 1
FENCE       XNM,1       PHI           initialize PHI
            XNM,1       HALF          remember halfway point
COMPAR      XMA,4       003           compare ITEM
            CMP,I,4     001           with fence item
            JOE         HIT           jump out when equal
            JOL         * + 4         or less
            XMA         = ADD   B     enter ADD
            XAM         CMND          at CMND
            UCJ         * + 3         then check beta
            XMA         = SUB   B     enter SUB
            XAM         CMND          at CMND
            XMA         B             compare beta
            CMP         = 1           to 1
            JOE         OUT           done if =
            ADD         = 1           add 1 to old beta
            XMD                       move
            MUL         = 0.5         and halve
            XAM         B             replace new beta
            XMA         PHI           bring phi
CMND        NOOP                      add or subtract beta
            XAM         PHI           and replace new phi
            XAN,1                     also put it into index 1
            UCJ         COMPAR
OUT         XMA         PHI           enter phi and
            CMP         HALF          compare to (HALF)
            JOG         TOP           item in top of list
BOTTOM      XMA         CMND          check to find if result of
            CPM         = ADD   B     last item compare was greater
            JOE         * + 2
            NMP,1       1             otherwise pointer moved back
            XNA,1                     put pointer
            XAM,4       4             in call sequence
            UCJ,4       5             and return to RRTRN
HIT         XMA         PHI           {put pointer
            XAM,4       4             {into call sequence
            CMP         HALF          {check if in top or bottom
            JOG,4       6             return to RRTRN
            UCJ,4       5             return to ARTRN
TOP                 (Similar to BOTTOM above)
```

Fig. 4.6.5 The binary search routine BISRCH.

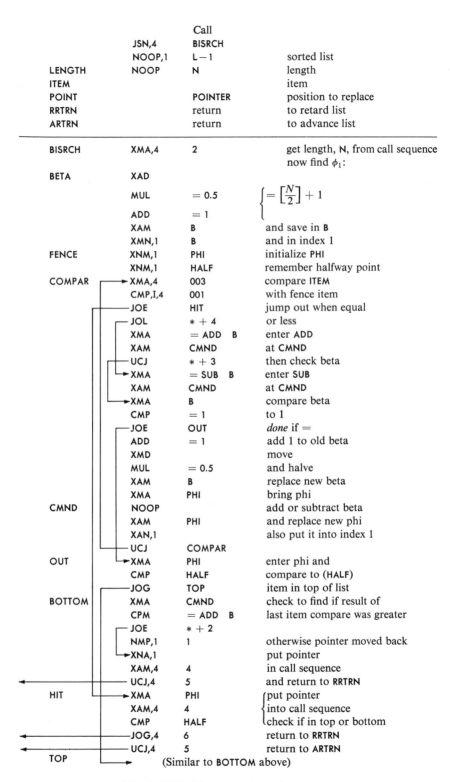

if so, we calculate a new fence. This calculation requires application of the beta operator which is added or subtracted to the old fence, using the command we have placed at CMND. When done, we return to COMPAR.

WINDUP

When we are at the bottom level of our list or if we have found the desired item earlier, we go to the section called OUT. Here we determine whether the position determined is in the top or bottom half of the list. If it is in the bottom, half, we go to BOTTOM and fill in the entries in the calling sequence. Otherwise we go to TOP, which has been omitted from the figure.

```
BISORT   XPN,3    OUTPUT+N−1   initialize output pointer
         XMA      R
         XAM,3    1            store first item
         XMA      R + 1        get second item
         CMP,3    1            compare to first
         JOG      * + 3        if greater, store
         XAM,3    1            if  less
         XMA      R            move first down
         XAM,3    2            and store
         XNM,3    LIST         store pointer in call
         XPN,2    2            initializes counter
LOOP     XMA,2    R            put next item into
         XAM      ITEM         call sequence
         XNM,2    LENGTH       put counter in call
         XNM,3    LIST         set list start in call sequence
         JSN,4    BISRCH       do binary search
LIST     NOOP,1   00           provided
LENGTH   NOOP                  provided
ITEM     NOOP                  provided
POINT    NOOP                  returned
RRTRN    UCJ      RETARD
ARTRN    XMN,1    POINT        put pointer into
         XNM,1    ATEST        limit test command
         XMN,1    LENGTH       place last item marker in index 1
         NPP,1    1            and add 1 to it
ADV      XMQ,1    LIST         { get next item
                               { advance pointer one place
         XQM,1    LIST + 1     { move item ahead
         NMP,1    1
ATEST    CMPN,1   000
         JOL      MOVE
         UCJ      ADV
MOVE     XMA      ITEM         insert item
         XAM,1    1
         NPP,2    1            advance counter to check
         CMPN,2   N + 1        if all items inserted
         JOL      LOOP         if not go to LOOP
RETARD   (similar to ARTRN)
```

Fig. 4.6.6 Sort by insertion using binary search routine, BISORT.

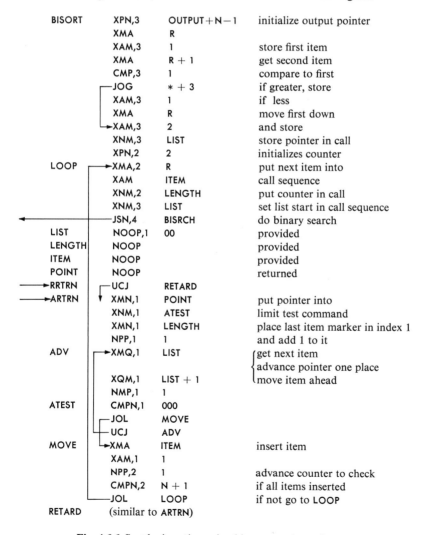

The sort program

The sort by insertion using binary search is called BISORT and is presented in Fig. 4.6.6. This can be perused by the reader without explanation.

PROBLEMS

4.1 Reprogram SINSRT for records of length **R**.

4.2 Reprogram SINSRT for records of length **R** where **R** is a parameter in the call sequence.

4.3 Reprogram BISORT for records of length **R**.

5 SORTING USING SUBLISTS

5.1 QUADRATIC SELECTION

Advantage of sublists

Analysis of selection sorting has shown that, as the size of the input list grows, so does the length of the list each time an item is selected. The list is reviewed once for each of its members. We obtain an advantage when we use selection and exchange: instead of reviewing the entire list, we only review a portion of it for each item. And this portion grows smaller as we examine later items. As we shall see, the best *number of sublists* is close to the square root of the *number of items* in the main list—this is the source of the name **quadratic sort.**

To save examining the complete list for each item regardless of how many are left, we now consider breaking up the list into sublists. Then when an item is taken from a sublist for output, only that sublist need be reviewed in its entirety.

However, we must, for each ouptut item, find the least remaining item for the *whole* list. To obviate examining the whole list, we establish a list, $\mathbf{L}'$, of *leasts* for each sublist. That is, suppose our original list $\mathbf{L}$ is divided into sublists, ${}^{1}\mathbf{L}$, ${}^{2}\mathbf{L}$, etc. L'_1 stores the present least of ${}^{1}\mathbf{L}$; L'_2 stores the present least of ${}^{2}\mathbf{L}$, and so forth.

To find the next output item for $\mathbf{S}$, we examine only $\mathbf{L}'$ and pick its least. Suppose it is found at L'_K; then we must update L'_K by picking a new least from ${}^{K}\mathbf{L}$.

Procedure

In outline form, we have:

1. Divide the list **L** into sublists $^i\mathbf{L}$.
2. Enter the least of each sublist $^i\mathbf{L}$ into a cell L'_i of an auxiliary list $\mathbf{L}'$.
3. Find the least of ($\mathbf{L}'$) for output, say ($\mathbf{L}'_K$)
4. Refill L'_K with the new least from $^K\mathbf{L}$.
5. Repeat (3) and (4) until ν (**S**) = ν (**L**).

DIVISION

The optimal number of sublists, (see later) N, is given by

$$\mathrm{N} = \sqrt{\mathrm{n}} \quad \text{if} \quad \mathrm{n} = \mathrm{N}^2 \tag{5.1.1}$$

or

$$\mathrm{N} = [\sqrt{\mathrm{n}} + 1] + 1 = [\sqrt{\nu \mathbf{L}} + 1] + 1 \tag{5.1.2}$$

Then divide **L** into N sublists so that

$$\mathbf{L} = \bigcup_1^{\mathrm{N}} {}^{\mathrm{i}}\mathbf{L} \tag{5.1.3}$$

where, further

$$\nu\, {}^{\mathrm{i}}\mathbf{L} \leq \mathrm{N} \tag{5.1.3}$$

In what follows, it is simpler to assume that the number of items in our original list, **L**, is a perfect square. The analysis in operational terms can be performed when this is not so, but this is left as an exercise for the reader. Henceforth we assume that either

$$\mathrm{n} = \mathrm{N}^2 \tag{5.1.4}$$

or

$$\nu\, {}^{\mathrm{i}}\mathbf{L} = \mathrm{N}_{\mathrm{I}} \tag{5.1.5}$$

To update the whole deal, sublists and auxiliary list, as we see later, we must examine the auxiliary list straight through, and then the entire sublist to which the item belongs. For $N = \sqrt{n}$, we examine $2\sqrt{n}$ items.

If N were chosen larger, the number of items for sublist would be smaller, but the number of sublists and, hence, the length of the auxiliary list would be greater. The total number of items examined would then be larger than $2\sqrt{n}$. Similarly, if N were made smaller, there would be fewer sublists and a shorter auxiliary list, but each sublist would be larger—again the number of looks would exceed $2\sqrt{n}$.

AUXILIARY LIST

The setup of $\mathbf{L}'$ is simply stated in operator form,

$$\overset{N}{\underset{i=1}{\mathbf{R}}} (\lambda\, {}^{i}\mathbf{L}) \longrightarrow \mathrm{L}'_{i} \tag{5.1.6}$$

Replenishment

After we select the first item for our sorted list, we select a new item for the auxiliary list to replace the chosen item. It comes from the same sublist as selected output item.

Suppose that (S_1) came from the Kth sublist of $\mathbf{L}$, ${}^{K}\mathbf{L}$. To replenish cell L'_K, we review ${}^{K}\mathbf{L}$, but we do not want to choose the same item chosen earlier. This is avoided if, whenever we choose an item from a sublist, we replace it by a maximum item, ƶ. Thus to (5.1.6), when we first fill the auxiliary lists, we should add

$$\overset{N}{\underset{i=1}{\mathbf{R}}}\, \text{ƶ} \longrightarrow \lambda\, {}^{i}\mathbf{L} \tag{5.1.7}$$

Call ${}^{K}\mathbf{L}$, after it has been altered the first time, ${}^{K}_{1}\mathbf{L}$; during the first replenishment, we find the least item from this list and place it in the Kth cell of $\mathbf{L}'$ thus

$$(\lambda\, {}^{K}_{1}\mathbf{L}) \longrightarrow \mathrm{L}'_{K} \tag{5.1.8}$$

The left subscript, 1, indicates that *one* of the items from the original list ${}^{K}\mathbf{L}$ has been replaced by ƶ. For the first replensihment, we enter ƶ at this position

$$\text{ƶ} \longrightarrow \lambda\, {}^{K}_{1}\mathbf{L} \tag{5.1.9}$$

GENERAL

The sort continues thus with repetitions of these steps:

$$(\lambda\, {}_{j}\mathbf{L}') = (\mathrm{L}_{K_j}) \longrightarrow \mathrm{S} \tag{5.1.10}$$

$$(\lambda'_{K_j}\mathbf{L}) \longrightarrow \mathrm{L}'_{K_j} \tag{5.1.11}$$

$$\text{ƶ} \longrightarrow \lambda\, {}^{K_j}\mathbf{L} \tag{5.1.12}$$

Eventually, some of the sublists of $\mathbf{L}$ will contain only ƶ's. As soon as this happens, we fill the auxiliary list cell corresponding to that sublist with ƶ,

$$\{(\lambda\, {}^{j}\mathbf{L}) = \text{ƶ}\}\, \text{ƶ} \longrightarrow \mathrm{L}'_{j} \tag{5.1.13}$$

Recapitulation

After a new item has been selected for our sorted list:

1. We review the sublist from which the item was drawn to find the minimum.
2. We place the minimum in the cell of the auxiliary list corresponding to that sublist.
3. Since the cell in the sublist from which the item was withdrawn still contains that item, we write ƶ into the cell over the item.
4. We review the auxiliary list to find its minimum.
5. This minimum is the next item for the sorted list.

Example

Several stages of an example of quadratic sorting appear in Figs. 5.1.1 through 5.1.4. It is left to the reader to state in operational notation the rou-

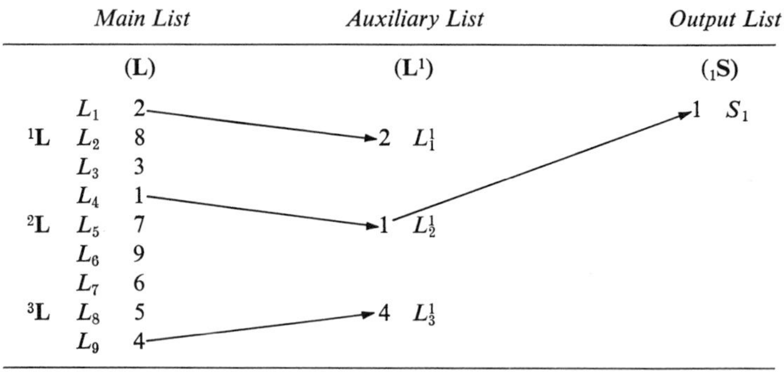

Fig. 5.1.1 Fillup stage of the quadratic sort and first quadratic selection.

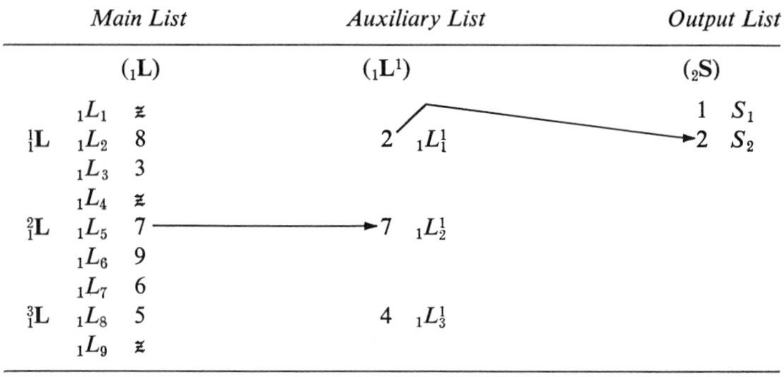

Fig. 5.1.2 Second quadratic selection and refill.

tine for quadratic selection. Since quadratic selection with presort is more effective, we devote the next section to its analysis and develop the routine for it.

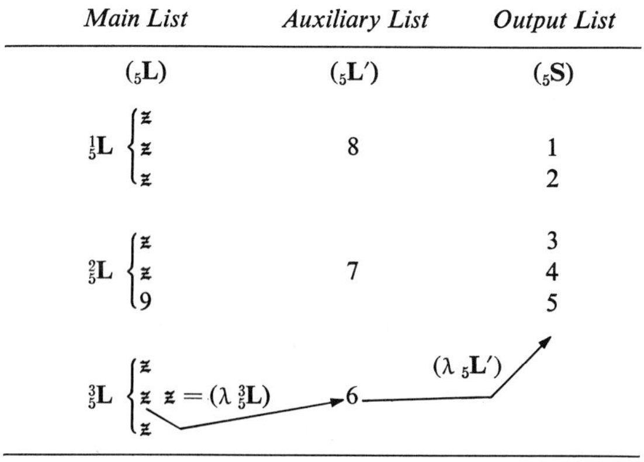

Fig. 5.1.3 At this stage of quadratic selection one cell of **L** receives ƶ.

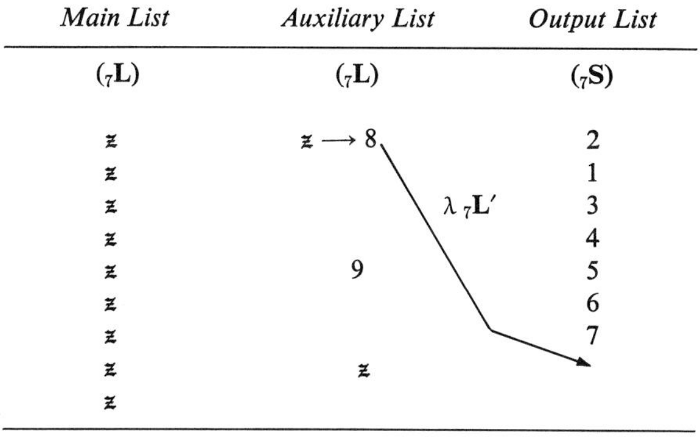

Fig. 5.1.4 Near the end of the quadratic sort.

5.2 QUADRATIC SELECTION WITH PRESORT

In Section 5.1 for the quadratic sort, each of the N items of a sublist is reviewed each time the cell of that auxiliary list is chosen for output. This happens N times—once for each item in the sublist. If this were not so, every item of the sublist would not appear in the output. Each sublist review amounts to a selection sort. The selection sort is highly inefficient. Why not arrange each sublist with a more efficient sort and then see if the quadratic selection procedure could be applied to the sorted sublists?

Suppose, then, that each ${}^{i}\mathbf{L}$ is presorted by some scheme. In the middle of the quadratic sort the procedure is like this.

1. Find the least of $(\mathbf{L}')$ for output; call it (L'_K).
2. Get the present top of the sublist ${}^{K}\mathbf{L}$; call it $({}^{K}L_j)$.
3. Put it in L'_K.
4. If ${}^{K}\mathbf{L}$ is empty, put ȥ in L'_K.
5. Move the pointer for ${}^{K}\mathbf{L}$ so that it points to ${}^{K}\mathbf{L}_{j+1}$.
6. Stop when all sublists are empty. ($L'_K =$ ȥ for all K.)

Auxiliary list

Before sorting gets under way, we fill the auxiliary list, $\mathbf{L}'$. Since the sublists are in order, this simply means taking the top sublist item and placing it in the proper auxiliary list cell,

$$\mathop{\mathbf{R}}_{i=1}^{N} ({}^{i}L_1) \longrightarrow L'_i \qquad (5.2.1)$$

then moving down the pointer for each ${}^{i}\mathbf{L}$.

Selection and Refill

During the sort proper, we select the smallest item in the auxiliary list. Suppose that it is the kth item in that auxiliary list. Then we have

$$(\lambda\, \mathbf{L}') = (L'_k) \longrightarrow S_1 \qquad (5.2.2)$$

We wish to go back to the sublist from which this item (L'_k) came. This item was withdrawn from sublist ${}^{k}\mathbf{L}$; it is the k_jth item in that sublist.

Recall that each sublist, including ${}^{k}\mathbf{L}$, has been presorted. The next item to be examined is at k_j *plus 1*. It is at ${}^{k}L_{k_j+1}$. Before we act, let's advance k_j

$$k_j + 1 \longrightarrow k_j \qquad (5.2.3)$$

The new item of the new sublist is placed in the kth position of the auxiliary list, $\mathbf{L}'_k$,

$$({}^{k}L_{k_j}) \longrightarrow L'_k \qquad (5.2.4)$$

One thing we must beware of is exceeding the length of the jth sublist. If we do, we will find that we are beginning the $(j + 1)$th sublist. To eliminate this eventuality, we check to see if there is still an element left in the sublist before placing it in the auxiliary list

$$\{k_j \leq N_j\}({}^{k}L_{k_j}) \longrightarrow L'_k \qquad (5.2.5)$$

Otherwise, we enter ȥ at the auxiliary location.

$$\{k_j > N_j\}\text{ȥ} \longrightarrow L'_k \qquad (5.2.6)$$

Notice that the check for sublist ending in (5.2.5) and (5.2.6) is simpler when the number of items in L is N^2 and, hence, that each sublist is comprised of N items.

Example

Figure 5.2.1 shows how quadratic selection with presort is done for a small input list of nine items. ${}_0\mathbf{L}$ is the subdivided but unordered input list. In going

	Main Unsorted (L)		*Group Sorted Main List* (${}_1$L)	*Auxiliary List* (L′)
	2		2	
${}^1_0\mathbf{L}$	8	${}^1_1\mathbf{L}$	3	
	3		8	2, , 3, 8,
	1		1	
${}^2_0\mathbf{L}$	7	${}^2_1\mathbf{L}$	7	1, 7, , ,
	9		9	
	6		4	
${}^3_0\mathbf{L}$	5	${}^3_1\mathbf{L}$	5	4, , , 5,
	4		6	

Fig. 5.2.1 Example of quadratic sort with presort.

to ${}_1\mathbf{L}$ we order each of the sublists by one of the techniques discussed earlier. The top item of each sublist is entered into the auxiliary list $\mathbf{L}'$.

For the first operation, the least of ($\mathbf{L}'$) is (L_2') which contains 1, that is, the first item chosen. To replace 1 in $\mathbf{L}'$, we go back to the second subgroup ${}^2\mathbf{L}$ and move its pointer forward one position. It now points to the item 7 at ${}^2\mathbf{L}$ which is placed at L_2'.

For the next operation, the least of ($\mathbf{L}'$) is selected. It is at L_1' which contains 2. This requires us to go to ${}^1\mathbf{L}$. We move the pointer to ${}^1\mathbf{L}$ which contains 3, which is entered into L_1'. The reader may follow how the rest of the quadratic selection process is performed.

Routine

The routine for quadratic selection is presented in Fig. 5.2.2. At (1) the sublists of ${}_0\mathbf{L}$ are ordered and become, ${}_1\mathbf{L}$. At (2) the top item of each sublist is entered into the corresponding location of the auxiliary list. At (3) all the subgroup counters are initialized. Step (4) sets up the output counter. At (5) we select the least of the auxiliary list and place it at the output. We advance the sublist index (6). The next sublist item is entered in the aux-

$$({}^{0}_{0}\mathbf{L}) \longrightarrow {}_{1}\mathbf{L} \tag{1}$$

$$\mathop{\mathbf{R}}_{i=1}^{N} ({}^{i}_{1}L_{1}) \longrightarrow L'_{i} \tag{2}$$

$$\mathop{\mathbf{R}}_{i=1}^{N} 1 \longrightarrow j_{i} \tag{3}$$

$$\hat{j} = \left(\sum_{i=1}^{N} j_{i}\right) - N + 1 \tag{4}$$

$$(\lambda\, \mathbf{L}') = ({}^{j}\mathbf{L}_{\mathrm{j_k}}) \longrightarrow S_{\hat{j}} \tag{5}$$

$$j_{k} + 1 \longrightarrow j_{k} \tag{6}$$

$$(j_{k} \leq N)\ \{({}^{i}\mathbf{L}_{j_{k}}) \longrightarrow L'_{j}\} \tag{7}$$

$$(j_{k} > N)\ \{\text{ẑ} \longrightarrow L'_{j}\} \tag{8}$$

Fig. 5.2.2 Quadratic selection routine.

iliary list, provided the sublist in question is not exhausted (7); if it is not exhausted, we enter ẑ into the auxiliary list.

FLAP Program

Let us now examine a FLAP program to do quadratic sorting with presorted sublists. This requires an auxiliary list. To facilitate the programming, the auxiliary list structure presented in Fig. 5.2.3 will be used. The FLAPJAC

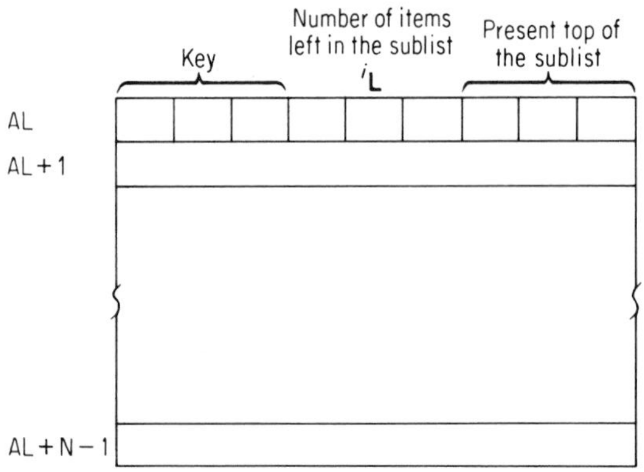

Fig. 5.2.3 Structure of the sublist for QUAD2 program for FLAPJAC.

word has 36 bits which may be considered as nine 4-bit numerical characters. Each word can be considered to consist of three fields as shown in the figure:

* The first field stores the three-digit key of the next available word of the sublist.

* The second field indicates three digits for the number of items left in the sublist.
* The third field has the absolute address of the top of the list—this is the location which contains the word the key of which is in the first field of this word.

An example of how the auxiliary list functions is found in Fig. 5.2.4. Here we are sorting nine items, each of which has a three-digit key. This requires an auxiliary list of three entries. The figure shows the state of the auxiliary list after three items have been chosen for output: item 101 from ${}^3L_1$ was first; 234 of ${}^1L_1$ second; 368 from ${}^1L_2$ was third. The use of pointers should be apparent.

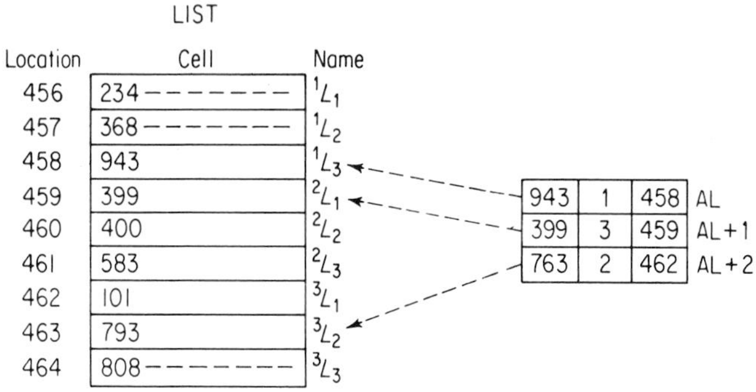

Fig. 5.2.4 Sorting nine items with QUAD2 using the auxiliary list structure of Fig. 5.2.3.

FLOW CHART

Figure 5.2.5 contains a flow chart for the quadratic sort, QUAD2. First we find N, the number of sublists. This is the function of n, the total number of items to be sorted. Then in box 2, the original list is broken into N sublists, and each of these is sorted by some method which is not considered here. We now have N ordered sublists ${}^i\mathbf{L}$ from which we must make up an auxiliarly list, $\mathbf{L}'$.

The routine START finds the next item for output by examining the auxiliary list. The routine CHOOSE prepares a new entry for the auxiliary list. These two new routines are now examined.

CHOOSE

CHOOSE in Fig. 5.2.6 is entered after having called LEAST, which has already determined the position of the item in the auxiliary list which contains

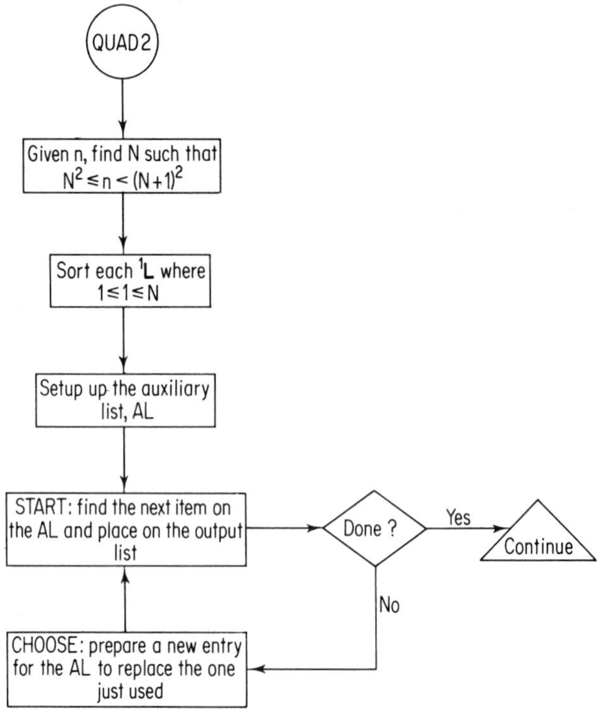

Fig. 5.2.5 Flow chart for the quadratic sort, QUAD2.

the least key. This position is referred to as ALPOS. The word at that position is brought into the accumulator where it is rotated rightward so that the number of items remaining in the sublist is contained in the right three digits of the accumulator. This count is transferred to index 2 where it is reduced by 1. As long as there are items left in the sublist, we go to NEXT to reposition the auxiliary word and advance the sublist position. The next steps bring in the item from the sublist and extract the key. The key is then placed in the auxiliary list word, and we return to the program.

Should a sublist become empty, we put z into the key position of the auxiliary list word.

QUAD2

The quadratic sort is presented in Fig. 5.2.7. First the subroutine LEAST is called to determine the item with the least key in the auxiliary list. The absoulte location of the item is extracted, and the item is brought into the accumulator. Once it is transferred from the output list a check is made

Step	Command		Description	A REGISTER			Q REGISTER			INDEX 1	INDEX 2
CHOOSE	XMA	ALPOS	bring *least* position	NOOP		501		x		x	x
+1	XAN,1		into index 1							501	
+2	XMA,1	AL	bring AL item	399	003	459					
+3	ERA	12	put "items left" at right	459	399	003					
+4	XAN,2		and then into index 2								003
+5	TDN,2	NEXT	{if there are items left in sublist after tally down, go to NEXT								002
+6	XMA	=Z	{put z into AL								
+7	XAM,1	AL									
+8	UCJ,4	1	and return to main program								
NEXT	XNA,2		restore "items left" to A	459	399	002					
+1	ELA	12	reposition AL word	399	002	459					
+2	ADD	=1	advance item position	399	002	460					
+3	XAN,2		position into index 2								460
+4	LSR	24	place "items left" "top" in Q	xxx	xxx	399	002	460	xxx		
+5	XMA,2	0	bring actual item	407	xxx	xxx					
+6	SRA	24	position key	000	000	407					
+7	LSL	24	shift into place in A	407	002	460	xxx	xxx	xxx		
+8	XMA,1	0	replace in AL								
+9	UCJ,4	1	return								

Fig. 5.2.6 CHOOSE SR for QUAD2.

to determine if sorting operation is completed. If not, we do the routine CHOOSE which refills the auxiliary list item.

```
START    JSN,4    LEAST     ⎧
         NOOP,1   AL        ⎪
         NOOP     N         ⎨Find least item in AL.
ALPOS    NOOP               ⎪
ALWORD   NOOP               ⎩
         XMA      ALWORD
         XAN,1              Put sublist item number in index 1.
         XMA,1    0         Put sublist item into A.
         XAN,3    S         Output item.
         NPP,3    1         Advance output list pointer.
         CMPN,3   n         Done?
         JOG      CONTINU   End of sort.
         JSN,4    CHOOSE    Reset AL.
         UCJ      START     Continue sort.
```

Fig. 5.2.7 Quadratic sort with present program, QUAD2.

5.3 CUBIC SELECTION

Philosophy

Cubic selection requires that, besides our original list **L**, we have two auxiliary lists **L′** and **L″**.

To determine the number of items in each of the auxiliary lists, we define the constant *M* thus

$$M = [\sqrt[3]{\nu\, \mathbf{L}}] + 1 \qquad (5.3.1)$$

The number of items in our original list therefore obeys the relationship

$$(M - 1)^3 < \nu\, \mathbf{L} \leq M^3 \qquad (5.3.2)$$

In what follows we assume that this simplifying relationship exists

$$\nu\, \mathbf{L} = M^3 \qquad (5.3.3)$$

and that the number of items in our original list is a perfect cube.

We divide the original list **L** into M^2 lists, each of *M* items. We then have

$$\mathbf{L} = \bigcup_{1}^{M^2} {}^{i}\mathbf{L} \qquad (5.3.4)$$

For each of these lists we select a minimum. The minimum is placed in the corresponding element in **L′**. There are M^2 elements in **L′**. There is one element corresponding to each sublist so that we have

$$\lambda\, {}^{i}\mathbf{L} \longrightarrow \mathbf{L}'_i \qquad (5.3.5)$$

The first auxiliary list hence consists of M^2 items thus

$$\mathbf{L}' = \bigcup_{1}^{M^2} \mathbf{L}'_i \qquad (5.3.6)$$

We divide L' into M sublists, each of M items, thus

$$\mathbf{L}' = \bigcup_{1}^{\mathrm{M}} {}^{\mathrm{j}}\mathbf{L}' \tag{5.3.7}$$

Second auxiliary list

We now make a second auxiliary list, $\mathbf{L}''$, in the same way that we made the first auxiliary list but this time using the first auxiliary list as the input. For each of the M sublists of $\mathbf{L}'$ we have one cell in $\mathbf{L}''$. We therefore have the correspondence

$$\mathbf{L}_{\mathrm{j}}'' \longleftrightarrow {}^{\mathrm{j}}\mathbf{L}' \tag{5.3.8}$$

The minimum for each sublist is inserted in each of these cells thus

$$\lambda\,({}^{\mathrm{j}}\mathbf{L}') \longrightarrow \mathbf{L}_{\mathrm{j}}'' \tag{5.3.9}$$

We have

$$\mathbf{L}'' = \bigcup_{1}^{\mathrm{M}} \mathbf{L}_{\mathrm{j}}'' \tag{5.3.10}$$

For an initial list $\mathbf{L}$ of 27 items we have the following relations

$$\mathbf{L} = \bigcup_{\mathrm{i}=1}^{9} {}^{\mathrm{i}}\mathbf{L}; \qquad \mathbf{L}' = \bigcup_{1}^{3} {}^{\mathrm{j}}\mathbf{L}'; \qquad \mathbf{L}'' = \bigcup_{1}^{3} \mathbf{L}_{\mathrm{j}}'' \tag{5.3.11}$$

Figure 5.3.1 presents graphically the relations among the lists and sublists.

$$\begin{array}{llll}
\mathbf{L} & & & \\
{}^{1}\mathbf{L}\left\{\begin{array}{l} L_1 \\ L_2 \\ \vdots \\ L_M \end{array}\right. & \lambda\,{}^{1}\mathbf{L} \longrightarrow L_1' & & \\
{}^{2}\mathbf{L}\left\{\begin{array}{l} L_{M+1} \\ \vdots \\ L_{2M} \end{array}\right. & \lambda\,{}^{2}\mathbf{L} \longrightarrow L_2' & & \\
{}^{3}\mathbf{L}\left\{\begin{array}{l} L_{2M+1} \\ \vdots \\ L_{3M} \end{array}\right. & \lambda\,{}^{3}\mathbf{L} \longrightarrow L_3' & \Bigg\}\ {}^{1}\mathbf{L}' & \lambda\,{}^{1}\mathbf{L}' \longrightarrow L_1'' \\
\vdots & & & \\
{}^{M}\mathbf{L}\left\{\begin{array}{l} L_{M^2-M+1} \\ \vdots \\ L_{M^2} \end{array}\right. & \lambda\,{}^{M}\mathbf{L} \longrightarrow L_M' & & \\
{}^{M+1}\mathbf{L}\left\{\begin{array}{l} L_{M^2+1} \\ \vdots \\ L_{M^2+M} \end{array}\right. & \begin{array}{l} \lambda\,{}^{M+1}\mathbf{L} \longrightarrow L_{M+1}' \\ \lambda\,{}^{2M}\mathbf{L} \longrightarrow L_{2M}' \end{array} & \Big\}\ {}^{2}\mathbf{L}' & \lambda\,{}^{2}\mathbf{L}' \longrightarrow L_2'' \\
\vdots & & \vdots & \\
{}^{M^2}L\left\{\begin{array}{l} L_{M^3-M+1} \\ \vdots \\ L_{M^3} \end{array}\right. & \lambda\,{}^{M^2}\mathbf{L} \longrightarrow L_{M^2}' & \Big\}\ {}^{M}\mathbf{L}' & \lambda\,{}^{M}\mathbf{L}' \longrightarrow L_M''
\end{array}$$

Fig. 5.3.1 Symbolic setup for cubic sort.

On the left is the list **L** with element L_j. It is divided (braces) into sublists ${}^i\mathbf{L}$ each containing elements ${}^iL_{j_i}$.

The first auxiliary list, $\mathbf{L}'$ in the center column consists of sublists ${}^j\mathbf{L}'$. The elements of $\mathbf{L}'$ are $\mathbf{L}'_i$, all *leasts* of ${}^i\mathbf{L}$ for present stage of the sort.

The second auxiliary list $\mathbf{L}''$ on the right contains one entry L''_j which is the *least* of each auxiliary sublist ${}^j\mathbf{L}'$. The output item is determined from the least of $\mathbf{L}''$.

Without presort

Let us examine how we do cubic selection without presort. This case is simpler notationally than when a presort is performed.

For the quadratic sort, it was preferable to place the *item* in the auxiliary list. For cubic and higher sorts, reference to the original list and group is best performed by sorting the *address* of the item in the first and higher auxiliary lists. The reason for this is the list manipulation procedure:

- there are several types of lists
- there are many lists of each type
- the lists have sublists

If we use addresses in the secondary lists, there is then room in each secondary list item for a pointer to alternative lists according to the result of the examination of that item. Then a secondary item consists of:

- a pointer to **L** in the address field
- a pointer to a higher auxiliary list

We then have the following relationships for our cubic sort.

- $\mathbf{L}''$ is the second auxiliary cell list.
- $(\mathbf{L}'')$ is a list of locations in **L**.
- $((\mathbf{L}'')$ is a list of keys. These keys belong to the list $(\mathbf{L})$.

Selection

We have established the first and second auxiliary lists. We now examine the locations found at $\mathbf{L}''$ to determine which one contains the least key. This key, which is the contents of this least location, is passed over to the output list **S** thus

$$(\lambda\,(\mathbf{L}'')) \longrightarrow \mathbf{S} \qquad (5.3.12)$$

It is important to realize the meaning of (5.3.12): λ operates upon cells, but it does not operate on cells of $\mathbf{L}''$. Actually, $\mathbf{L}''$ is a list of pointers to cells in **L**; then (L''_i) is an address of a cell in **L**. $\lambda\,(\mathbf{L}'')$ is the *location* of the minimum of the items whose addresses appear in $\mathbf{L}''$. The minimum item itself is hence $(\lambda\,(\mathbf{L}''))$.

We must now eliminate this element from consideration. We do this by placing a $\not z$ there. The location under consideration is L_K. It is a member of the main subgroup i_K.

$$\not z \longrightarrow \lambda\,(\mathbf{L}'') = \mathrm{L}_K \in {}^{i_K}\mathbf{L} \tag{5.3.13}$$

FIRST AUXILIARY LIST

We now have to find the location of the minimum in the sublist and place this in the proper first auxiliary list location L'_{i_K}. This belongs to a first auxiliary subgroup whose number is j_K. All this is conveyed thus

$$\lambda\,{}^{j_K}\mathbf{L} \longrightarrow \mathrm{L}'_{i_K} \in {}^{j_K}\mathbf{L}' \tag{5.3.14}$$

We next seek the minimum of the location recorded in the auxiliary subgroup under examination. This is to be inserted in the proper second auxiliary list location. We do this thus

$$\lambda\,({}^{j_K}\mathbf{L}') \longrightarrow \mathrm{L}''_{j_K} \tag{5.3.15}$$

Routine

The operator routine for the cubic sort is presented in Fig. 5.3.2. steps (1), (2), and (3) report the main and auxiliary list components. We fill the first auxiliary list (4) and then the second auxiliary list (5). We select the first element for output (6) and replace that element with $\not z$ (7). We place the main sublist minimum location in the auxiliary list (8). We place the minimum location from the first auxiliary sublist into the second auxiliary sublist location (9). This is repeated until we exhaust the main list.

$$[\sqrt[3]{\nu\,\mathbf{L}} + 1] = M$$

$$\mathbf{L} = \bigcup_{i=1}^{M^2} {}^{i}\mathbf{L} \tag{1}$$

$$\mathbf{L}' = \bigcup_{i=1}^{M} {}^{i}\mathbf{L}' \tag{2}$$

$$\mathbf{L}'' = \{L''_1, L''_2, \ldots, L''_M\} \tag{3}$$

$$\underset{i=1}{\overset{M^2}{\mathbf{R}}}\ \lambda\,{}^{i}\mathbf{L} \longrightarrow \mathrm{L}'_i \tag{4}$$

$$\underset{i=1}{\overset{M}{\mathbf{R}}}\ \lambda\,({}^{j}\mathbf{L}') \longrightarrow L''_j \tag{5}$$

$$\underset{k=1}{\overset{\nu\mathbf{L}}{\mathbf{R}}} \begin{cases} (\lambda\,(\mathbf{L}'')) = (L_K) \longrightarrow S_k & (6) \\ \not z \longrightarrow L_K \in {}^{i_K}\mathbf{L} & (7) \\ \lambda\,{}^{i_K}\mathbf{L} \longrightarrow L'_{i_K} \in {}^{j_K}\mathbf{L}' & (8) \\ \lambda\,({}^{j_K}\mathbf{L}') \longrightarrow L''_{j_K} & (9) \end{cases}$$

Fig. 5.3.2 Operator routine for cubic sort.

5.4 HIGHER ORDER SORTS

Principle

There is no theoretical limit to the number of auxiliary lists which we may use. The quartic sort has one main list, **L**, and three auxiliary lists, **L**′, **L**″, and **L**‴. The first auxiliary list contains minimums from each of the main sublists. **L**′ is divided into sublists for which minimums are found and placed into **L**″. Minimums of the second auxiliary list are placed into the third auxiliary list.

Q order sorts require Q different types of lists, one main list, **L**, and $Q - 1$ auxiliary lists, **L**′, **L**″, . . ., $\mathbf{L}^{Q-1}$. We will be using higher order sorts of variable order when we examine the tournament sort in Section 5.5.

Presort

It is, of course, possible to presort the initial list by subgroup. Then, to get the next item, we merely advance the subgroup pointer by 1, making sure that we do not go outside of the subgroup then. Auxiliary subgroups can and should also be sorted, but only if we are dealing with keys and not locations.

There is still an advantage to using a presorted main list. Yet, by storing *locations* in the auxiliary lists, we find that an advantage is gained. Advancing an index simplifies the next minimum location in the presorted main list. The determination of addresses of minimums from auxiliary lists proceeds as described in Section 5.3.

5.5 TOURNAMENT SORT

Introduction

The tournament sort is so called because it matches items against each other just as people are matched against each other in setting up a tennis tournament. The original list is divided into pairs. The winner of each pair is determined, and this set becomes the first auxiliary list. First-stage winners are paired and compared; second-stage winners are chosen from this set. The second winners list, in turn, is paired; and so forth. The final *pair* of winners is matched to determine a final winner. When we replace "winner" by "lesser" above, we find the tournament sort defined; the least item is produced as the first item on our sorted list. We then review our list again to find the next *winner*, or the next item for our output list. A systematic procedure for this should be developed.

Example

Figure 5.5.1 presents an example of the tournament sort. The main list **L** contains 16 items. We select the minimum of each pair and place it in $\mathbf{L}^1$. Thus 2 is the lesser of 2 and 6 and goes to $\mathbf{L}^1_1$; 3 is the lesser of 3 and 9 and goes to $\mathbf{L}^1_2$; . . . ; 10 is the lesser of 14 and 10 and goes to $\mathbf{L}^1_8$. We now pair off the items in $\mathbf{L}^1$ and find the minimum of each pair: the lesser of 2 and 3 is 2 which goes to $\mathbf{L}^2_1$; . . . ; the lesser of 7 and 10 is 7 and goes to $\mathbf{L}^2_4$.

In a similar way, we fill $\mathbf{L}^3$ which contains only 2 and 1. From it we select the lesser, 1, which is the item for output.

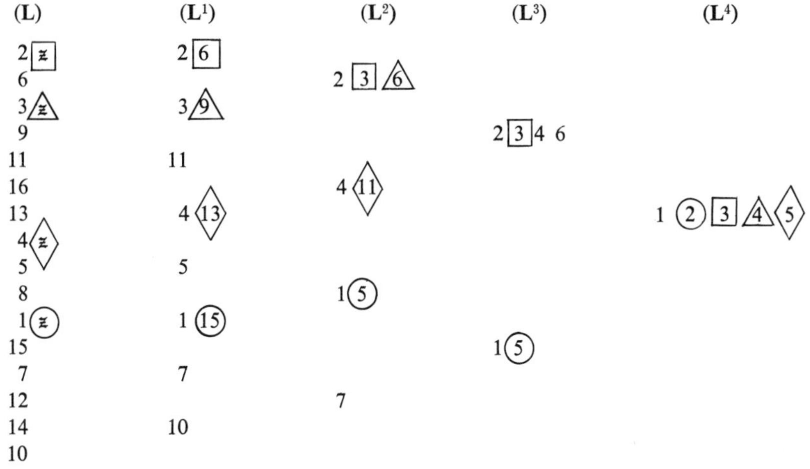

Fig. 5.5.1 Example of tournament sort.

Refill

Now that we have selected the item with key 1, we return to adjust the list using the sentinel ƶ. We replace 1 by ƶ at L_{11} (in circle). We now correct the winners all the way up the line; this is noted by the circled items in the figure. The next overall total winner is 2, noted by the circled 2 opposite $\mathbf{L}^4$.

2 is replaced by ƶ as noted in the square next to that item. We then go up the line and adjust each of the auxiliary lists as noted by items within squares.

Subsequent items are withdrawn, and they appear as the triangles and diamonds in the figure.

Notation

We find our beta operator indispensable in providing a notation to present the tournament sort. In what follows, we assume that the number of items is a power of 2. This is not a necessity of the sort—it would be a serious drawback if this were the case. However, after understanding the theory for a power of 2, it is easy to extrapolate to other cases. Then we have,

$$\nu\,\mathbf{L} = 2^{q} \tag{5.5.1}$$

then we have

$$\beta_1 = \beta\,\nu\,\mathbf{L} = 2^{q-1} \tag{5.5.2}$$

and

$$\beta_2 = \beta^2\,\nu\,\mathbf{L} = 2^{q-2} \tag{5.5.3}$$

so that

$$\beta_q = \beta^q\,\nu\,\mathbf{L} = 2^{q-q} = 1 \tag{5.5.4}$$

SUBGROUPS OF **L**

The main list is comprised of β_1 sublists thus

$$\mathbf{L} = \bigcup^{\beta_1} {}^{i}\mathbf{L} \tag{5.5.5}$$

Each of these sublists is defined as

$$\begin{aligned} {}^{1}\mathbf{L} &= \mathrm{L}_1 \cup \mathrm{L}_2 \\ {}^{2}\mathbf{L} &= \mathrm{L}_3 \cup \mathrm{L}_4 \\ {}^{\beta_1}\mathbf{L} &= \mathrm{L}_{2\beta_1-1} \cup \mathrm{L}_{\nu\mathrm{L}} \end{aligned} \tag{5.5.6}$$

In a similar way, we define sublists of the first auxiliary list by

$$\mathrm{L}^1 = \bigcup^{\beta_1} \mathrm{L}^1_i = \bigcup^{\beta_2} {}^{i}\mathrm{L}^1 \tag{5.5.7}$$

We define sublists of the second auxiliary list thus

$$\mathrm{L}^2 = \bigcup^{\beta_2} \mathrm{L}^2_i = \bigcup^{\beta_3} {}^{i}\mathrm{L}^2 \tag{5.5.8}$$

The next to the last auxiliary list is given by

$$\mathrm{L}^{q-1} = \mathrm{L}^{q-1}_1 \cup \mathrm{L}^{q-1}_2 \tag{5.5.9}$$

The final list consists of a single item and is hence defined thus

$$\mathrm{L}^q = \mathrm{L}^q_1 = \mathrm{L}^q \tag{5.5.10}$$

Fill operations

To fill the first auxiliary list we have to choose the minimum of each sublist of **L** thus

$$\mathop{\mathsf{R}}_{1}^{\beta_1} \lambda\, {}^{i}\mathbf{L} \longrightarrow \mathrm{L}^1_i \tag{5.5.11}$$

To fill the second auxiliary list, we examine the contents of the locations contained in the first auxiliary list by pairs thus

$$\overset{\beta_2}{\underset{1}{\mathbf{R}}} \lambda ({}^{i}\mathbf{L}^{1}) \longrightarrow \mathrm{L}_{i}^{2} \tag{5.5.12}$$

In general, to find the item for the *j*th auxiliary list, we perform

$$\overset{\beta_j}{\underset{1}{\mathbf{R}}} \lambda ({}^{i}\mathbf{L}^{j-1}) \longrightarrow \mathrm{L}_{i}^{j} \tag{5.5.13}$$

Notice that in (5.5.11) through (5.5.13), *addresses* not items are entered into the auxiliary lists. For (5.5.11), $\lambda\ {}^{i}\mathbf{L}$ is the *location* of the lesser† of the pair which comprises the *i*th sublist of **L**. In (5.5.13), ${}^{i}\mathbf{L}^{j-1}$ is the *i*th sublist of the $(j - 1)$th auxiliary list, a *pair of locations*. $({}^{i}\mathbf{L}^{j-1})$ are the contents of this cell; but they are addresses, too. $\lambda\ ({}^{i}\mathbf{L}^{j-1})$ chooses the lesser of the contents of these addresses and then forms the address corresponding to it. This *address* is placed at $\mathbf{L}_i^j$, the *i*th item cell in the *j*th auxiliary list.

Refill

Anywhere in the sort, the next item for output is determined by examination of the contents of $\mathbf{L}^q$. Recall $\mathbf{L}^q$ has only one member L^q. It contains the *address* of the cell of interest. The *contents* of cell of interest are entered into the output thus

$$((\mathrm{L}^{q})) \longrightarrow \mathrm{S}_{i} \tag{5.5.14}$$

The double parentheses read "the contents of the contents of L_q."

We now have to enter ℨ at the spot whose address is in L_q,

$$\mathfrak{Z} \longrightarrow (\mathrm{L}^{q}) \tag{5.5.15}$$

We then select winners from successive updated sublists. The first winner is chosen thus

$$\lambda\ ({}^{\beta K}\mathrm{L}) \longrightarrow \mathrm{L}_{\beta K}^{1} \tag{5.5.16}$$

Notice, here, how the beta operator selects the proper group number by operating on the *position*, *K*, of the selected item in the main list. Since it is at cell L_K, it belongs to subgroup *K*. Similarly we have

$$\lambda\ ({}^{\beta^2 K}\mathbf{L}^{1}) \longrightarrow \mathrm{L}_{\beta^2 K}^{2} \tag{5.5.17}$$

and, in general

$$\lambda\ ({}^{\beta^j K}\mathbf{L}^{j-1}) \longrightarrow \mathrm{L}_{\beta^j K}^{j} \tag{5.5.18}$$

†This is only one alternative: instead of entering the winner's address, the *loser's* address may be entered. In fact, it is said that greater efficiency can be achieved with the *loser's* address, although I have seen no substantiation of this.

Observe that

$$ {}^{i}\mathbf{L} = \{\mathbf{L}_{2i-1}, \mathbf{L}_{2i}\} \tag{5.5.19} $$

Suppose that during the sort we eventually found

$$ (\mathbf{L}_{2i-1}) = (\mathbf{L}_{2i}) = \not{z} \tag{5.5.20} $$

Then from (5.5.16) we have

$$ \not{z} \longrightarrow \mathbf{L}_{i}^{1} \tag{5.5.21} $$

Similarly

$$ {}^{j}\mathbf{L}^{1} = \{\mathbf{L}_{2j-1}^{1}, \mathbf{L}_{2j}^{1}\} \tag{5.5.22} $$

If

$$ (\mathbf{L}_{2j-1}^{1}) = (\mathbf{L}_{2j}^{1}) = \not{z} \tag{5.5.23} $$

Then

$$ [\not{z}] \longrightarrow \mathbf{L}_{j}^{2} \tag{5.5.24} $$

Finally, when

$$ (\mathbf{L}^{q}) = [\not{z}] \tag{5.5.25} $$

the sort is done.

Routine

The tournament sort routine appears in Fig. 5.5.2. At (1) we select the addresses for the first axuiliary list. A similar operation is performed in (2) to select the addresses for succeeding auxiliary lists. We initialize the output

$$ \underset{i=1}{\overset{\beta\nu\mathbf{L}}{\mathsf{R}}} \lambda\, {}^{i}\mathbf{L} \longrightarrow L_{i}^{1} \tag{1} $$

$$ \underset{j=1}{\overset{q}{\mathsf{R}}}\ \underset{i=1}{\overset{\beta_{j}\nu}{\mathsf{R}}} \lambda\, ({}^{i}\mathbf{L}^{j-1}) \longrightarrow L_{j}^{i} \tag{2} $$

$$ 1 \longrightarrow K \tag{3} $$

$$ \underset{k=1}{\overset{\nu\mathbf{L}}{\mathsf{R}}} \begin{cases} ((L^{q})) = (L_{K}) \longrightarrow \mathrm{O}_{K} & (4) \\ [\not{z}] \longrightarrow (L^{q}) & (5) \\ \lambda\, {}^{\beta K}\mathbf{L} \longrightarrow \mathbf{L}_{\beta K}^{1} & (6) \\ \underset{j=2}{\overset{e}{\mathsf{R}}} \lambda\, ({}^{\beta^{j}K}\mathbf{L}^{j-1}) \longrightarrow \mathbf{L}_{\beta^{j}K}^{j} & (7) \end{cases} $$

Fig. 5.5.2 Tournament sort routine.

list (3) and then select an item for it (4). The item must be replaced with $\not{z}$ (5). Winners for the first auxiliary list are selected (6), and we continue up the line (7), determining winner *locations* and placing them in auxiliary lists.

The whole select and refill operation is continued as long as there are items in the main list to be selected as determined by the limits in the repeat operation.

5.6 TOURNAMENT SORT PROGRAM

Memory arrangement

The memory arrangment for the FLAP program to do the tournament sort, **TSORT**, is found in Fig. 5.6.1. To make it easy to get to the main list

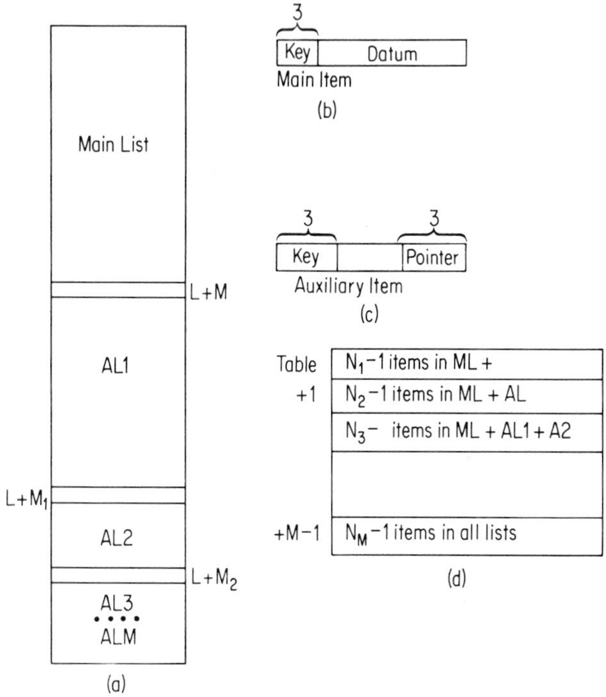

Fig. 5.6.1 Data layout for **TSORT**.

and to each of the auxiliary lists, the lists occupy contiguous locations in memory. Recall that there are N items to be sorted, where N is a perfect power of 2. Thus,

$$N = 2^M \tag{5.6.1}$$

Besides the main list, there are M auxiliary lists which, for facility, let us call AL1, AL2, . . . , ALM.

The starting point of the main list is L. Each entry in this main list consists of two parts as shown in Fig. 5.6.1b: There is a key of three digits; the rest of the word is the datum.

Each of the items in the auxiliary list is comprised as shown in Fig. 5.6.1c: The key occupies three digits; there is garbage in the next three digits; the final three digits comprise a pointer to the corresponding item in the main list.

Since the main list consists of a number of items and this number is a power of 2, the first auxiliary list is half the size of the main list; each of the other auxiliary lists is just half the size of its predecessor. Thus, AL1 contains $N/2$ items, AL2 contains $N/4$ items and ALM contains exactly one item. When we add the sizes of the AL's together we have

$$\nu\,(\bigcup_{i} \mathrm{AL}) = \frac{N}{2} + \frac{N}{4} + \cdots + 1 = N - 1 \qquad (5.6.2)$$

Hence auxiliary lists require $N - 1$ cells. Therefore, the main list and the auxiliary list use up $2N - 1$ cells.

The main problem the programmer faces with this tournament sort is wending his way through the auxiliary lists. To accomplish this, a table is set up as illustrated in Fig. 5.6.1d. This table acts as a pointer to the beginning of any given auxiliary list. Thus, the entry at TABLE is the numbers of items in the main list; when this is added to the location L, it gives the starting point of AL1. The second entry in the table at TABLE + 1 is the number of items contained in the main list and AL1 together. When this is added to L, we get the starting point of AL2.

Example

Let us now examine a numerical example, presented in Fig. 5.6.2. The main list consists of 64 items. The auxiliary list AL1 contains 32 entries, and so forth, as shown in that figure. The starting point L, of ML is 500. The starting place of the auxiliary list is 564. The other points are similarly determined. TABLE shown in Fig. 5.6.2 contains the progressive entries 64, 96, 112 and so forth, which permits us to enter each of the auxiliary lists.

Example of Use

Now let us get down to the specific problem preented in Fig. 5.6.3. This assumes that all the auxiliary tables have been set up. We will see later how this is done. The next item for output is withdrawn from the final auxiliary list ALM which, as noted, contains a single item. The item is placed into the output by means of the pointer contained in ALM.

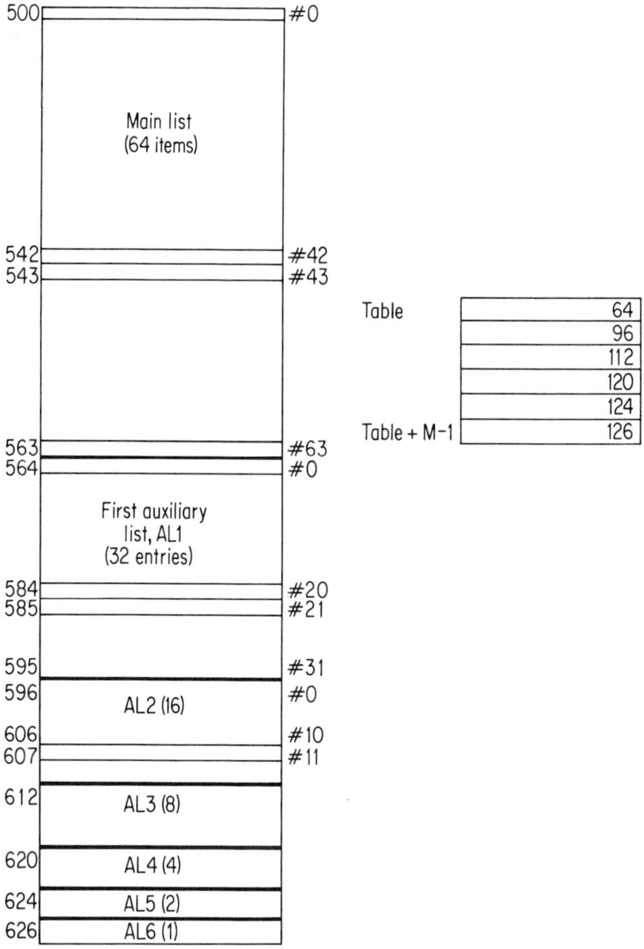

Fig. 5.6.2 Example of contents of memory for one use of TSORT.

The next activity is to update the main list and all the auxiliary lists. In the numerical example presented, the pointer in ALM shows that the 43rd item in the main list was the one chosen for output. Its twin is the item at 542. The next step is to insert ᴢ at cell 543 and pick up its twin from cell 542.

We then calculate the corresponding entry in the first auxiliary list, using the beta function. This is found to be at cell 20, with its twin at cell 21. To get to the proper cell, we enter the AL table and pick up 64. We add 20, the AL1 ordinal cell number, and the 500, the sort area start, to get 584, the location of L_{20}^1. The item from the previous step is inserted at cell 20. In so doing, we compare it with its twin, L_{21}^1, which is necessarily at 585, to determine which of these is the lesser. This is picked up for the next operation.

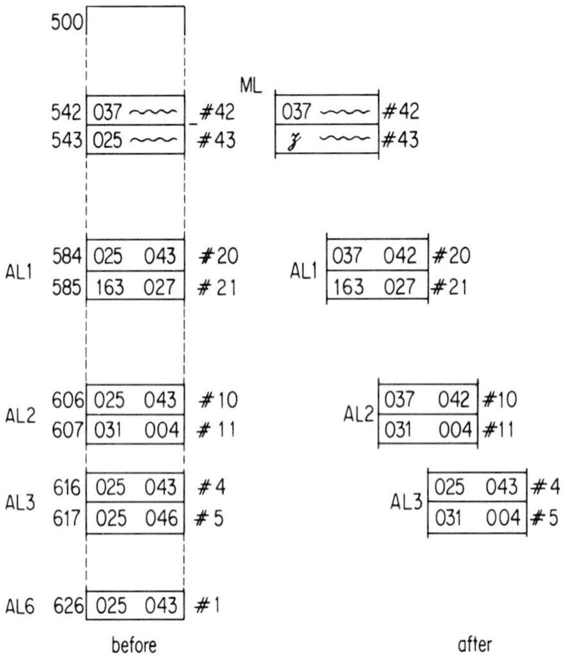

Fig. 5.6.3 How **TSORT** makes changes in the main and auxiliary lists to keep them updated.

Since we have

$$(584)_K : (585)_K, \qquad 037 < 163 \tag{5.6.3}$$

then

$$(L^1_{20}) \longrightarrow L^2_{10} \tag{5.6.4}$$

To find $[L^2_{10}]$ we enter the AL table, pick up 96, and add 10 and 500 to get 606.

Next we have

$$(L^2_{10})_K : (L^2_{11})_K \equiv (606)_K : (607)_K \equiv 37 > 31 \tag{5.6.5}$$

and

$$(L^2_{11}) \longrightarrow L^3_5 \tag{5.6.6}$$

We continue thus. The proper cell is in the next auxiliary list. We go there and place the item we have just picked up. We compare it with its twin, which is picked up for the next activity. In so doing, we update each of the auxiliary lists, ending up with the final auxiliary list, in this case, AL6.

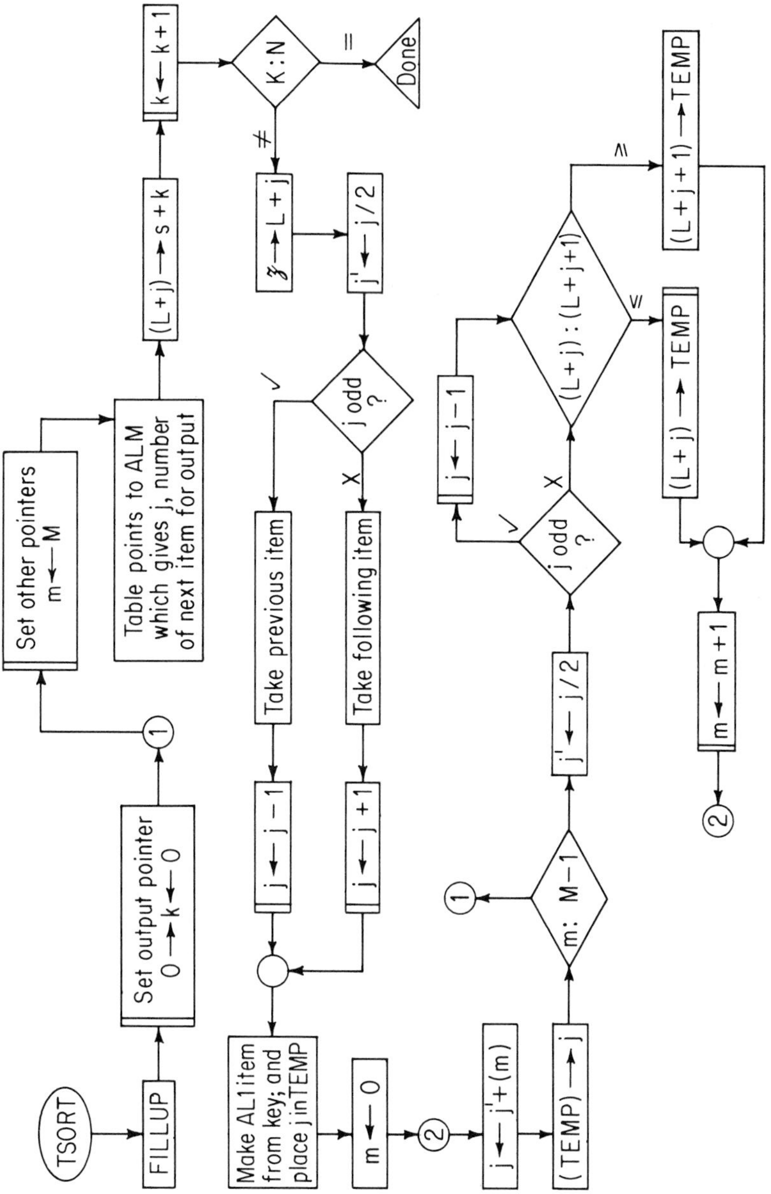

Fig. 5.6.4 Flow chart for tournament sort, **TSORT.**

```
OUTPUT   XPN,5    0            Initialize output pointer.
         XPN,3    0            Initialize TABLE pointer.
         XMN,1    L + 2N − 2   ALM pointer from TABLE to index 1.
         XMA,1    L            Get item at L + (ALM)
         XAM,5    S            and output it.
+5       NPP,5    1            Tally output.
         CMPN,5   N            Last item?
         JOE      return       End of sort.
         XMA      = ƶ          } ƶ to item.
+10      XAM,1    L            }
         XNA,1                 } Get item number.
         XAD                   }
         MUL      =1/2         Apply beta
         XAM      NEXT         and save.
+15      XQA                   Get roundoff.
         CMP      =0           Compare to 0 (odd or even?).
         JOE      * + 3
         NMP,1    1            If odd (remainder) look back.
+20      UCJ      * + 2
         NPP,1    1            If even (no remainder) look ahead.
         XMA,1    L            Get item twin from L for AL1.
         ANDTA    KEY          Mask out key.
         XNA,1                 Mask in pointer
+25      XAM      TEMP         and save.
COMPARE  XMA,3    TABLE        Get pointer to next AL.
         ADD      NEXT         Add in AL element pointer to set AL
                                 element location.
         XAN,1                 Save in index 1.
         XMA      TEMP         Get new AL word
         XAM,1    L            and place in this AL list.
TEST     CMPN,3   M − 1        Is this last TABLE entry?
         JOE      OUTPUT + 1   If so, go to OUTPUT + 1; all AL's updated.
         XMD      NEXT         Get NEXTPT to move to next list.
         MUL      =1/2         Apply beta function
         XAM      NEXT         to get new NEXT.
         XQA                   Save roundoff.
         CMP      =0           Compare to zero.
         JOE      * + 2
         NMP,1    1            If nonzero, move back THISPT.
         XMA,1    L            Get first of pair at THISPT.
         CMP,1    L + 1        Compare with second of pair at THISPT.
         JOG      * + 2        }
         XMA,1    L + 1        } Place lesser in TEMP.
         XAM      TEMP         }
         NPP,3    1            Move TABLE pointer.
         UCJ      COMPARE      Loop back.
```

Fig. 5.6.5 Program OUTPUT phase of TSORT.

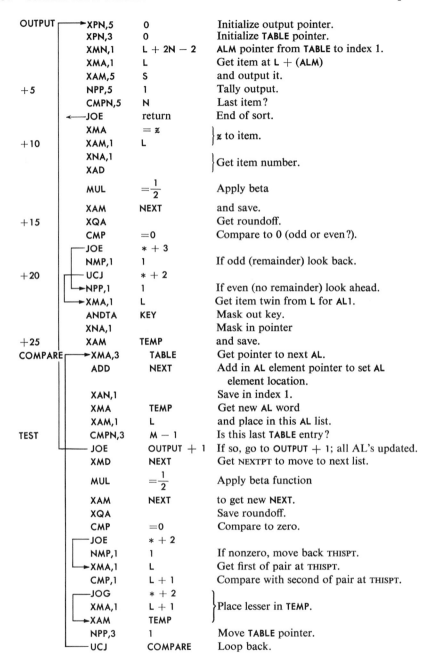

Flow chart

The output phase of the tournament sort TSORT is called OUTPUT and is flow charted in Fig. 5.6.4. In (1), the routine is initialized. At (2, 3) the initialization for the selection of the next item for output is performed. At (4), the location of the item for output, L + j, is determined from the final auxiliary list, ALM. The output pointer is updated (5) and checked (6), and we halt if done (7). If not done, return to the list cell from which the item was withdrawn and place ≋ in there (8).

Now find the place in the first auxiliary list (9, 10) and get the proper item at that point (11, 12, 13, 14). Assemble an *auxiliary list item* consisting of a key and location (15). Now check the other auxiliary lists and set the index counter, m, to 0 (16). Update the pointer (17) and place the auxiliary item at its proper location (18). Check to see if there are more auxiliary lists to examine (19) and, if not, return for another output item (a).

Next go to the next auxiliary list (20) and get the proper item from the pair (21, 22). Check the items of the pair to see which one is to be carried to the next higher list (23). Place this in a temporary location TEMP (24, 25) and set each pointer to the next auxiliary list (26), returning via (b) for further auxiliary list examination.

OUTPUT

The portion of TSORT which places items on output and updates the auxiliary list is called OUTPUT and is presented in Fig. 5.6.5. The first three steps initialize this section. Next we get the pointer from ALM and use it to obtain the item which is then put in the next place on the output list. It may be the last item, and this is checked before we go on. If it is the last item, the sort is considered complete.

When there are more items, we place the ≋ in the spot where the item was withdrawn. This occurs at OUTPUT + 9. The steps for calculating the beta function are found at OUTPUT + 12. This consists simply of multiplication by $\frac{1}{2}$. Notice, however, that the multiplication command used is MUL. This command does not do rounding. What is left in the Q REGISTER determines whether we move forward or backward to get the twin of this item. At OUTPUT + 16 we check the remainder to decide the direction in which to move. At OUTPUT + 22 we get the twin, mask out the key, and mask in the pointer, saving this in a location called TEMP. This is the new item for AL1. Notice it is correct even if its key is ≋, for then we wish AL1 to contain ≋ too.

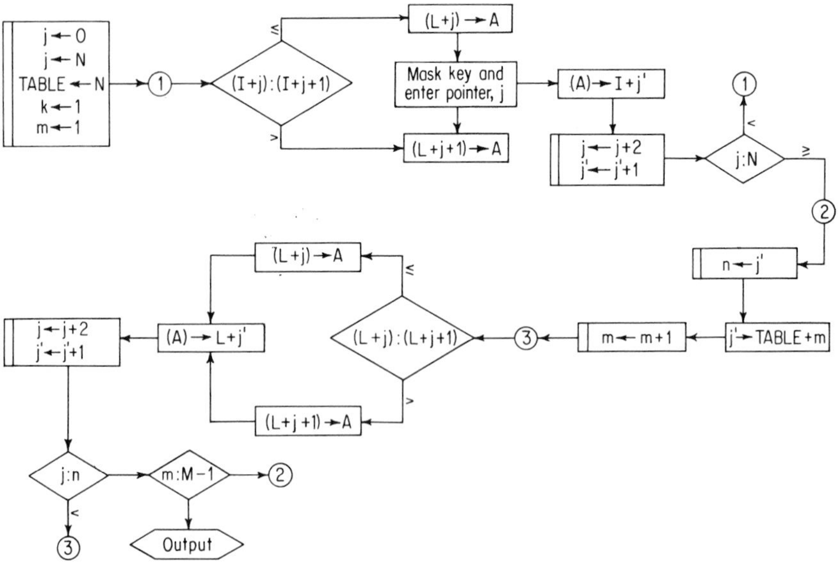

Fig. 5.6.6 Flow chart for FILLUP phase of TSORT.

The next task appears in the program at COMPARE. Here we enter TABLE to get the pointer to the next auxiliary list, being careful to determine at TEST that this is not the last auxiliary list. If it is, we return to the beginning of the routine, OUTPUT, since all AL's have been updated.

What follows at TEST + 2 is to apply the beta function to get the next auxiliary list item. The roundoff quantity in the Q REGISTER is checked against 0 to determine the twin of this list item. We make a comparison to determine the item for the next auxiliary list. This is placed in TEMP, and we continue to update the auxiliary lists by looping around through COMPARE.

Filling up the auxiliary lists

The flow chart for filling up the auxiliary lists is found in Fig. 5.6.6. This phase of TSORT is called FILLUP. It begins in (1) where we initialize the activity. In (2) we compare an item with its upper twin. Whichever is lesser is entered into the accumulator (3, 4). The datum is removed from the item presently in the accumulator, and for it is substituted a pointer to the original item (5). This is the proper item for AL1, and it is entered into a position in AL1 at a distance j^1 from $L(6)$. We advance: to the next pair in our main

The program for FILLUP is found in Fig. 5.6.7.

```
FILLUP    XPN,1     0         Set main list pointer (THISPT).
          XPN,2     N         Set AL pointer (NEXTPT).
          XPN,3     1         Set TABLE pointer.
          XNM,2     TABLE     Enter N into TABLE.
MAKEAL1   XMA,1     L         }Compare this pair of items.
          CMP,1     L + 1     }
          JOL       * + 2     }Place smaller in A.
          XDA                 }
          ANDTA     KEY       Mask key
          XNA,1               }
          JOL       * + 2     }and enter pointer.
          ADD       =1        }
          XAM,2     L         Store small item word in AL1.
          NPP,1     2         Advance THISPT.
          NPP,2     1         Advance NEXTPT.
          CMPN,1    N         Finished?
          JOL       MAKEAL1   If not, continue with AL1.
MAKEJ     XNM,2     CHECK     Enter limit of AL(J - 1) into CHECK
          XNA,2
          XAM,3     TABLE     and also place in TABLE.
          NPP,3     1         Advance TABLE pointer.
STARTJ    XMA,1     L         }Compare this pair of AL(J - 1) items.
          CMP,1     I + 1     }
          JOL       *+ 2      }Smaller to.
          XDA                 }
          XAM,2     L         Place in ALJ.
          NPP,1     2         Advance ALJ - 1 pointer.
          NPP,2     1         Advance ALJ pointer.
CHECK     CMPN,1              Done with ALJ? number comes from MAKEJ.
          JOL       STARTJ    Continue to make ALJ at STARTJ.
          CMPN,3    M - 1     If finished ALJ then finish ALM?
          JOL       MAKEJ     If not, continue with ALJ + 1 at MAKEJ.
          go to     OUTPUT
```

Fig. 5.6.7 Program for FILLUP phase of TSORT.

list by adding 2 to j; to the next entry in our auxiliary list by adding 1 to j^1(7). If we have not examined all the main list items (8) we continue ①.

The foregoing steps fabricate AL1. Its production is different from the other auxiliary lists. They, however, can be manufactured by the same rule in the boxes that follow.

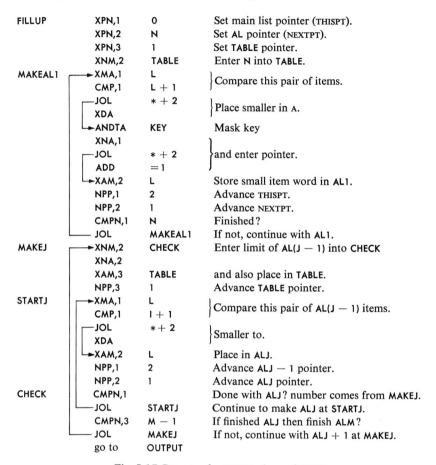

We set up the start of the next AL using j^1, which now points to the next available AL cell (9). We set up the TABLE entry and advance the TABLE entry counter (10, 11). Now we compare a pair of auxiliary list items (12). The lesser is brought into the accumulator (13, 14) and, since it is in proper form, it is transferred directly to its proper position in the next auxiliary list (15). This list pointer is advanced by 2 (for the next pair), and the *next* list pointer is advanced by 1 (16). We check to see if all the AL items for this AL have been prepared (17) and, if not, we return to (12) via ③. If we have completed processing *this* auxiliary list, we check to see if it is the last (18). If not, we return to (9) to reset pointers for a new AL. Otherwise, this fabrication is complete, and we continue the sort at OUTPUT.

PROBLEMS

5.1 Explain why quadratic selection is more effective than linear selection. Why is $N = \sqrt{n}$ more effective than another choice of N?

5.2 What are the advantages of a presort for the main subgroups over a given sort during the main sort?

5.3 Describe and flowchart a quadratic sort of records R words (key in first word). Why might we not use a presort?

5.4 Program QUAD1, a one-record quadratic sort without presort, using macros such as MOVE where necessary. Either tag records or enter 999 there to distinguish that it has been used.

5.5 Program QUAD1R an R-word record quadratic sort without presort as in Problem 5.4.

5.6 Flowchart and program a cubic sort CUB1 without a presort assuming the establishment of auxiliary lists.

5.7 Flowchart and program a presort cubic sort CUB2 assuming presorted groups and established auxiliary lists.

5.8 Flowchart and program a cubic sort CUB1R to sort record of length R.

5.9 Flowchart and program a one-word record quartic sort QUAR1 with presort assuming the auxiliary lists established.

5.10 Flowchart and program a tournament sort of R-word records, TSORTR, assuming auxiliary lists have been established.

6 ADDRESS CALCULATION

6.1 ADDRESS CALCULATION PRINCIPLES

Calculation of address

Address calculation sorting depends upon the presence of an acceptable **address calculation operator ω** which converts the key of a record to an address in the output list. Sort effectiveness depends, of course, upon the effectiveness of the operator, ω. This, in turn, depends upon several things.

- The relation of the sample universe, (**L**), the items in the list to be sorted, to the population universe $\mathscr{L}$—all the items which might be in the list.
- This, in turn, depends upon the distribution function $D(\mathscr{L})$.

The distribution is said to be **rectangular** if the probability of a chosen key being any one of the population keys is equal. There are many other key distributions, ranging from those which are almost rectangular to those which are normal (in the statistical sense). A nonrectangular distribution, for instance, occurs when some duplicate keys may arise.

Relation of output to input list

The efficiency with which the address calculation works depends upon the relative size of working storage in main memory. It has been shown that, if there are *twice* as many temporary *output* locations as there are *input* items, address calculation sort can be very efficient. If we pack items close together so that there are not many more output locations than there are input items, the sort becomes more and more inefficient. The inefficiency arises when we try to place an incoming item in a spot that is already occupied. When this occurs, we have to move the item at this position either backward or forward. If locations adjacent to it are also occupied, this requires moving several items as well as testing to determine how many items need be moved and in which direction they should be moved.

Case 1—perfect aim

In Fig. 6.1.1 the address calculated is empty. We have calculated the address where the item with key 27 should be placed. When we go to this location in $_1S$, we find it is empty. Therefore, we place the incoming item at this position to generate $_2S$.

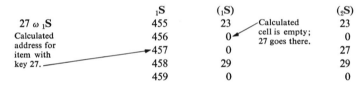

	$_1S$	$(_1S)$		$(_2S)$
$27\ \omega\ _1S$	455	23	Calculated	23
Calculated	456	0	cell is empty; 27 goes there.	0
address for item with key 27.	457	0		27
	458	29		29
	459	0		0

Fig. 6.1.1 Address sort, case 1, $27\ \omega\ _1S = 457$.

Case 2—cell full; room at the top

In Fig. 6.1.2 the address at which we look is full, and the key at the calculated address is smaller than the item key to be placed. Hence the new item belongs at a higher address. We look at successively higher addresses to find a vacant one. Since the next address past the calculated one is empty, it is a simple matter to insert this item at that address.

	$_1S$	$(_1S)$		$(_2S)$	
Calculated address	455	23	Calculated cell is	23	After 27 is
	456	24	occupied with item with key less than	24	placed in space fol-
	457	25	that of incoming	25	lowing cal-
	458	0	item. Next cell is	27	culated address.
	459	0	empty.†	0	

†*Note:* In general, there may be occupied cells between the occupied calculated cell and the next empty cell, but all must contain keys less than that of the item to be inserted.

Fig. 6.1.2 Address sort, case 2, $27\ \omega\ _1S = 457$.

Case 3—squeeze in the item

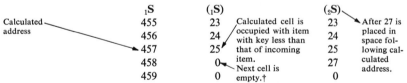

Figure 6.1.3 illustrates case 3, where the calculated address is full, as are several succeeding addresses; but, more important, the desired item must

be inserted *between* two already filled addresses. We must first find the place where the item belongs. Then we must move succeeding items forward. We cannot move them forward until we find a vacant address. Once we have found the vacant cell, we advance the contents of each of the cells *after* the cell where the item belongs and including that cell to form ${}_2S$ of the figure. Now it is possible to insert the present item in its proper location.

	${}_1S$	$({}_1S)$		*After moving; before insertion* $({}_2S)$	*After insertion* $({}_3S)$
$27\ \omega\ {}_1S$	455	23	Calculated cell is occupied.	23	23
Calculated address	456	24	Item must be placed *after* these items.	24	24
→	457	25	Item must be placed *before* these items; they must be moved.	25	25
	458	26		26	26
	459	28		28	27
	460	29	First empty cell after calculated address.	28	28
	461	0		29	29
	462	0		0	0

Fig. 6.1.3 Address sort, case 3, $27\ \omega\ {}_1S = 457$.

Case 4—room at the bottom

For case 4, illustrated in Fig. 6.1.4, the calculated address is preempted, and the key in that cell is higher than the item key. The cell below is also full, and its key is also higher than the item key. Finally, two cells back from the calculated address, we find an empty cell. Since this cell precedes a cell containing a higher key than the item key, we place the item at that cell to form ${}_2S$.

	${}_1S$	$({}_1S)$		*After placement of* 27. $({}_2S)$
	455	23		23
	456	0	Vacant; since key of next item ahead is also greater than key of incoming item, the incoming item goes here.	27
	457	29	Next lower cell is occupied by item with key greater than key of incoming item.	29
Calculated address →	458	31	Calculated cell is occupied by item with key greater than that of incoming item.	31
	459	0		0
	460	0		0

Fig. 6.1.4 Address sort, case 4, $27\ \omega\ {}_1S$.

Case 5—another squeeze

Here the calculated address is occupied, the present item has a key lower than that of the item at the address, and several previous addresses are filled.

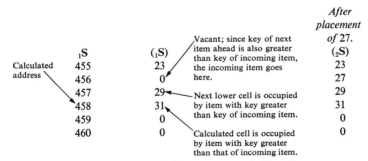

Some of the items in cells have higher keys than the item key, but some have lower keys. Hence, the item must be squeezed in between those cells which have higher keys and those that have lower ones. But first we find an empty location ahead of the full cells which precede the calculated address. Then we move some of the items backwards to form a space for this item. This is shown in Fig. 6.1.5, where $_2$**S** and $_3$**S** are produced.

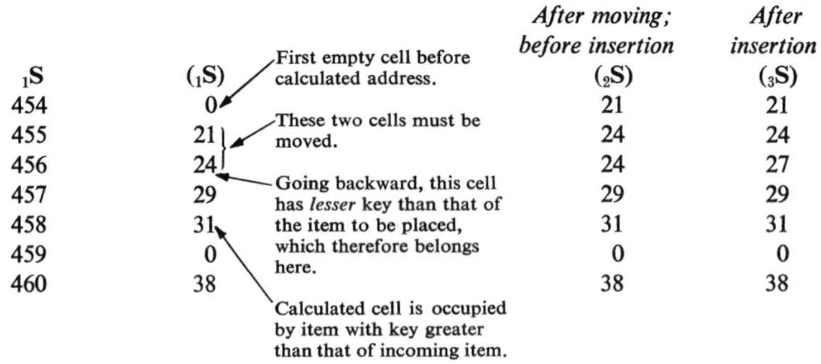
$_1$S
454
455
456
457
458
459
460
($_1$S)
0
21
24
29
31
0
38
First empty cell before calculated address.
These two cells must be moved.
Going backward, this cell has *lesser* key than that of the item to be placed, which therefore belongs here.
Calculated cell is occupied by item with key greater than that of incoming item.
After moving; before insertion
($_2$S)
21
24
24
29
31
0
38
After insertion
($_3$S)
21
24
27
29
31
0
38

Fig. 6.1.5 Address sort, case 5, 27 ω $_1$S.

NOTE

A computernick realizes that a cell is never *truly* empty; it's gotta contain something! The sort programmer must "clear" all unused cells at the beginning of the sort by entering some sentinel into each. He may use **a**, **z** or something else distinctive. The program checks for this sentinel immediately after calculating each $L_i\ \omega\ \mathbf{S}$ to find if the cell is "occupied."

6.2 ADDRESS CALCULATION OPERATION

The address calculation operator, ω, determines the address of an item from its key. Let us think of this as a mapping of a given input list cell L_i into one of the cells of the output list **S**, indicated as

$$\mathbf{L_i\ \omega\ S} \tag{6.2.1}$$

For case 1, this cell is empty, indicated as

$$(\mathbf{L_i\ \omega\ S}) = \Lambda \tag{6.2.2}$$

It remains to place the current item at the calculated address,

$$\{(\mathbf{L_i\ \omega\ S}) = \Lambda\}(\mathbf{L_i}) \longrightarrow \mathbf{L_i\ \omega\ S} \tag{6.2.3}$$

For the four remaining cases, the calculated address is ocuupied.

Cases 2 and 3

For cases 2 and 3, the calculated address is occupied by a key *smaller* than the current key.

$$(L_i) > (L_i \, \omega \, \mathbf{S}) \tag{6.2.4}$$

We have to look ahead from the address calculated for an empty cell using σ. We look in the list $\mathbf{G}_i$ consisting of the locations in $\mathbf{S}$ which are above the calculated location. Here $\mathbf{G}_i$ is given by

$$\mathbf{G}_i = \{L_i \, \omega \, \mathbf{S} + 1, L_i \, \omega \, \mathbf{S} + 2, \ldots S_{\nu S}\} \tag{6.2.5}$$

Looking ahead for an empty cell in this list is hence described by

$$\Lambda \, \sigma \, \mathbf{G}_i \tag{6.2.6}$$

CASE 2 VERSUS CASE 3

Which case are we now examining, 2 or 3? This depends upon the contents of the occupied cells which precede the empty cell. If the keys remain less than the key of this item as we look ahead, this is case 2; if at least one of the keys is larger than the item key, we are faced with case 3. These cases can be distinguished by examination of the cell just before the empty cell,

$$\Lambda \, \sigma \, \mathbf{G}_i - 1 \tag{6.2.7}$$

If this cell contains a key less than or equal to the item key, we place the item at the empty cell

$$\{(\Lambda \, \sigma \, \mathbf{G}_i - 1) \leq (L_i)\} \, \{(L_i) \longrightarrow \Lambda \, \sigma \, \mathbf{G}_i\} \tag{6.2.8}$$

Case 3

For case 3, the examination of the cell previous to the empty one reveals that it contains a key greater than the present item

$$(\Lambda \, \sigma \, \mathbf{G}_i - 1) > (L_i) \tag{6.2.9}$$

This requires that we look backward over the cells we have just scanned.

The cells we examine are those between the calculated address and the empty cell, but excluding the empty cell. Call this the **target group,** $^T\mathbf{G}_i$. It is embraced by our notation thus

$$^T\mathbf{G}_i = \{L_i \, \omega \, \mathbf{S} + 1, L_i \, \omega \, \mathbf{S} + 2, \ldots, \Lambda \, \sigma \, \mathbf{G}_i - 1\} \tag{6.2.10}$$

FINDING AND ADVANCING

We look in the target group, $^T\mathbf{G}_i$ for those cells which must be advanced. Call the group of cells whose contents must be advanced the **advance group,**

$\mathbf{A}_i$. This group is bounded on the top by an empty cell. The last cell it contains on the bottom has a key greater than the item key; the cell just below this (and not in $\mathbf{A}_i$) has a key less than or equal to the item key. To find $\mathbf{A}_i$, we apply γ to ${}^T\mathbf{G}_i$ thus

$$\mathbf{A}_i = \lceil L_i \, \gamma \, {}^T\mathbf{G}_i \rceil \tag{6.2.11}$$

Notice that the quantity between the $\lceil \quad \rceil$ represents all cells past the calculated address; $\mathbf{A}_i$ are the cells between the sought cell and the empty one.

To make room for the item, we apply α to $\mathbf{A}_i$ thus

$$\alpha \, \mathbf{A}_i \tag{6.2.12}$$

Next we insert the item at the space we have made

$$(L_i) \longrightarrow L_i \, \gamma \, {}^T\mathbf{G}_i \tag{6.2.13}$$

Cases 4 and 5

For cases 4 and 5, the cell that we are led to by the address calculation contains a key which is *greater* than the present item

$$(L_i) < (L_i \, \omega \, \mathbf{S}) \tag{6.2.14}$$

We wish to examine the list **S** backwards from the location calculated.

BACKWARDS OPERATOR

To indicate that we are searching for equal but in the reverse direction, we use the operator σ, placing the search item on the right instead of the left of the operator. We look below $L_i \, \omega \, \mathbf{S}$ for the next empty cell. First call $\mathbf{H}_i$ the set of cell in **S** below $L_i \, \omega \, \mathbf{S}$,

$$\mathbf{H}_i = \{S_1, S_2, \ldots, L_i \, \omega \, \mathbf{S} - 2, L_i \, \omega \, \mathbf{S} - 1\} \tag{6.2.15}$$

We look for the first empty cell from the *top* of $\mathbf{H}_i$

$$\mathbf{H}_i \, \sigma \, \Lambda \tag{6.2.16}$$

The target set ${}^T\mathbf{H}_i$ starts there and goes upward

$${}^T\mathbf{H}_i = \{\mathbf{H}_i \, \sigma \, \Lambda + 1, \mathbf{H}_i \, \sigma \, \Lambda + 2, \ldots, L_i \, \omega \, \mathbf{S} - 2, L_i \, \omega \, \mathbf{S} - 1\} \tag{6.2.17}$$

To distinguish cases 4 and 5, after we find an empty cell, we have to look at the cell just ahead of it. We check its contents against the item key. When the item key is less than the key in that cell, we have case 4. If this cell contains an item with key greater than or equal to the search key, we place the item in the empty cell,

$$\{(\mathbf{H}_i \, \sigma \, \Lambda + 1) \geq (L_i)\}\{(L_i) \longrightarrow \mathbf{H}_i \, \sigma \, \Lambda\} \tag{6.2.18}$$

Case 5

If the condition in the left braces of (6.2.18) is not true, then we have

$$(\mathbf{H}_i\, \sigma\, \Lambda + 1) < (\mathrm{L}_i) \qquad (6.2.19)$$

We then look for a subset of $\mathbf{H}_i$ to retard. This, in turn, is a subset of the target group ${}^T\mathbf{H}_i$ defined in (6.2.17). It is found by applying the operator $\bar{\gamma}$ to that set thus

$$\mathbf{B}_i = \lfloor \mathrm{L}_i\, \bar{\gamma}\, {}^{\mathrm{T}}\mathbf{H}_i \rfloor \qquad (6.2.20)$$

where $\mathbf{B}_i$ is the *retard* group. After the retard operation,

$$\rho\, \mathbf{B}_i \qquad (6.2.21)$$

we place the item at the proper position

$$(\mathrm{L}_i) \longrightarrow \mathrm{L}_i\, \bar{\gamma}\, {}^{\mathrm{T}}\mathbf{H}_i \qquad (6.2.22)$$

Routine

Figure 6.2.1 presents the address calculation sort in operator notation (1)–(3). Definitions are given below, (4)–(9). Notice that cases 2 and 3 are not distinguished; neither are cases 4 and 5. For case 2, $\mathbf{A}_i$ is empty and no operation $\alpha\, \mathbf{A}_i$ is performed; similarly, $\mathbf{B}_i$ is empty for case 4.

$$\{(L_i\, \omega\, \mathbf{S}) = \Lambda\}(L_i) \longrightarrow L_i\, \omega\, \mathbf{S} \qquad (1)$$
$$\{(L_i) > (L_i\, \omega\, \mathbf{S})\}\{\alpha\, A_i; (L_i) \longrightarrow L_i\, \gamma\, {}^T\mathbf{G}_i\} \qquad (2)$$
$$\{(L_i) < (L_i\, \omega\, \mathbf{S})\}\{\rho\, B_i; (L_i) \longrightarrow L_i\, \gamma\, {}^T\mathbf{H}_i\} \qquad (3)$$
$$\mathbf{A}_i = \lceil L_i\, \gamma\, {}^T\mathbf{G}_i \rceil \qquad (4)$$
$$\mathbf{B}_i = \lfloor L_i\, \gamma\, {}^T\mathbf{H}_i \rfloor \qquad (5)$$
$${}^T\mathbf{G}_i = \{L_i\, \omega\, \mathbf{S} + 1, L_i\, \omega\, \mathbf{S} + 2, \ldots, \Lambda\, \sigma\, G_i - 1\} \qquad (6)$$
$${}^T\mathbf{H}_i = \{H_i\, \sigma\, \Lambda + 1, H_i\, \sigma\, \Lambda + 2, \ldots, L_i\, \omega\, \mathbf{S} - 2, L_i\, \omega\, \mathbf{S} - 1\} \qquad (7)$$
$$\mathbf{G}_i = \{L_i\, \omega\, \mathbf{S} + 1, L_i\, \omega\, \mathbf{S} + 2, \ldots, S_{\nu \mathrm{S}}\} \qquad (8)$$
$$\mathbf{H}_i = \{S_1, S_2, \ldots, L_i\, \omega\, \mathbf{S} - 2, L_i\, \omega\, \mathbf{S} - 1\} \qquad (9)$$

Fig. 6.2.1 Operation notation for address calculator sort.

6.3 FLOW CHART AND PROGRAM

Flow chart

The flow chart for the address calculation sort is presented in Fig. 6.3.1. In (1) we initialize the program. At (2) we enter a subroutine which calculates the address, P, for the item presently under consideration, I. The better we make this subroutine, the better the sort will work out. We now check the contents of the calculated address (3) to determine if we have an empty space.

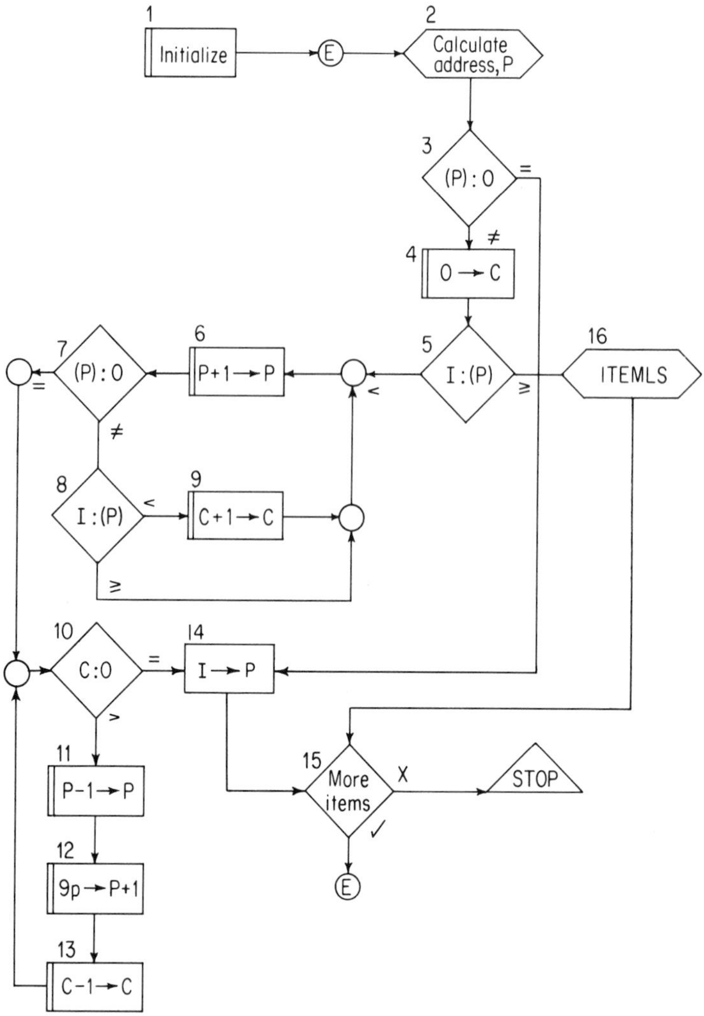

Fig. 6.3.1 Flow chart for address calculation sort.

If so, the item can be placed there, and we exit to (14). In some cases, the calculated cell is occupied. If so, we set a counter C, which we may use later. Next we check the item against the contents of the cell to see if we look ahead or behind the calculated cell. We consider only cases 2 and 3 here; cases 4 and 5 are similary handled in the subroutine ITEMLS (16). When the comparison (5) yields *less*, we will be looking ahead: We advance the output pointer so that we look at the next address (6). If it is empty (7), we begin moving items if necessary (10).

If the present address is occupied (7), we check its contents against the item to be placed there (8). If the item to be placed there is greater than the present cell contents, we have case 2, which requires no movement of items; we return to (6). When items are to be moved, case 3, we use the counter, C, to tell us how many items must be moved. Each time we go around the loop, we add one to this counter (9). Of course, this is predicated upon sequenced items in the sort area; if the procedure was used from the beginning, we are guaranteed of that.

Eventually we pop out of the loop, having found an empty cell (7). When this happens, we take a look at the counter (10). If the counter is empty, no items need be moved, and we place the new item at the position currently pointed to (14). If there are more items (15), we calculate the address of the next item, (2).

The loop (10 through 13) moves the proper number of items ahead one position in the output area. When doen, we continue to (14) as before. A *retard* loop is required for ITEMLS.

FLAP program

The program in FLAP to do sorting by address calculation is presented in Fig. 6.3.2. The sort starts by initializing the input pointer. We bring in the first item to the accumulator at NEXT and immediately jump to the routine for address calculation ADCALC. This routine calculates the predicted ordinal position in the output area, placing this number in index 2. At NEXT+2 we get the contents of the calculated cell and check to see if it is actually empty. If so, we jump to FILL.

If the calculated cell is not empty then we do not have case 1. Hence we set the counter, index 3.

Now we compare the input item to the contents of the cell to determine if we have case 4 and 5 named ITEMLS or whether we have case 2 and 3, which follows directly below and is called ITEMGR.

ITEMGR

We move the cell pointer ahead, get the cell contents, and check if it is zero. If it is, this is the exit from box 7 of the flow chart, causing us to go the subroutine called MOVEUP.

If we do not go to MOVEUP, we check to see if we have case 2 or 3 by comparing the item to the cell contents. For case 3, we tally the counter at MOVEUP+2.

MOVEUP

We check the counter, and if it is zero, we go to FILL. Otherwise, the rest of the steps move the contents of a cell to its successor.

```
ADRSRT   XPN,1    0             Initialize input pointer.
NEXT     XMA,1    IN            Put next item in A.
         JSN,4    ADCALL        Do address calculation; item
                                number is placed in N2.
         XMA,2    OUT           Get cell calculated.
         CMP      =0            Is it empty?
         JOE      FILL          Yes, fill it.
         XPN,3    0             Clear counter.
         CMP,1    IN            Cell contents: item.
         JOG      ITEMLS        Jump to less segment.
ITEMGR   NPP,2    1             Move cell pointer ahead.
         XMA,2    OUT           Get this cell contents
         CMP      =0            and compare it to 0.
         JOE      MOVEUP        If equal, stop looking.
         CMP,1    IN            Cell contents: item.
         JOL      ITEMGR        Item is still larger than
         JOE      ITEMGR        contents of cell being examined.
         NPP,3    1             If not, tally counter.
         UCJ      ITEMGR        When counter is empty, fill cell.
MOVEUP   JNZ,3    FILL
         NMP,2    1             } Move an output
         XMA,2    OUT           } item ahead one cell.
         XAM,2    OUT + 1       } Check if more
         TDN,3    MOVEUP + 1    } items are to be moved.
         UCJ      FILL          }
         NPP,3    1             }
ITEMLS   NMP,2    1             }
         XMA,2    OUT           } Check items behind
         CMP      =0            } calculated address
         JOE      MOVEDN        } for empty cell.
         CMP,1    IN            }
         JOL      ITEMLS - 1    }
         UCJ      ITEMLS        }
MOVEDN   JNZ      FILL          }
         NPP,2    1             } Move cell contents back
         XMA,2    OUT           } to make room for item.
         XAM,2    OUT - 1       }
         TDN,3    MOVEDN+ 1     }
FILL     XMA,1    IN            Get item
         XAM,2    OUT           and place in assigned cell.
         NPP,1    1             Advance item index.
         CMPN,1   NUM           Check if done.
         JOL      NEXT          Go back to place next item.
         UCJ      CONTINUE      Done.
```

Fig. 6.3.2 Address calculation sort program in FLAP.

FILL

Once we have made space for the input item, it is simply placed in this space. The rest of the subroutine simply checks if more items are waiting to be sorted.

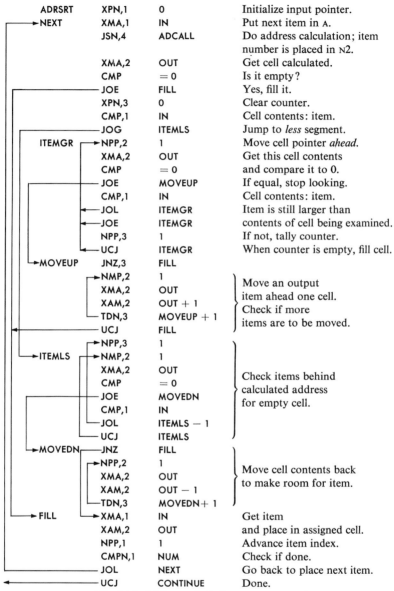

OTHERS

The two subroutines, ITEMLS and MOVEDN, are similar to their namesakes and can be easily followed by the reader.

6.4 COMMENTS ON ADDRESS CALCULATION SORT

The address calculation sort is very fast. Its speed is determined by two things:

- the effectiveness of the address calculation formula
- the fullness ratio, R

The fullness ratio is defined as the ratio of the size of the output area to the number of items to be sorted. For values of R greater than 2, and with a fairly good address calculation formula, we almost always find an empty cell on the first shot. For fullness ratios less than 2, and especially for values approaching 1, we have frequent conflicts, and the address calculation sort is less useful.

CALCULATION

The formula for determining the address can be looked upon as a mapping. This function maps the universe into the sample or sort area. Hence it is a many-to-one transformation. To make it an one-to-one transform would require a sort area as large as the universe.

Most address calculations provide a neighborhood within which the desired item is to be placed, generally requiring the movement of others around it, as we have seen.

When several item keys map into the same address, we generally have an effective sorting formula. If the same item key could map into different addresses at different times, we have an ambiguousness which will defeat our purposes.

Example

To illustrate how address caulculation is done here is a most simple example. Suppose that we have a million items in our universe and these items are numbered from 000,000 to 999,999. Suppose also that, each day, up to a thousand items are active. These are to be posted onto our ordered master file. Before posting, we would like to order these items using an internal sort by address calculation. If a uniform or rectangular distribution of item numbers is assumed, an address calculation sort can be very efficient, especially if 2000 or more cells of memory are provided. A simple approach is to truncate the item number by dropping the three final digits. Thus when item

278,453 is to be entered into storage, it would be placed at 278. However, this would take care of only 1000 cells. We should actually double the number 278 to get 556. Again, this is an absolute location and would have to be offset by the cell number which begins the sort area.

Another item coming in would have its address calculated in the same way. Obviously, there are many items whose relative address, when calculated, would be 556—those from 278,000 through 278,499. We rely on the statistical properties of the sample which would reproduce a rectangular distribution. This means that while we would expect some duplications of address in almost any sort, they would average out so that the sort would eventually appear more efficient than most.

Popularity

For reasonable formulas and for fullness ratios greater than 2, the address calculation sort is better than any other available sort. This being the case, why is it not in more general use? An effective formula depends not only on the data form at being used, but also upon the distribution of the items in the key universe. In other words, the formula is data dependent.

Most business applications today use generalized sorting routines furnished by the computer manufacturer. There is no generalized address-calculating formula which is universally efficient. A sort generating routine would have to be informed not only of data format but also of its statistical distribution. This would become especially complicated for sorts performed on multiple keys.

Address calculation sorts are best for recurring applications within an installation where sorts are designed and written by installation programmers. In the future, installations which write their own sorts may and should find more uses for the address calculation sort.

PROBLEMS

6.1 An active file of about one hundred records is to be sorted. It stems from a master file of ten thousand. Hence the key for each record is a four-digit number and the distribution is linear. Describe the operator ω_1 for the address calculation sort.

6.2 Consider an alphabetic name file by last names. This distribution is not linear. The first letter of the last name points to a table entry which contains the starting point and length of the area devoted to that letter in the sort. The second letter is used to home in on a location as a starting point for the address culculation sort. Describe ω_2 for this purpose.

6.3 Assume that the table for Problem 6.2 starts at 900. Then the entry for *D* is at 903. In FLAP the entry looks like this: 000 *length start*. Here *start* is the place where the D's begin in memory; *length* is the number of such entries. Flowchart the activities for ω_2.

6.4 Program Problem 6.3 where NUM is an SR which converts a six-bit letter code into its numerical value, eight bits.

6.5 The indexed sequential file (ISF) system implemented by many manufacturers is really a multistage address calculation procedure. Justify this statement.

6.6 For an ISF using a track index and a cylinder index (two search tables), flowchart a sort. Assume a multiword record for both the file and the tables. The key is in the first word.

6.7 Program the lookup procedure for Problem 6.6 in FLAP.

6.8 Explain the meaning and need of $\mathbf{G}_i$ (6.2.5), ${}^T\mathbf{G}_i$ (6.2.9), and $\mathbf{A}_i$ (6.2.10). What is their relation to $\mathbf{H}_i$, ${}^T\mathbf{H}_i$, and $\mathbf{B}_i$?

7 MERGE SORTING

7.1 MERGE PRINCIPLES

Introduction

Merging requires two or more lists, each consisting of ordered sublists. These are merged into a single list of ordered sublists. A list of ordered sublists can be produced from a single unordered list by the merging process. Assume first two lists of ordered sublists **A** and **B** thus

$$\mathbf{A} = \bigcup {}^{oi}\mathbf{A}; \qquad \mathbf{B} = \bigcup {}^{oi}\mathbf{B} \tag{7.1.1}$$

Combine together one sublist from list **A** and another one from **B** to form a single ordered sublist

$${}^{i}\mathbf{O} = {}^{i}\mathbf{A} \overset{o}{\bigcup} {}^{i}\mathbf{B} \tag{7.1.2}$$

where the little circle within the union sign indicates that we are taking the *ordered* union. The entire output list, **O**, is the union of the ordered sublists.

$$\mathbf{O} = \bigcup {}^{i}\mathbf{O} \tag{7.1.3}$$

FURTHER MERGES

When we combine **A** and **B**, we get *one* list of ordered sublists **O**. It is impossible to merge with only one list! The remedy is to distribute the merged list into two new lists, **C** and **D**. Thus

$${}^{2j-1}\mathbf{O} \longrightarrow {}^{j}\mathbf{C}; \qquad {}^{2j}\mathbf{O} \longrightarrow {}^{j}\mathbf{D}; \qquad j = 1, 2, \ldots, \nu\mathbf{O} \tag{7.1.4}$$

We take ordered strings from **O** and alternately place them on **C** and **D**.

$$\mathbf{C} = \bigcup {}^i\mathbf{C}; \qquad \mathbf{D} = \bigcup {}^i\mathbf{D} \tag{7.1.5}$$

C and **D** can be merged into an ordered list **O′** which can, in turn, be distributed into new lists, **E** and **F**. By merging and distributing enough times, we get one single ordered list.

NUMBER OF SUBLISTS

In (7.1.2), when one of the sublists, ${}^i\mathbf{A}$ or ${}^i\mathbf{B}$ is empty, ${}^i\mathbf{O}$ is identical to the other or nonempty sublist. This is true if there are more ordered sublists in one list than in the other and the merge copies the *extra* strings from the longer *list* onto the output list. That is the merge operation (7.1.2) implies *copying* when one or more of the sublists is empty.

Example

To visualize merging, examine the example presented in Fig. 7.1.1 where ${}^1\mathbf{A}$ and ${}^1\mathbf{B}$ are merged into ${}^1\mathbf{O}$.

	A	B	O
1	${}^1\mathbf{A}$: 1, 6, 7, 9, 13	${}^1\mathbf{B}$: 2, 4, 8, 10, 12, 14	${}^1\mathbf{O}$: 1, 2, 4, 6, 7, 8, 9, 10, 12, 13, 14
2	${}^2\mathbf{A}$: 5, 15, 16, 19	${}^2\mathbf{B}$: 11, 17, 18, 20, 21	${}^2\mathbf{O}$: 5, 11, 15, 16, 17, 18, 19, 20, 21
3	${}^3\mathbf{A}$: 6	${}^3\mathbf{B}$: 13	${}^3\mathbf{O}$: 6

Fig. 7.1.1 Example of the merge operation.

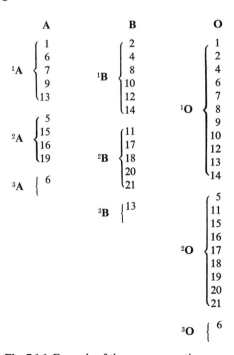

TECHNIQUE

We look at the top two items and choose the smaller one as the first item for output. In these examples, sublists are in *ascending* order from top to bottom. We remove the top item from **A** from consideration, leaving us a 6 from **A** and a 2 from **B**. Again we choose the smaller item, this time 2. We continue this, choosing the smaller item. Our first approach to a rule is: *Examine the top item of both lists; choose the smaller as the next item for output, thereafter eliminating it from consideration.*

When do we get into trouble? After we choose 13 from **A** to go onto ^{1}**O**! Then the next item on **A** is 5. However, it should be ignored because it is not part of ^{1}**A** but is rather part of ^{2}**A**. Therefore, we should continue by taking 14 from ^{1}**B** as the next output item for ^{1}**O**. Having done this, we find 5 at the top of **A** and 11 at the top of **B**. These belong, respectively, to ^{2}**A** and ^{2}**B**. Therefore it is the lesser of these two which is taken and becomes part of the ordered group ^{2}**O**.

Merge conditions

We distinguish three merge conditions which determine the choice and disposition of the next item.

NO STEPDOWN

When items at the top of both lists are larger than or equal to the last item placed on the output list, we have a **no stepdown condition:** we choose the lesser as the output item. For instance, suppose we have placed 1 and 2 on the output list **O** in Fig. 7.1.1. 6 and 4 are at the top of **A** and **B**, respectively. Since they are both larger than 2, the last item placed on **O**, we choose the lesser, 4, as the output item.

SINGLE STEPDOWN

When we have completed examination of an ordered sublist on one of the lists, the next item key is smaller than the previous item on that input list. A **single stepdown condition** occurs when the next item on one input list is *smaller* than the last item placed on **O** *and* when the next item on the other input list is *larger* than the last item placed on **O**. We choose the *larger* item for output as long as the single stepdown prevails.

For instance, after having placed 19 into ^{2}**O**, we find 6 at the top of **A**, which is lesss than 19, and 20 at the top of **B**, which is greater than 19. We place 20 onto ^{2}**O** and later 21 onto ^{2}**O**. This reveals the item 13 and, since both 6 and 13 are *less* than 21, a **double stepdown** (and we choose the lesser item, 6.)

DOUBLE STEPDOWN

We sense that the situation changes from one stepdown to double stepdown. This is treated like *no stepdown;* now we are starting a new sublist of **O**.

Multiway merges

We have examined two-way balanced merges, using two input lists. Multiway merges, where several input lists are merged into a single output list, are discussed in Section 7.4.

7.2 MERGE OPERATION

We examine the two-way merge, assuming that the input lists **A** and **B** need not be of equal size but that the sum of the number of items on each of these lists is equal to the number of items on the output list.

$$\nu\,\mathbf{A} + \nu\,\mathbf{B} = \nu\,\mathbf{O} \tag{7.2.1}$$

The first item on the output list will be O_1. To make our comparisons universal, we need to compare with the output item "before the first." Let us call this item O_0 and set it equal to the minimum element thus

$$(\mathrm{O}^0) = \mathbf{a} \tag{7.2.2}$$

Conditions

NO STEPDOWN

The *no-stepdown* condition occurs when the lesser of either input items is greater than or equal to the last selected item.

$$(\lambda\ \mathrm{A_iB_j}) \geq (\mathrm{O_{i+j-2}}) \tag{7.2.3}$$

The lesser of the two items becomes the next output item.

$$(\lambda\ \mathrm{A_iB_j}) \longrightarrow \mathrm{O_{i+j-1}} \tag{7.2.4}$$

SINGLE STEPDOWN

For the single stepdown condition, the last output item lies between the greater and the lesser of the input items.

$$(\mu\ A_iB_j) \geq (O_{i+j-2}) > (\lambda\ A_iB_j) \tag{7.2.5}$$

In this case we choose the greater of the input items to become the next output item thus

$$(\mu\ A_iB_j) \longrightarrow O_{i+j-1} \tag{7.2.6}$$

DOUBLE STEPDOWN

In the case of the double stepdown, the last item chosen is larger than either of the input items

$$(O_{i+j-2}) > (\mu\ A_iB_j) \tag{7.2.7}$$

In this case we choose the lesser of the two input items as the next output item.

$$(\lambda\ A_iB_j) \longrightarrow O_{i+j-1} \tag{7.2.8}$$

Runout

There is one more eventuality: Since the lists may contain an unequal number of sublists and since sublists are matched during merging, one of the lists becomes exhausted before the other. In this case the remaining items on the unexhausted list are copied onto the output list.

Routine

The merge in operational notation appears in Fig. 7.2.1. At (1) we initialize the indices of the items on the two input sublists. The item number on the output sublist is a function of the input item numbers.

$$1 \longrightarrow i, j \tag{1}$$

$$\underset{\substack{i \leq \nu\mathbf{A} \\ \&\ j \leq \nu\mathbf{B}}}{\mathsf{R}} \quad \begin{aligned} &(\lambda\ A_iB_j) \geq (O_{i+j-2}) \vee (O_{i+j-2}) > (\mu\ A_iB_j) \\ &\quad \{(\lambda\ A_iB_j) \longrightarrow O_{i+j-1}; && (2) \\ &\quad j + \{(A_i) > (B_j)\} \longrightarrow j; \quad i + \{(A_i) \leq (B_j)\} \longrightarrow i && (3) \\ &(\mu\ A_iB_j) \geq (O_{i+j+2}) > (\lambda\ A_iB_j)\{(A_iB_j) \longrightarrow O_{i+j-1}; && (4) \\ &\quad i + \{(A_i) \geq (B_j)\} \longrightarrow i; \quad j + \{(A_i) < (B_j)\} \longrightarrow j\} && (5) \end{aligned}$$

$$\underset{i \leq \nu\mathbf{A}}{\mathsf{R}} \quad (A_i) \longrightarrow O_{i+j-1}; \quad i + 1 \longrightarrow i \tag{6}$$

$$\underset{j \leq \nu\mathbf{B}}{\mathsf{R}} \quad (B_j) \longrightarrow O_{i+j-1}; \quad j + 1 \longrightarrow j \tag{7}$$

Fig. 7.2.1 Two-way merge onto a single output.

At (2) we check for *no stepdown* (first condition) or *double stepdown* (second relation); if either is present, we choose the lesser of the input items for output. On line (3) we advance the index in the list from which we have taken the item so that when we perform the next comparison, it will be with the proper item. Here "$(A_i) > (B_j)$" and "$(A_i) \leq (B_j)$" are Boolean functions which may only have the values 0 or 1. We add 0 or 1 to opposite indices, according to where the item came from. At (4), for a single stepdown, the greater input item is chosen for output. Its index is advanced when a single stepdown occurs at (5); again, a Boolean function is used for addition determination.

The repeat operator, **R**, applies as long as there are items in *both* input lists. As soon as this is denied (one list exhausted), we reach a runout condition. If **A** contains further items, these are placed on the output list (6); if **B** contins further items, these are placed on the output list, (7). Only one of these options, (6) or (7), will be exercised since the *other* list has run out.

Distribution

We distribute sublists from the output list onto new input lists as shown in Fig. 7.2.2. We introduce here the sublist count operator ${}^1\nu$ which counts the number of sublists rather than the number of items. Hence ${}^1\nu$ **O** is the number of sublists on the output list **O**.

$$\overset{{}^1\nu\,\mathbf{O}}{\underset{i=0}{\mathsf{R}}} \qquad ({}^{2i}\mathbf{O}) \longrightarrow {}^{i}\mathbf{C}; \qquad ({}^{2i+1}\mathbf{O}) \longrightarrow {}^{i}\mathbf{D}$$

Fig. 7.2.2 Two-way merge distribution routine.

Figure 7.2.2 is presented for notational simplicity. The sublist operator is not actually required since the criterion for determining the end of a sublist is a *double stepdown*. The reader should be able to rephrase the routine of Fig. 7.2.2 without resorting to the subgroup number operator ${}^1\nu$.

7.3 TWO-WAY MERGE FLOW CHART AND PROGRAM

Flow chart

It is useful to examine a flow chart of the two-way merge, Fig. 7.3.1, before approaching the FLAP program for this task. We assume two input tapes, A and B, with input records on these tapes labelled A_a and B_b, respectively. Output is placed on units C and D, and records are labelled C_c and D_d, respectively. The flow chart includes a *distribute* routine which alternates sorted output strings onto the output units. Since distribution must also be done during rollout, the rollout switch, e, is used.

We set all the indices, a, b, c, and d, and the switch, e, to zero (1). In (2) C is identified as the output unit and carries the pseudonym, X. Thus, X will

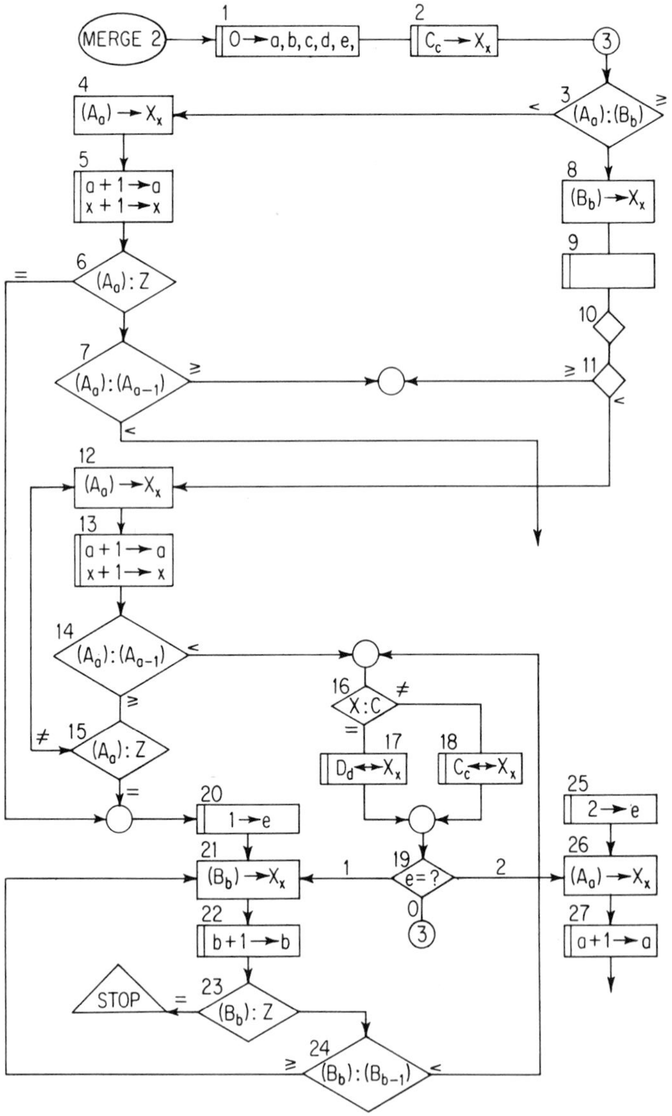

Fig. 7.3.1 Flow chart for two-way merge.

be the name of the output unit regardless of whether it is actually C or D. We always enter the top comparison box (3) for *no stepdown*. If the smaller record came from A, it goes to output (4). Indices a and x are incremented (5). We then check the next record on A against the terminal flag to see if there are more records (6). If so, we check the A file for a *single stepdown* (7). If none occurs, we continue (3).

A similar set of occurrences applies to *B* (8–11).

SINGLE STEPDOWN

Should the *B* comparison (11) indicate a *single stepdown*, we place the next *A* record on output (12), advance the indices (13), and check for *double stepdown* (14). If a second stepdown is absent, we check the termination flag (15); if the flag is absent, we return to *single stepdown* processing of *A* (12).

DOUBLE STEPDOWN

When a *double stepdown* is encountered (14), we have placed a complete ordered string into the output; the next record for output will be the first of a new string. It will be placed on the *other* output unit. We determine the present output unit (16) and designate the *other* unit as the new output unit (17, 18).

Since distribution is also performed during rollout, rollout switch, *e*, is checked. If we are not doing rollout, *e* reads zero, and we return to *no stepdown* processing (3).

ROLLOUT

Rollout can occur in either file *A* or *B*. We examine only the latter condition.

Rollout is performed for file *B* when a terminal flag is noted on file *A* in either (6) or (15). As we start rollout of *B*, we set the rollout switch, *e*, to 1 (20) (when we rollout file *A*, the rollout switch, *e*, is set to 2).

The next record on file *B* is sent to output (21). Index *b* is advanced. We then check for a terminal flag on file *B*. If we should find it, this is the end of our merge.

We check for stepdown (24); if absent, we continue rollout (21). For a stepdown, we switch output files (15).

FLAP program

At the beginning of the FLAP program, Fig. 7.3.2, we initialize all the files and the output switch by entering 0 into indexes 1 through 4 and 6. Index 6 is used to switch from one output file to the other. A cell in memory called SWITCH is used during distribution to determine to which point in the program to return. It is now set to return to NOSTEP at (6, 7). (The numbers in parentheses show correspondence with the flow chart, Fig. 7.3.1.) The actual comparison is made at (9). If the *A* record is small, we do not jump at (10)

```
1   MERGE2   XPN,1      0               A input.
2            XPN,2      0               B input.
3            XPN,3      0               C output.
4            XPN,4      0               D output.
5            XPN,6      0               Output switch.
6            XMA        LOC (NO STEP)   Set switch for TWOSTEP to
7            XAM        SWITCH          return to NOSTEP.
8   NOSTEP   XMA,1      A               For no stepdown, find
9            CMP,2      B               smaller of A and B.
10           JOG        BSMALL          Jump when B is smaller.
11  ASMALL   XAM,I,6    OUT             Put A on output indirectly
                                        indexed.
12           EXEC,6     OUT + 2         Advance output index.
13           NPP,1      1               Advance input index.
14           XMA,1      A               Get next input item.
15           CMP        ENDFLAG         If it is last
16           JOE        RUNOUTB         runout other (B) list.
17           CMP,1      A - 1           Check for single stepdown
18           JOG        ONESTEPB        and jump if present;
19           UCJ        NOSTEP + 1      loop if absent.
20  OUT      NOOP,3     C             } These cells permit indirect ad-
21           NOOP,4     D             } dressing of indexed output list.
22           NPP,3      1             } These cells execute incremen-
23           NPP,4      1             } tation of output index.
24  BSMALL   XMA,2      B             }
25           XAM,I,6    OUT           }
26           EXEC,6     OUT + 2       }
27           NPP,2      1             }
28           XMA,2      B             } This is very similar
29           CMP        ENDFLAG       } to ASMALL
30           JOE        RUNOUTA       }
31           CMP,2      B - 1         }
32           JOG        ONESTEPA      }
33           UCJ        NOSTEP        }
```

Fig. 7.3.2 Internal merge and distribution routine in FLAP.

but continue to ASMALL (11). This command places the contents of the accumulator, using indirect and indexed addressing, on the output. It goes indirectly through location OUT which does a second indexing, using index 3, to get to the proper position in the output area.

At ASMALL the first command is

$$\text{XAM,I,6} \qquad \text{OUT} \tag{7.3.1}$$

This takes us to OUT + (6), OUT plus the contents of index 6, to look for the desired address. Now index 6 was originally set to 0 because we use file *C* first for output. During the merge, we alternate between *C* and *D* by alternating (6) between 0 and 1. This causes (7.3.1) to alternate between OUT and OUT + 1 for indirection.

The *C* file is indexed by index 3, by indirection through the use of OUT;

```
34  ONESTEPA   XMA,1      A                    Next A item
35             XAM,I,6    OUT                  is outputted
36             EXEC,6     OUT + 2              and output index incremented.
37             NPP,1      1                    Input is incremented;
38             XMA,1      A                    next A item obtained
39             CMP,1      A - 1                and compared to last
40             JOL        TWOSTEP              jump on double stepdown.
41             CMP        ENDFLAG              Check for end of A list.
42             JOE        RUNOUTB              If so, do runout for B;
43             UCJ        ONESTEP A + 1        otherwise continue single step-
                                               down processing.
44  TWOSTEP    JNNZ,6     * + 3                When (6) = 0
45             XPN,6      1                    make (6) = 1
46             UCJ,I      SWITCH               and return via SWITCH
47             XPN,6      0                    If (6) = 1 make (6) = 0
48             UCJ,I      SWITCH               and return via SWITCH
49  RUNOUTA    XMA        LOC (RUNOUTA) + 2    Reset switch to return
50             XAM        SWITCH               from TWOSTEP
51             XMA,1      A                    Get A item.
52             CMP        ENDFLAG              If there are no more
53             JOE        STOP                 then merge is completed;
54             XAM,I,6    OUT                  otherwise, output A item
55             EXEC,6     OUT + 2              and increment output index
56             NPP,1      1                    and input index.
57             XMA,1      A                    Get next A item.
58             CMP,1      A -1                 Check for stepdown and,
59             JOL        TWO STEP             when present, switch output;
60             UCJ        * - 8                otherwise continue runout.
```

Fig. 7.3.2 Internal merge and distribution routine in FLAP (Cont.)

the *D* file is indexed by index 4, by indirection through the use of OUT + 1. Hence (7.3.1) gets us to *C* indexed by 3 via OUT when (6) = 1.

But, having used an output file, we should advance the corresponding index. The command for index advance again depends on the setting of index 6. We use

$$\text{EXEC,6} \qquad \text{OUT} + 2 \tag{7.3.2}$$

Here EXEC enables us to execute one command at a chosen location and return immediately to the instruction stream. If (6) = 0, we have used the *C* file and should increment index 3; NPP,3 at OUT + 2 does this. If (6) = 1, we have used the *D* file and increment index 4 using NPP,4 at OUT + 3. Index 6 enables us to choose which command we use and, therefore, which index is incremented.

We advance the input index at ASMALL + 2, get the next *A* item at ASMALL + 3 (14), check it against the termination flag at ASMALL + 4 (15), and jump if runout is required at ASMALL + 5 (16). We then check for a single stepdown at ASMALL + 6 (17), and if absent, we go back to NOSTEP + 1 (9).

If comparison indicated that the record from file *B* is smaller at NOSTEP

+ 2 we go to the segment called BSMALL at (24). This is almost identical to ASMALL, and it is left for the reader to figure out. It corresponds to (8–11) of the flow chart, Fig. 7.3.1.

SINGLE STEPDOWN

The single stepdown segment is called ONESTEPA. It follows fairly closely to (12–15) of the flow chart.

DOUBLE STEPDOWN

The double stepdown segment is called TWOSTEP. Its purpose is to alter the output switch, index 6: if index 6 contains 0, place 1 there, TWOSTEP + 1; if it contains 1, place 0 there, TWOSTEP + 3.

RUNOUT

Runout for file *A* is performed at RUNOUTA. The first task is to reset SWITCH so that, when we return from TWOSTEP, we will enter RUNOUTA at RUNOUTA + 2—rather than go to NOSTEP. The rest of the runout routine should be clear from the figure.

Example

Figure 7.3.3 is an example of what happens during a merge. It also shows

To be merged

A	(A)	B	(B)
4	8		
3	3	3	7
2	5	2	8
1	2	1	4

Step	*(A)*	*(B)*	(O)	*Relation*	*Use*	*Next*	*String*
1	2	4		(O) < (*A*) < (*B*)	λ	2	first
2	5	4	2	(O) < (*B*) < (*A*)	λ	4	first
3	5	8	4	(O) < (*A*) < (*B*)	λ	5	first
4	3	8	5	(*A*) < (O) < (*B*)	μ	8	first
5	3	7	8	(*A*) < (*B*) < (O)	λ	3	second
6	6	7	3	(O) < (*A*) < (*B*)	λ	6	second
7	8	7	6	(O) < (*A*) < (*B*)	λ	7	second

Fig. 7.3.3 Merge example.

three kinds of stepdowns noting that the operator λ is used for no stepdown and double stepdown, whereas the μ operator is used for the single stepdown.

7.4 MULTIWAY MERGE

Philosophy

For a K-way merge, we have K input lists, $^1\mathbf{A}$ through $^K\mathbf{A}$. Each of the lists consists of ordered sublists. One sublist from each list is merged into a single output sublist and placed on the output list **O**. Later we distribute the ordered sublists from **O** onto new lists, $^1\mathbf{C}$ through $^K\mathbf{C}$.

Notation

To simplify our notation, let us call the number of items in the jth input list I_j thus

$$\mathrm{I_j} = \nu\, {}^j\mathbf{A} \tag{7.4.1}$$

The total number of items to be merged into the output list is then $\hat{I}$, given by

$$\hat{\mathrm{I}} = \sum_{\mathrm{j}=1}^{\mathrm{K}} \mathrm{I_j} \tag{7.4.2}$$

SUBSCRIPTS

To keep track of the items currently available on a given sublist, we have to use a subscripted subscript. In examining the jth list $^j\mathbf{A}$, we see that the present item of interest uses the subscript i_j. The location of this item is then $^jA_{i_j}$. The contents of this cell is then $(^jA_{i_j})$.

The subscript, $\hat{\imath}$, of the item on the output list is the sum of all the subscripts of the items examined to find $O_{\hat{\imath}}$, less $K - 1$. Then $\hat{\imath}$ is given as

$$\hat{\mathrm{i}} = 1 - \mathrm{K} + \sum_{\mathrm{j}=1}^{\mathrm{K}} \mathrm{i}_j \tag{7.4.3}$$

Working set

The working set of items, **W**, is the set of all items currently under examination. We define **W** and $^jW_1 \in \mathbf{W}$. Here the left superscript indicates that $^j\mathbf{A}$ is the source of ^jW. If $^iA_{i_j} - 1$ was the last item examined in $^j\mathbf{A}$ then we have

$$\mathrm{W_j} = (^\mathrm{j}\mathrm{A}_{\mathrm{i_j}}) \tag{7.4.4}$$

and

$$\mathbf{W} = \{^\mathrm{j}\mathrm{W}_1\}; \qquad \mathrm{j} = 1 \text{ to } \mathrm{K} \tag{7.4.5}$$

Further, let **W** be ordered, with the order indicated by the right subscript so that

$$\mathbf{W} = \{{}^{j}W_1, {}^{k}W_2, {}^{l}W_3, \ldots, {}^{m}W_K\} \tag{7.4.6}$$

where

$$W_1 \leq W_2 \leq W_3 \leq \cdots \leq W_K \tag{7.4.7}$$

We need one more definition for proper subscript advance. The operator, ι, selects the source superscript or subscript from a cell. For instance, we have

$$\iota\, {}^{j}W_i = j \tag{7.4.8}$$

More importantly, this will be associated with the minimum operator for selecting a subscript, and we have

$$\iota\, \lambda\, \mathbf{a} = j \supset a_j \leq a_i; \qquad \text{all} \quad a_i \in \mathbf{a} \tag{7.4.9}$$

Conditions and consequences

There are several conditions which occur.

NO STEPDOWN

When the item just chosen is less than all the working items, we have *no stepdown*, described by

$$(O_{\hat{\imath}-1}) \leq (W_1) = (\lambda\, \mathbf{W}) \tag{7.4.10}$$

For this condition, we choose the least item on the working list as the next output item

$$(W_1) \longrightarrow O_{\hat{\imath}} \tag{7.4.11}$$

To advance the pointer, we must first determine the file to which W_1 belongs. Call it k; thus

$$\iota\, W_1 = k \tag{7.4.12}$$

The item to which it corresponds in ${}^{k}A$ is

$${}^{k}W_1 = {}^{k}A_{i_k} \tag{7.4.13}$$

The latter subscript is advanced thus

$$i_k + 1 \longrightarrow i_k \tag{7.4.14}$$

Of course, the new set **W** will reflect this change. It should be subscripted by $\hat{\imath}$ to reflect the time at which the set is being used. Thus ${}_{\hat{\imath}}\mathbf{W}$ would be the working set when $O_{\hat{\imath}}$ is being chosen. The order within **W** may change; ${}_{\hat{\imath}}\mathbf{W}$ changes to ${}_{\hat{\imath}+1}\mathbf{W}$ because ${}^{k}_{\hat{\imath}}\mathbf{W}$ may occupy a different position (rank) than ${}^{k}_{\hat{\imath}+1}\mathbf{W}$.

ALL STEPDOWN

When the item just placed in the output is greater than all the items on the working list, we have finished an output sublist. This condition is given as

$$(\mathrm{O}_{\hat{\imath}-1}) > (\mathrm{W}_{\mathrm{K}}) = (\mu\, \mathbf{W}) \tag{7.4.15}$$

We are ready to start a new string. We choose the least from the working list and place it on the output,

$$(\mathrm{W}_1) \longrightarrow \mathrm{O}_{\hat{\imath}} \tag{7.4.16}$$

We must then advance the index for this list with (7.4.12) through (7.4.14).

INTERMEDIATE CONDITIONS

Most prevalent will be an intermediate condition where one or more of the ordered sublists have become exhausted, and the top of the new sublist from that list appears in the working list. This condition is described by

$$(\lambda\, \mathbf{W}) \leq (\mathrm{O}_{\hat{\imath}-1}) < (\mu\, \mathbf{W}) \quad \text{or} \quad (\mathrm{W}_1) \leq (\mathrm{O}_{\hat{\imath}-1}) < (\mathrm{W}_{\mathrm{K}}) \tag{7.4.17}$$

For this condition, we want to choose the smallest item in the working list which is greater than or equal to the item last chosen. Since $\mathbf{W}$ is ordered, we apply γ to choose the first item greater than $(\mathrm{O}_{\hat{\imath}-1})$; thus

$$(\mathrm{O}_{\hat{\imath}-1}\, \gamma\, \mathrm{W}) \longrightarrow \mathrm{O}_{\hat{\imath}} \tag{7.4.18}$$

The index corresponding to this item must be increased. Strip the superscript from chosen item thus,

$$\iota\, \mathrm{O}_{\hat{\imath}-1}\, \gamma\, \mathbf{W} \longrightarrow \mathrm{k} \tag{7.4.19}$$

and advance the subscript i_k for the kth file,

$$\mathrm{i}_{\mathrm{K}} + 1 \longrightarrow \mathrm{i}_{\mathrm{K}} \tag{7.4.20}$$

Runout

As the multiway merge process continues, eventually one or more of the input lists become exhausted. When this occurs, we place a maximum symbol, $\mathfrak{z}$ in the proper position of our working list so that we no longer choose elements from this list. Another way to do this is to eliminate elements from the working list $\mathbf{W}$ for an expired file so that $\nu\, \mathbf{W}$ becomes smaller.

Lists continue to drop out until there is just one list left. Since the working list consists of exactly one item, runout is then performed automatically.

ROUTINE

Figure 7.4.1 shows a collection routine for the K-way merge.

$$
\underset{j=1}{\overset{K}{\mathsf{R}}}\left\{\begin{array}{l}
1 \longrightarrow i_j \\
{}^jA_1 \longrightarrow {}^jW \\
\nu\, {}^j\mathbf{A} \longrightarrow I_j
\end{array}\right.
\begin{array}{r}(1)\\(2)\\(3)\end{array}
$$

$$\sum I_j \longrightarrow I \tag{4}$$

$$1 \longrightarrow \hat{\imath} \tag{5}$$

$$
\underset{\hat{\imath}=1}{\overset{I}{\mathsf{R}}}\left\{\begin{array}{l}
\mathbf{W} = \{{}^jW_i\}, \qquad (W_j) \leq (W_{j+1}) \\
\{(O_{\hat{\imath}-1}) \leq (W_1) \vee (O_{j-1}) \geq (W_K)\}(W_1) \longrightarrow O_{\hat{\imath}} \\
\&\, {}_{\iota}W_1 \longrightarrow k \\
\{(W_1) < (O_{\hat{\imath}-1}) < (W_K)\}(O_{\hat{\imath}-1}\, \gamma\, \mathbf{W}) \longrightarrow O_{\hat{\imath}} \\
\&\, {}_{\iota}(O_{\hat{\imath}-1}\, \gamma\, \mathbf{W}) \longrightarrow k \\
i_k + 1 \longrightarrow i_k \\
\{i_k > I_k\}\, \not z \longrightarrow {}^kW \\
\hat{\imath} + 1 \longrightarrow \hat{\imath}
\end{array}\right.
\begin{array}{r}(6)\\(7)\\(8)\\(9)\\(10)\\(11)\\(12)\\(13)\end{array}
$$

Fig. 7.4.1 Collection routine for K-way merge.

PROBLEMS

7.1 Why must two lists to be merged be in order? Can they be in descending order? In opposite orders? Why are four lists required at any given time during the merge?

7.2 Why do we consider *sublists* during merge?

7.3 Explain the *stepdown* conditions. Why are they considered during a merge?

7.4 In merging ascending lists, what is comparable to *stepdowns*? How do we treat these?

7.5 Make up three lists of sublists ${}^1\mathbf{A}$, ${}^2\mathbf{A}$, and ${}^3\mathbf{A}$ using small numbers as keys. Show the state of the working set $\mathbf{W}$ during the merging and distribution of these lists into ${}^1\mathbf{C}$, ${}^2\mathbf{C}$, and ${}^3\mathbf{C}$.

7.6 Repeat Problem 7.5 for a four-way merge.

7.7 Make a flow chart of a K-way merge.

7.8 Managing is a big problem for the merge. Describe how this would be done using these alternative approaches:

(a) $\mathbf{W}$ is a sorted list in terms of absolute size. How do we select the next item for $\mathbf{W}$? How do we update $\mathbf{W}$?

(b) $\mathbf{W}$ is partitioned into two sublists which are sorted: those lists from which records may come, and those which have already reached stepdown.

(c) $\mathbf{W}$ is kept in order by list number, not by size.

7.9 Replace Figs. 7.2.1 and 7.2.2 with one routine, eliminating the subgroup operator.

8 REPLACEMENT SORTING

8.1 THE REPLACEMENT PRINCIPLE

Introduction

We have found an inherent inefficiency in earlier sorting methods because often we eradicate a selected item from the input list by replacing the chosen item with $\mathfrak{z}$. The entire list must be reviewed regardless of the number of $\mathfrak{z}$'s on it.

The next alternative examined was to eliminate the selected item by reducing the size of the input list. This required an exchange procedure.

An alternative examined here replaces the selected item within the input list by an entirely new item. The advantages to this are:

- Each review of the list now examines a collection of useful items.
- Extra moving around is eliminated.

Application

Replacement sorting is not applicable to selection and exchange and to such techniques where we actually shorten the list examined.

Replacement sorting is applicable to straight selection. Its use is similar to that for the counting technique. This may be more or less efficient, depending on the record specifications and the machine being used. It is easiest to explain replacement for sorting by counting, as done in Section 8.2.

Extension to quadratic sorting is left as an exercise. The replacement technique especially enhances the tournament sort as detailed in Section 8.4.

8.2 REPLACEMENT COUNTING

Method

We consider several memory areas:

1. *Input*. One or more input areas each contain a reservoir of items to be sorted. They are replenished automatically as they become exhausted (by the input/output control system, perhaps).
2. *Input list*, **L**. This is a temporary storage area which holds a small record, or a record pointer called the **key word,** continuing the record key and the address of the record.
3. *Counter*, **C**. This area contains one word for each word in the list **L**. The word indicates the relative rank of the key word in **L**.
4. *Output*, **S**. This is an output area of variable size, approximately double that of the list area, **L**.

STARTUP

To start the operation, we perform a counting sort, settting up the counters in **C** as items are entered into **L**, as in Section 3.6. At the end of this procedure, **L** is full and **C** contains numbers from 0 to ν **L** − 1 which rank the items in **L**.

OUTPUT

The item for which a counter in **C** reads 0 is withdrawn from **L** and placed in the output list **S**. Then a new input item is placed in **L** where the old item was withdrawn. As this is done, the counters are reset so that the new list is ranked just as the old one was.

Example

Examine Fig. 8.2.1. After one output cycle, we are ready to take the next item from **L**. A glance at ${}_1\mathbf{C}$ shows that the new item is at L_4 (and is 6) because ${}_1C_4$ is 0. The new input item 29 is to be inserted at L_4 as the output item is withdrawn. It is stored temporarily in the register I. There is also a rank register R which contains 0. Its function will be examined later. Finally, there is an item counter containing a count corresponding to the present item.

Step	*List* (L)	*Present Count* ($_1$C)	*Augmented Count* ($_2$C)	*Item Count Register* (IC)	*Output List* (S)	*Input Item* (I)	*Rank Register* (R)
1	27	3	2	1	3	29	0
2	36	4	4	1			
3	18	2	1	2			
4	6	0	X	X			
5	55	5	5	2			
6	7	1	0	3			

Fig. 8.2.1 Replacement count, frame 1.

REPLACEMENT

Before we insert 29 at L_4, we scan the list **L** to update the counters **C**. In the figure, the first column shows the list cell contents; the third and fourth columns show the count for 0 cell before and after examination, while the fifth shows the item count register reading for this step. The output list, static, appears in column six. The input item and rank register contents appear in the two rightmost columns. This format is followed for the rest of this section.

RULES

We review **L**, comparing each item in **L** with the new item 29 contained in I.

If the item contained in I is greater than that contained in a given location in **L**, we subtract 1 from the corresponding counter in **C** and add 1 to the item counter, IC. Symbolically, the rule is

$$(\mathrm{I}) > (\mathrm{L_i})\{(\mathrm{IC}) + 1 \longrightarrow \mathrm{IC}; \qquad (\mathrm{C_i}) - 1 \longrightarrow \mathrm{C_i}\} \tag{8.2.1}$$

EXAMPLE

In Fig. 8.2.1, as we review **L**, 29 is greater than $(L_1) = 27$, so we reduce the count in C_1 and increase IC; 29 is less than $L_2 = 36$, so we leave both counters $_1C_2$ and IC alone.

We continue down the list in the same way except that, when we reach L_4, this is where (I) will go. Here we notice that $C_4 = 0$. Hence this is where the item for **S** comes from, and we leave both C_4 and IC alone, ignoring the relation of L_4 and I.

When we complete a scan of the list:

- we place the selected item, 6, in the output list, **S**;

- we replace 6 in L_4 by the new item, 29.
- we place the contents of the item counter, IC, into counter C_4.

The list then looks as shown in Fig. 8.2.2.

Step	*List* (L)	*Present Count* ($_1$C)	*Augmented Count* ($_2$C)	*Item Count Register* (IC)	*Output List* (S)	*Input Item* (I)	*Rank Register* (R)
1	27	2	2	0	3	4	0
2	36	4	4	0	6		
3	18	1	1	0			
4	29	3	3	0			
5	55	5	5	0			
6	7	0	X	X			
7	61	6	6	0			

Fig. 8.2.2 Replacement count, frame 2.

New item smaller

Figure 8.2.2 shows what happens when the new item brought in is 4. It is less than any of the items, inluding the one for output. We proceed with the list scan exactly as before. However, notice that the input counter remains set to 0, as do all the other counters.

When we are ready to output the item from L_6 onto the list **S**, we compare it with 4 contained in I. Since the output item, 7, is greater than the incoming new item, 4, we adjust the rank register, **R**: we add 1 to it.

Rank register

The rank register keeps track of items which do not belong in the present sorted output string. As we prepare items for the sorted string **S**, we come across those which are smaller than items last placed there. Without the rank register, the item placed at L_6, with a count of 0 placed at C_6, would be chosen for output, spoiling our sorted string; longer items should be chosen first. This is taken care of by means of a rank register, R, which tells us the rank of the next item for output. We choose the item whose count is identical with R:

- items with smaller count belong in the next string;
- items with larger count belong in this string.

In Fig. 8.2.3, the rank register contains 1. As we go through the list, **L**, to find the next item for output, instead of looking for an item whose key

Step	*List* (L)	*Present Count* ($_1$C)	*Augmented Count* ($_2$C)	*Item Count Register* (IC)	*Output List* (S)	*Input List* (I)	*Rank Register* (R)
1	27	2	1	1	3	44	1
2	36	4	3	2	6		
3	18	1	X	X	7		
4	29	3	2	3			
5	55	5	5	3			
6	4	0	0	4			
7	61	6	6	4			

Fig. 8.2.3 Replacement count, frame 3.

counter is 0, we look for one whose key is 1. All other operations are the same.

When we come to the end of our examination, we compare the item for output, in this case 18 from L_3, with the incoming item 4 at I. In Fig. 8.2.3, since 18 is less than 44, the rank register remains set at 1. The reader can examine further examples in Figs. 8.2.4 and 8.2.5.

Step	*List* (L)	*Present Count* ($_1$C)	*Augmented Count* ($_2$C)	*Item Count Register* (IC)	*Output List* (S)	*Input Item* (I)	*Rank Register* (R)
1	27	1	X	X	3	5	1
2	36	3	3	0	6		
3	44	4	4	0	7		
4	29	2	2	0	18		
5	55	5	5	0			
6	4	0	0	1			
7	61	6	6	1			

Fig. 8.2.4 Replacement count, frame 4.

Step	*List* (L)	*Present Count* ($_1$C)	*Augmented Count* ($_2$C)	*Item Count Register* (IC)	*Output List* (S)	*Input List* (I)	*Rank Register* (R)
1	5	1	1	1	3	5	2
2	36	3	2	2	6		
3	44	4	3	3	18		
4	29	2	X	X	27		
5	55	5	5	3			
6	4	0	0	4			
7	61	6	6	4			

Fig. 8.2.5 Replacement count, frame 5.

History register

It is equally and often more desirable to the programmer to store the *key* of the last item placed on **S** rather than its rank. Then we compare the **L** key with the history key for each item scanned; when the former is smaller, it indicates a lower rank, and appropriate action is taken.

8.3 REPLACEMENT COUNTING ROUTINE

Assumptions

We have two areas: **L** consisting of ν **L** items; a set of counters, **C**, one for each item on the list. We have set up the counters for the sort as in Section 3.6. The counter corresponding to the least item in the list **L** contains O; the counter corresponding to the largest item in **L** contains $\nu \mathbf{L} - 1$. The list of counters thus set up is labelled $_1\mathbf{C}$.

There is an output list, **S**, in which the next empty space is S_j. There is also a rank register, *R*, which indicates the rank of the item next to be selected for the output list. An item is withdrawn from **L** and is placed in **S**; it is replaced from an input item in the reservoir, **I**. This item is stored in a register, I. A count for this item is established in the incoming item counter, IC.

LIST PARTITION

In the middle of a replacement sort, **L** contains a number of items; some are eligible for output and others are not. Say that we have assembled an output string in ascending order and the last item we have placed on that string is 27. Items in **L** which are less than 27 cannot be placed on this sorted string. Items equal to or greater than 27 in **L** *are* eligible for output.

An effective method for separating eligible from ineligible items is the rank register. Each item in **L** has a rank designated by the counter in **C**. Suppose the rank register reads 8. Items with rank less than 8 in **L** are ineligible; the item with rank 8 in **L** is the next item for **S**; items with rank above 8 are eligible for future output. Ranks of both eligible and ineligible items may change as replacement takes place.

The incoming item in I determines whether we advance the rank register, R. If it is greater than the next item selected, it is eligible for future placement in this string. Therefore, the number of eligible items does not change, and the rank register is not advanced.

If the new item is less than the selected item, it is ineligible. Since it replaces a previously eligible item, the number of eligible items decreases;

the number of ineligible items increases, and hence, the rank register increases so that these items will not be selected during the next examination.

Routine

Operator notation for replacement counting is presented in Fig. 8.3.1.

$$
\begin{array}{llr}
 & 0 \longrightarrow R & (1) \\
 & 1 \longrightarrow j & (2) \\
 & \nu\mathbf{L} + 1 \longrightarrow k & (3) \\
\underset{\nu\mathbf{I}}{\mathbf{R}} \left\{ \begin{array}{l} \\ \\ \\ \\ \\ \\ \\ \\ \\ \\ \end{array} \right. & \begin{array}{l}
I_k \longrightarrow I \\
0 \longrightarrow IC \\
\underset{i=1}{\overset{\nu L}{\mathbf{R}}} \left\{ \begin{array}{l}
({}_jC_i) = (R)\{(L_i) \longrightarrow S_j; \quad i \longrightarrow K\} \\
({}_jC_i) \neq (R)\ \&\ (I) > (L_i) \\
\quad \{(R) > ({}_jC_i)\{({}_jC_i) - 1 \longrightarrow {}_jC_i\}_j \\
\quad (IC) + 1 \longrightarrow IC\}
\end{array} \right. \\
(I) < (L_K)\{(R) + 1 \longrightarrow R\} \\
(I) \longrightarrow L_K; \quad (IC) \longrightarrow {}_jC_K \\
j + 1 \longrightarrow j \\
k + 1 \longrightarrow k
\end{array} & \begin{array}{r} (4) \\ (5) \\ (6) \\ \\ \\ (7) \\ (8) \\ (9) \\ (10) \\ (11) \end{array}
\end{array}
$$

Fig. 8.3.1 Sort by replacement counting.

STRING SETUP

For setup, we clear the rank register (1), and set up the outgoing index to 1 to place the first item selected in S_1 (2). Then we set up the incoming index so that the next item from the incoming area will be just one more than a number of items in **L** (3).

ITEM SETUP

We bring the next item into I and clear the counter, IC (4, 5).

COMPARISON

We examine the counters, looking for one with contents of the same rank as those of the rank register. When found, we place the corresponding item from **L** onto the output list and note its relative number in the list as K (6). During the same scan and for items for which the count is different from the number in the rank register, we compare I with the item L_i. If the new item is greater, we reduce the counter for the old item C_i by 1 and increase the counter for the new item, IC, by 1 (7). Otherwise, we leave C_i and IC alone. This is done for *each* counter in **C** in one scan.

Next we compare the item selected for output L_K with the incoming item.

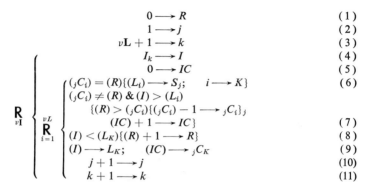

If the latter is smaller, it is ineligible for consideration for the string; we advance the rank register R (8).

We place the incoming item in the spot from which we withdrew the item for the sorted string. In the counter corresponding to it, we also place C_K, the contents of the IC which has kept track of the rank of I (9).

We advance the indices to be set for the next item (10, 11).

Tape and disk procedure

Figure 8.3.2 shows how we might actually use a replacement count sort when we get the items to be sorted from a magnetic tape unit or from a disk drive. This same procedure is adopted for the replacement tournament sort discussed in succeeding sections. Hence the discussion will not be repeated later.

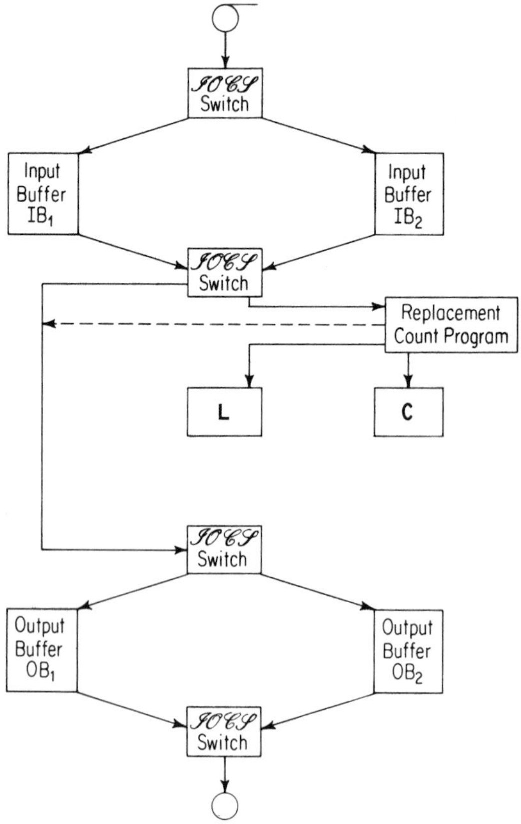

Fig. 8.3.2 How the tape sort is accomplished.

INPUT

Records for sorting are placed in two input buffer areas. One input area will suffice, but with present monitors and $\mathcal{IOCS}$, systems swinging buffers are easy to come by. The switching for communication with these buffers using a good $\mathcal{IOCS}$ is automatic.

ITEM PREPARATION

The replacement count program contains an item preparation segment. It reviews each record and extracts from it its key. The segment then fabricates an item consisting of the key and the absolute location of the record in the buffer. Keys are entered in random order in **L**.

COUNTER SETUP

By means of the counting scheme discussed earlier, a counting segment goes through the list, **L**, and ranks items, placing the ranks in corresponding counters.

SELECTION

One more item is prepared from the next record in the input buffer, and this item is placed in I. The selection segment scans through the counters, **C**, until the next item for output is attained. This is turned over to the output segment, and the counting process continues to completion. The new item is inserted in **L**, and the counter list **C** is updated. Further, the rank register is incremented if necessary.

OUTPUT

The output section of the sort routine performs a transfer of the complete record from the input buffer area to the output buffer area. With a good $\mathcal{IOCS}$, this area is filled up and automatically written when it has become full. Advance of the input buffer area also makes it appear as though it were a single string of records.

8.4 REPLACEMENT TOURNAMENT SORT

Introduction

In Chapter 5 for the tournament sort, we begin with a list, **L**, select the minimum of each pair of items, and place it on $\mathbf{L}^1$. We take pairs of items on $\mathbf{L}^1$, select the minimum, and place it on $\mathbf{L}^2$. We continue thus until we have a list with but a single item on it. This item is the one for output.

Actually, the secondary lists contain item addresses rather than items themselves; but for the introductory explanation, we pretend that items are contained there.

For replacement sorting, the item which has been placed on the output list is replaced in **L** by an incoming item instead of $\mathfrak{z}$. We then update each secondary list. We make a search for the next output item as we go along and end up in list $\mathbf{L}^q$ with a single item, the next one for output.

PROBLEM

The main problem to be faced is the same one encountered with replacement counting: how do we handle new items which are *less* than the last outgoing item? We take up this problem after we see how the method works for incoming items greater than the last selected item.

EXAMPLE, NO PROBLEMS

In Fig. 8.4.1 we see a list, **L**, of 16 items. Auxiliary lists $\mathbf{L}^1$ and $\mathbf{L}^2$ and $\mathbf{L}^3$ contain 8, 4, and 2 items, respectively. $\mathbf{L}^4$ is the item for output.

	Main		*Secondary*		*Tertiary*		*Fourth*	*Fifth*
$^1\mathbf{L}$	L_1: 17, 63	$^1\mathbf{L}^1$	L_1^1: 17, 32	$^1\mathbf{L}^2$	L_1^2: 5, 8, 17, 32	$^1\mathbf{L}^3$	L_1^3: 4, 5, 6, 8, 17, 19, 23, 29	$^1\mathbf{L}^4$: L_1^4: 4, 5, 8, 15, 17, 18, 19, 23, 28
	L_2: 32							
$^2\mathbf{L}$	L_3: 8, 99		L_2^1: 5, 8, 38					
	L_4: 5, 38							
$^3\mathbf{L}$	L_5: 19, 12	$^2\mathbf{L}^1$	L_3^1: 4, 6, 19		L_2^2: 4, 6, 19, 23, 28			
	L_6: 4, 6, 3							
$^4\mathbf{L}$	L_7: 23, 98		L_4^1: 23, 28					
	L_8: 28							
$^5\mathbf{L}$	L_9: 31	$^3\mathbf{L}^1$	L_5^1: 31	$^2\mathbf{L}^2$	L_3^2: 31		L_2^3: 15, 18, 31	
	L_{10}: 59							
$^6\mathbf{L}$	L_{11}: 36		L_6^1: 36					
	L_{12}: 41							
$^7\mathbf{L}$	L_{13}: 18, 11	$^4\mathbf{L}^1$	L_7^1: 18, 66		L_4^2: 15, 18, 48			
	L_{14}: 66							
$^8\mathbf{L}$	L_{15}: 48		L_8^1: 15, 48					
	L_{16}: 15, 2							

I_{17}:	6	I_{22}:	63
I_{18}:	38	I_{23}:	11
I_{19}:	3	I_{24}:	12
I_{20}:	99	I_{25}:	98
I_{21}:	2	I_{26}:	20

Fig. 8.4.1 Example of replacement tournament sort.

The input list, **I**, contains new items which replace sorted items. These come in, in order, from top to bottom as indicated at the bottom of the figure.

For each cell in each list, a series of numbers is recorded. Each is the key of the contents of a cell as it varies with time: The oldest appears at the left; newer items, separated by commas, appear to the right; the rightmost is the most recent.

FIRST SELECTION

By glancing at the secondary lists from left to right, we find that L^4 contains the first item for output, 4. It came from L_6. After being outputted from **L**, it is replaced by the next incoming item: 6 goes into L_6 to replace 4. Since 6 is greater than 4, no problem arises.

First we examine $^3\mathbf{L}$ because 4 came from L_6 and L_6 is in $^3\mathbf{L}$. $^3\mathbf{L}$ consists of L_5 and L_6. Since now $(L_5) = 19$ and $(L_6) = 6$, the latter goes to L_3^1; L_3^1 now corresponds to $^3\mathbf{L}$.

Now L_3^1 is a member of $^2\mathbf{L}^1$; the other member is L_4^1. We compare them: Since $(L_3^1) = 6$ and $(L_4^1) = 23$, we choose 6 to be placed at L_2^2—the correspondent in $\mathbf{L}^2$ for $^2\mathbf{L}^1$.

The twin of L_2^2 is L_1^2; together they comprise $^1\mathbf{L}^2$. Since $(L_1^2) = 5$ and $(L_2^2) = 6$, we choose 5 to place into L_1^3, which corresponds to $^1\mathbf{L}^2$.

The twin of L_1^3 is L_2^3; together they comprise $^1\mathbf{L}^3$. Since $(L_1^3) = 5$ and $(L_2^3) = 15$, we choose 5 to become $\mathbf{L}_1^4$, the sole member of $^1\mathbf{L}^4$. The next item for output is (L_1^4) or 5.

The reader may follow how 38 replaces 5 at L_4 and how the next item is selected by comparisons trickling down through the secondary lists.

New item smaller

Suppose that the item on the input list is samller than the one just selected. It must be prevented from trickling down to the output. Different techniques are used with **L** than with the secondary lists. We examine three techniques now.

Ineligible item in L pair

The item just brought in is ineligible and must not be placed on $\mathbf{L}^1$. However, the other item compared with it may be eligible and, if so, it goes to $\mathbf{L}^1$.

Let us see how this works with our example. Difficulty occurs when 6 is chosen for output and 3 is the incoming item placed at L_6. Notice that 19 is greater than the item just outputted, and so it is eligible for L^1. Hence, instead of selecting 3, we select 19 and place it at L_3^1. Next 19 is compared with 23 at L_4^1, the former being selected and placed into L_2^2. Comparisons continue until the output item, 8, is finally determined.

Ineligible pair in *L*

Notice what happens after 19 has been selected for output. The item to replace it is 12. Now both 12 and 3 are less than the selected item 19. Neither of them should be placed onto L^1. Therefore, a special tag or z is entered at L_3^1; when it is matched with its pair at L_4^1, 28, we find 28 to be smaller. *Any item is smaller than z.*

OTHER SUBLISTS

When both items of a pair on L^1 are z's what do we place on L^2? Of course z goes onto L^2 also. Sorting continues until all sublists contain only z's.

TERMINATION OF STRING

At this juncture, no sublist contains an eligible item. Depending upon how you look at it, *no* list item is eligible or *all* of them are eligible.

How do we reach this condition? We replace an item, making a main list pair ineligible. If as we plow through the auxiliary lists (AL's), we only encounter z's (or tags), then *no* AL item is eligible—an eligible item would show up on at least one AL.

Tags

Although we have described placing z's on the AL, it is preferable to enter an item which is tagged as ineligible. That is, eligible items are tagged 0, ineligible 1, this time; this is reversed next time. Then this time we have:

- If both items in the list are eligible, the lesser item, tagged 0, is placed in the AL.
- If only one list item is eligible, that item is tagged 0 and placed in the AL.
- If both list items are ineligible, both items are tagged 1 and the lesser is placed in the AL.

New strings

If the earlier procedure of entering z's in AL's had been adopted, at the end of the production of a sorted string, all AL's would contain z's. This would require an entire AL fill procedure.

With tags, the AL's are all set up for a new string sort immediately after the last one is produced. Each AL has been tagged as though it contains $\mathfrak{z}$'s. Actually, it contains the lesser of the pair from the preceding AL or from the main list. This is what is required during setup.

DETECTION

Assume eligible AL items are tagged 0. Use the rules of the previous subsection. When an AL item is ineligible because it corresponds to key less than the last output item, it is tagged 1. When the only eligible item on the main list is replaced by an ineligible one, the AL1 entry is tagged 1; so is the AL2; etc. Finally, the last AL, the one with only one item, also becomes tagged 1.

Now a string is complete! And the first item of the *new* string (in the last AL) is ready for output! We must just make sure to reverse our tagging and detection procedure: eligible items are 1; ineligible items are 0.

Another alternative

A new item becomes ineligible when its key is less than that of the last output item—the item it replaces in **L**. If we hold on to the key of the last output item, *it* can be the means for judging eligibility all the way up the line.

For **L** we have:

- If the twin is eligible, it goes to $\mathbf{L}^1$.
- If neither is eligible, the smaller goes to $\mathbf{L}^1$.

This philosophy holds for the AL's too. Thus if we are examining a pair in $\mathbf{L}^{j-1}$, we have:

- If both are eligible, the smaller goes to $\mathbf{L}^j$.
- If only one is eligible, it goes to $\mathbf{L}^j$.
- If neither is eligible, the smaller goes to $\mathbf{L}^j$.

A string is complete when we encounter ineligible items right up to the last AL, L^8. We then start a new string, change the eligibility requirement.

Contrast

Entering $\mathfrak{z}$'s requires a new initialization after each string is constructed. Tagging requires extra space in the key word. For the third alternative, each entry in an AL not only requires comparison with its twin but also with the eligibility criterion (the last item out). If there is room in the key word, tagging is undoubtedly the best approach. Otherwise, the third alternative should be used.

Addresses in auxiliary lists

The foregoing explanation assumed complete items in the AL's. This is messy from the point of view of list manipulation.

An auxiliary list item L_i^j, the ith item in the jth auxiliary list, ALJ, in what follows, consists of

- a pointer to a cell in **L**;
- a pointer to an item in ALJ + 1 (or $\mathbf{L}^{j+1}$);
- a key if it will fit;
- a tag.

8.5 THE REPLACEMENT TOURNAMENT SORT PROCEDURE

The replacement tournament sort description, in operator terms in Fig. 8.5.1, is based on the use of the sentinel $\not{z}$ to distinguish ineligible pairs in AL's. This is very inefficient but easy to describe. The programmer can easily manipulate the tags as described earlier, obtaining the more efficient procedure.

$$
\underset{k>\nu\mathbf{I}}{\mathsf{R}}\left\{\begin{array}{ll}
1 \longrightarrow \ell & (1) \\
\nu\,\mathbf{L}+1 \longrightarrow k \qquad 2^q=\nu\,\mathbf{L} & (2) \\
\overset{\beta\mathbf{L}}{\underset{i=1}{\mathsf{R}}}\ \lambda\,{}^{i}\mathbf{L} \longrightarrow L_i^1 & (3) \\
\underset{((\mathbf{L}^q))\neq\not{z}}{\mathsf{R}}\left\{\begin{array}{l}
\overset{q}{\underset{j=2}{\mathsf{R}}}\ \overset{\beta j\mathbf{L}}{\underset{i=1}{\mathsf{R}}}\ \lambda\,({}^{i}\mathbf{L}^{j-1}) \longrightarrow L_i^j \qquad (4) \\
((\mathbf{L}^q)) = (L_K) \longrightarrow O_1 \qquad (5) \\
(I_K) \longrightarrow L_K \qquad (6) \\
(L_K),\ ({}^{\beta K}\mathbf{L}-L_K) \geq (O_1)\{\lambda\ {}^{\beta K}\mathbf{L} \longrightarrow L_{\beta K}^1 \qquad (7) \\
(L_K) \geq (O_1)\ \&\ ({}^{\beta K}\mathbf{L}-L_K) < (O_1)\{L_K \longrightarrow L_{\beta K}^1\} \qquad (8) \\
(L_K) < (O_1)\ \&\ ({}^{\beta K}\mathbf{L}-L_K) \geq (O_1)\{{}^{\beta K}\mathbf{L}-L_K \longrightarrow L_{\beta K}^1\} \qquad (9) \\
(L_K)_1({}^{\beta K}\mathbf{L}-L_K) < (O_1)\{\not{z} \longrightarrow L_{\beta K}^1\} \qquad (10) \\
\overset{q}{\underset{j=2}{\mathsf{R}}}\ \lambda\,({}^{\beta j_K}\mathbf{L}^{j-1}) \longrightarrow L_{\beta j_K}^j \qquad (11) \\
\ell+1 \longrightarrow \ell \\
R+1 \longrightarrow k
\end{array}\right. &
\end{array}\right.
$$

Fig. 8.5.1 Operations for replacement tournament sort.

Setup

First we set up the auxiliary lists (1–4); the sort occurred in lines (1) through (4).

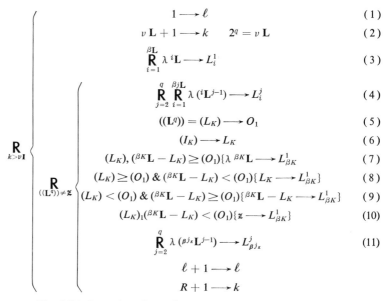

We initialize the output process by setting up the output item number and input item number (1, 2). The tournament sort area contains 2^q items in **L**. Another $2^q - 1$ cells are for the AL's; this totals $2^{q+1} - 1$.

We select *addresses* from **L** to be placed into $\mathbf{L}^1$ (3). This is done separately for the first AL since the AL's contain addresses, not items. For subsequent AL's, we go to a pair of addresses in *this* AL, select the address of the lesser item, and place it in the proper cell of the corresponding item in the *next* AL (4).

Output and input

For output (5) $\mathbf{L}^q$ contains the *address* of the cell where the item is to be found (the double parentheses). The output *item* is from position K in **L**. We bring the next input item from I_K and place it in L_K (6).

Reset of L^1

Lines (7) through (10) reset the first secondary list. We use the β operator to distinguish the item in **L** paired with the item just entered, L_K. We know that L_K belongs to the sublist βK. If we subtract or remove L_K from this *pair*, the item left is the twin of L_K (twin meaning the other item of the pair).

BOTH LARGER

If both L_K and its twin are larger than the selected item, the *address* of the lesser of these is placed in the corresponding slot of $\mathbf{L}^1$ (7).

ONE OF PAIR GREATER

If the incoming item is eligible but its twin is ineligible, the address of the incoming item is selected for the secondary list (8). If the incoming item is ineligible but its twin is eligible, the addres of the twin is selected for the secondary list (9).

NEITHER ELIGIBLE

When both the new item and its twin are less than the last selected item —neither item is eligible—the secondary list should be so tagged. Here we set up a location where $\mathfrak{z}$ is stored. Its address [$\mathfrak{z}$] is placed on the secondary list: further comparisons igonore this AL entry (10).

Updating of other lists

Again the β operator permits us to identify corresponding pairs in subsequent AL's (11).

Suppose that we are working with the jth secondary list. On line (11) we have found one of the *this* pair from the last repeat operation. *This* operation requests that we examine both items of the current AL pair: two addresses of cells in **L**. One or both of the addresses may be of the cell which contains $\mathfrak{z}$. In all cases, we select the *address* of the lesser item to place in the next higher AL. If both addresses in the pair refer to items in **L**, the lesser item goes into the next higher AL. If only one of the items is in **L**, *it* goes into the next AL. If neither of the items is in **L**, then the address of $\mathfrak{z}$ goes into the next higher AL. The completion of line (11) leaves us with the address of the next item for output in $\mathbf{L}^q$.

Advance and termination

We advance the output list and the input list pointers (12, 13), and return to line 5.

Notice that we repeat the operations specified in lines (5) through (13) as long as $\mathbf{L}^q$ does not contain $\mathfrak{z}$ (leftmost repeat). When it does, we know that the output string is complete, and we go back to line (1) to make a completely new setup of the secondary lists. This last setup operation is obviated when tags keep track of ineligible items.

PROBLEMS

8.1 For replacement sorting, what are (a) the advantages? (b) the disadvantages?

8.2 Why is it necessary to keep track of the last item sorted in replacement sorting?

8.3 Contrast these two methods of "keeping track": (a) rank, (b) item key.

8.4 Rewrite the replacement counting routine in operator notation, Fig. 8.3.1, using key instead of rank for "keeping track."

8.5 Write a FLAP routine to do replacement counting by the method of Fig. 8.3.1.

8.6 Write a routine in FLAP to implement Problem 8.4.

8.7 Is the replacement tournament sort of Section 8.4 an improvement over the simple tournament sort? What is its main disadvantage?

8.8 What is the average string length produced in the replacement tournament sort of Section 8.4?

8.9 We place $\mathfrak{z}$'s in AL's when neither of the input twins is ineligible. Consider ways to enter ineligible keys in the AL's using

(a) a last item sorted register, *R*.
(b) a tag, *t*, in an AL key.

8.10 Flowchart the replacement tournament sort of Section 8.5.

8.11 Program Problem 8.10 in FLAP.

8.12 Flowchart Problem 8.9.

8.13 Program Problem 8.12 in FLAP.

9 TAPE SORT OPERATION

9.1 BALANCED TWO-WAY MERGE

Common aim

A tape sort program is supplied with an input tape containing records to be placed in order on the final output tape. Tape sort programs are adaptable to the type of record being sorted, the length and placement and multiplicity of keys, the number of records per block, and so forth. These sorting programs have a monitor built into them to initialize their operation by entering these parameters into the program. Here we investigate only actions which take place after the sort program has been initialized.

The balanced two-way merge requires four tape units and the sort program which, in turn, contains an internal sort, a merge, and a distribute routine.

To make reading and writing information efficient during the sorting procedure and to make the writing of the sort program itself more efficient, an $\mathscr{IOCS}$ is assumed. The input-output (IO) control system has been discussed elsewhere† in great detail. The reader is assumed to have a sufficient knowledge of how $\mathscr{IOCS}$ performs blocking, deblocking, and buffering so as to make simple macro commands to $\mathscr{IOCS}$ suffice for the writer of the sort program.

Diagrams in the rest of this chapter are based on an $\mathscr{IOCS}$ using swinging buffers. If buffer pools are used, the description does not change. $\mathscr{IOCS}$ manages the switches so that it seems to the program that there is always a full input area available and always an empty output area available.

Internal sort and distribution

Figure 9.1.1 illustrates the first cycle: internal sort and distribute are performed. Two input buffer areas are managed by $\mathscr{IOCS}$. When one of these becomes empty, $\mathscr{IOCS}$ starts an input operation from the input tape I to the empty buffer, either IB_1 or IB_2. At the same time, the second switch makes the other input area available to the sort routine.

†Ivan Flores, *Computer Software*. Prentice-Hall, Inc., Englewood Cliffs, N.J., 1965.

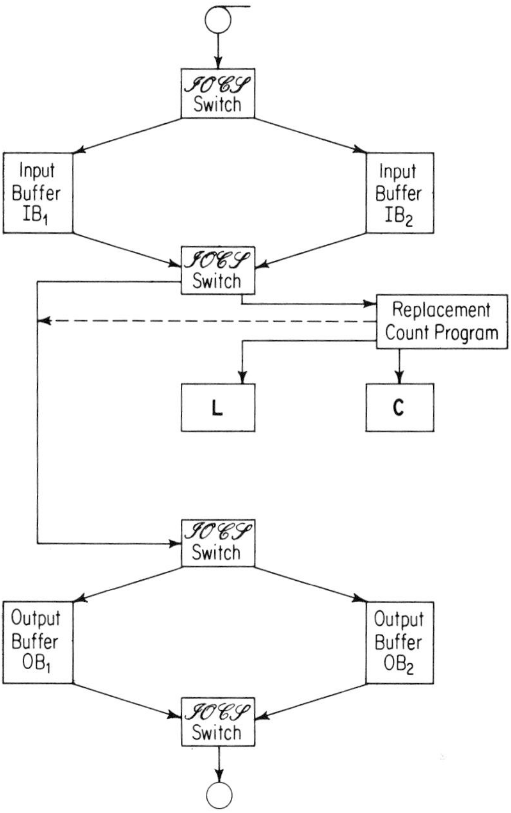

Fig. 9.1.1 How the tape sort is accomplished.

ITEM ASSEMBLY

The internal sort routine has an input buffer constantly available to it from which it assembles an item. This item consists of

- a key upon which sorting is done;
- an address giving the starting location of the record in the buffer area;
- a record length tag, where variable length records are being sorted.

The method being outlined assumes, of course, that the records are of moderate size; if they were all of small size, the records themselves could be sorted into the sort area.

It would be possible to do tape sorting using only merge operations. But more time is spent in IO during a merge than in processing. The earlier stages of merge sorting are eliminated in favor of internal sorting. The whole job could not generally be done by an internal sort because, the larger the strings, the more internal memory is required—soon the capacity of the computer is exceeded. Hence a combination is employed.

To reiterate, a combination of internal sort and merge offers

- greater IO efficiency during the internal sort;
- use of reasonable amounts of core memory during merge.

INTERNAL SORT

When the internal sort does not involve replacement, it is fixed in length, can be done in a single area, and is reinstated after each output operation. For the replacement sort, the sorting operation is ongoing: input, item sort, and output become one continuous operation, facilitated by $\mathscr{IOCS}$.

OUTPUT

When an item becomes distinguished as the next one for output, the sort routine looks up this item in the input buffer and transfers the entire record from the input buffer to the output buffer through the output buffer switch controlled by $\mathscr{IOCS}$.

DISTRIBUTE

As an output block becomes full, it is automatically dispatched by the $\mathscr{IOCS}$. The output tape upon which it is written depends upon the *distribute* philosophy. This is incorporated into the $\mathscr{IOCS}$ statements: the balanced merge simply involves alternation.

Merge

After the initial sort, we have two tapes, *A* and *B*, each of which consists of ordered sublists or strings. Blocks (numbers of strings) from each are entered by $\mathscr{IOCS}$ into one of a pair of input areas, as shown in Fig. 9.1.2. Blocks from *A* are entered into either AB_1 or AB_2; those from *B* go into BB_1 or BB_2.

The merge extracts item information. It then determines whether the next item for the current merged string is to come from *A* or *B*. This decision is handed to the *merge distribute* subroutine which determines whether the selected item is for output on *C* or *D*.

DISTRIBUTION

Recall that the merge activity takes pairs of strings from *A* and *B*, respectively, and produces a combined string of double length for ouput. To make

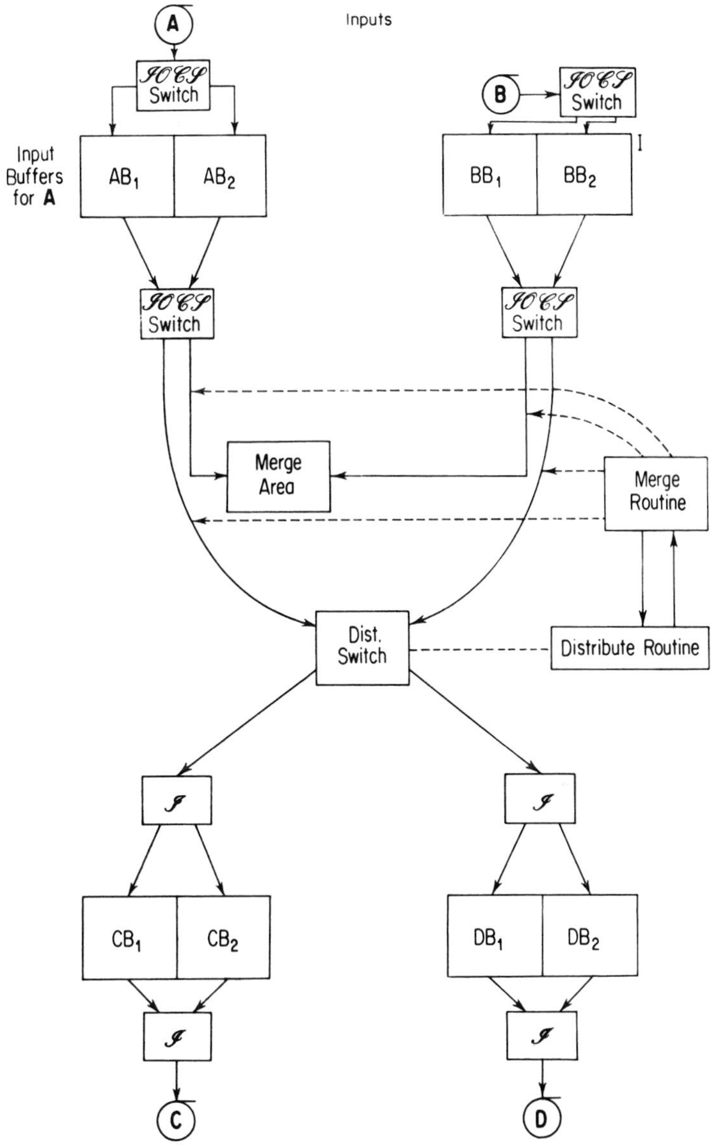

Fig. 9.1.2 A two-way balanced tape merge.

two output tapes, the selected strings are alternated between two outputs, *C* and *D*.

The *distribute* subroutine simply takes the *stepdown* information provided by the merge routine to determine when the next alternation takes place. This is built with the $\mathscr{IOCS}$ statements.

Merge completion

When all the records from *A* and *B* have been merged and distributed to *C* and *D*, *this* merge operation is complete. Next a switchover routine re-identifies *C* and *D* as inputs for the next merge action. *A* and *B*, in turn, must be designated as output tapes (and relabelled for our example as *E* and *F*).

In general, before the next merge operation begins, all the tapes used are rewound. Then we can begin our merge operation, taking strings from *C* and *D* and writing them out onto *E* and *F*.

Some manufacturers provide tape units which the computer can actuate to read backwards. This requires that the merge routine be reinitialized on alternate passes so that record keys can be properly examined: the keys are looked for in a different location; they are examined with respect to *descending* instead of *ascending* order; and so forth.

If the manufacturer provides a read-reverse facility but organizes the records as though they had been read forward, this leads to difficulty when string length becomes greater than block size. It is left as an exercise for the reader to see what this difficulty is and how it may be overcome.

Termination

As in the theoretical investigation of merging, termination is established when the output string appears on a single tape. This is detected since there is no alternation to the other tape.

9.2 MULTIWAY BALANCED MERGE

The multiway balanced merge resembles the two-way balanced merge except that several output and input tapes are provided instead of two each. For the *K*-way balanced merge, the first phase distributes ordered strings onto *K* output tapes, $^{1}\mathbf{A}$, $^{2}\mathbf{A}$, . . . , $^{K}\mathbf{A}$. Subsequent merges take the *K* output tapes, designate them as input tapes, and perform a merge operation onto *K* former input tapes redesignated as outputs.

From the terse description above, it is apparent that, for a *K*-way balanced merge, 2*K* tapes are required.

Internal sort and distribution

Figure 9.2.1 shows in block form how an internal sort and distribution phase is performed for the multiway merge. The operation is performed as described for Fig. 9.1.1. Again, only two input buffers are required; simi-

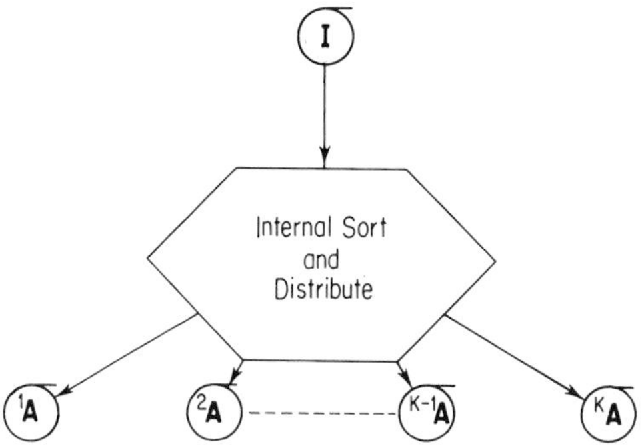

Fig. 9.2.1 Internal sort and distribution for multiway merge.

larly, only two output buffers are necessary. A block comprising an ordered string or part thereof is assembled in the output buffer. When the block is complete, it is released to an output tape. If there is more information for that string, it is assembled in the twin of the output buffer. When the string is complete, the last block, complete or not, is released from its output buffer.

The next string is to go to another tape drive. The choice of drive is made by a simple alternation algorithm which can be incorporated into the program with compound $\mathscr{IOCS}$ statements.

Merges

The merge activity is illustrated in Fig. 9.2.2. Here the tapes formerly designated as output tapes, $^i\mathbf{A}$, are redesignated as input tapes for the next merge operation. A new set of K tapes, $^i\mathbf{B}$, is initiated as the output set.

Separate buffering is supplied for each of the input tapes. Strings from input blocks are now called upon by the merge routine, which assembles suc-

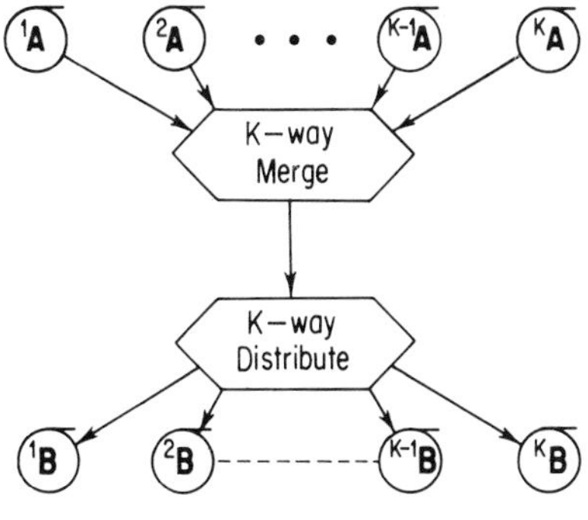

Fig. 9.2.2 Merge operation K-way balanced merge sort.

cessive output blocks in the output buffer as switched, to write on succesive output tapes by simple $\mathscr{IOCS}$ statements. The multiway merge proceeds as described in Sections 7.4 and 7.5. Stepdowns occur for inputs one after another. As each stepdown occurs, that input area is no longer mergedinto the current string. Eventually, there are only two areas which are being merged. A stepdown occurs in one of these, leaving only one area whch is to be rolled out. Finally, this area too produces a stepdown, so that one has been noted in all K input areas.

The long string produced from the K-way merge is presented to $\mathscr{IOCS}$, which makes blocks out of it and releases them one at a time to *one* output tape.

When the K-way stepdown occurs, it is time to switch to a new output tape. Input areas become exhausted in no particular pattern, and new buffers, previously filled, are automatically switched into service by $\mathscr{IOCS}$. Distribution onto the K output tapes follows a simply round robin, using $\mathscr{IOCS}$ commands.

Efficiency

As seen in the analysis of merging, the K-way merge achieves a time advantage because, at each pass, we produce strings of approximately K times the length of those of the previous pass. The two-way merge doubles the length of ordered strings. Production of longer strings on each pass reduces the number of passes for the sort and, as a consequence, the length of time to do the entire sort. The difficulty for large K is that it ties up many tape units. With more complicated techniques, discussed in the remainder of this chapter, we decrease the number of tape units involved without substantially decreasing the efficiency of the sort in general.

9.3 CASCADE SORT

Principle

The first attempt to do higher order merges with fewer tapes was dubbed the *cascade sort*. It performs initial distribution unequally onto *all* working tapes assigned (except the input.) This permits the majority of working tape drives to participate in forthcoming merges. For instance, with six tapes, we distribute items unequally after the internal sort onto five of the drives. We then merge all five tapes onto the original input tape. Since one of the five tapes contains fewer strings than the others, it becomes empty first. What we do next depends upon whether we are using a cascade or polyphase sort.

For the cascade sort, after the five-way merge, we continue with a four-way merge; a three-way merge follows; then a two-way merge; finally, a simple copy operation ends this *set* of merge operations.

Example

The technique is best explained by an example. Figure 9.3.1 shows each phase of each operation in a four-tape cascade sort.

Unit Strings Passed	*Tape Name*				*Comment*	
	A	*B*	*C*	*D*		*Line*
—	14_1	11_1	6_1	0	from internal sort	1
18	8_1	5_1	0	6_3	three-way merge	2
10	3_1	0	5_2	6_3	two-way merge	3
3	0	3_1	5_2	6_3	copy	4
18	3_6	0	2_2	3_3	three-way merge	5
10	3_6	2_5	0	1_3	two-way merge	6
3	3_6	2_5	1_3	0	copy	7
14	2_6	1_5	0	1_{14}	three-way merge	8
11	1_6	0	1_{11}	1_{14}	two-way merge	9
6	0	1_6	1_{11}	1_{14}	copy	10
31	1_{31}	0	0	0	three-way merge	11
124						

Fig. 9.3.1 A cascade merge sort for 31 US's.

Note: For the remainder of the book, a subscript indicates the present length of strings being dealt with in terms of the number of the original or unit strings (US's) produced by the internal sort. Then 5_4 refers to five strings, each of which is made up of four substrings of unit length (as produced by the internal sort).

In Fig. 9.3.1, the internal sort produces 14 unit strings for tape *A*, 11 for tape *B*, and 6 strings on tape *C*. Tape *D* is either initially empty or is the tape of origin from which the internal sort was produced.

The first phase of the first set of merges does a three-way merge of strings from tapes *A*, *B*, and *C*. Six strings of length 3 are produced on tape *D*, leaving tape *C* empty. The column *Unit Strings Passed* records that 18 unit strings have been moved, line 2 (tape *D* contains six strings, each of length 3).

Next we do a two-way merge of items from tapes *A* and *B* onto tape *C*, producing five strings of double length. On line 4, the three remaining strings on tape *A* are copied to tape *B*. This saves rewinding of the other tapes where read backwards is possible.

Next, on line 5, a three-way merge is done; strings of single length from tape *B*, strings of double length from tape *C*, and strings of triple length from tape *D* are merged to form strings of length six, which are placed on tape *A*. After three merges, tape *B* is exhausted. Next, line 6, two two-way merges are performed from tapes *C* and *D* onto tape *B* to produce strings of length 5. Finally, a copy operation is shown on line 7.

On line 8, one three-way merge produces a string of length 14. On line 9, a two-way merge produces a merge of length 11 on tape *C*. Finally, a three-way merge unites one long string from each of tapes *B*, *C*, and *D* onto tape *A*.

Comment

The cascade sort performs merges starting first with one whose order is one less than the number of available tapes. However, as a set of merges progresses, the order of the merge decreases until we finally do a copy operation. This is contrasted with the more efficient polyphase sort which always does merges of the highest order, namely, one less than the number of available tapes.

As far as the other requirements are concerned (such as selecting the number of strings involved at each level), the problems are no less complicated than for the polyphase sort. Hence it is apparent that the cascade sort has no advantages which the polyphase sort does not possess; it has one big disadvantage: the order of merge does not remain maximum.

9.4 POLYPHASE SORT

Principle

The aim of the polyphase sort is to make use of as many tape drives as possible by always performing high order merges. The method stems from an unequal initial distribution. However, on succeeding merges, all but one of the available tape units are used for transmitting, and the remaining unit receives merged strings.

Example

The polyphase sort example appears as Fig. 9.4.1. The initial transmitting unit, *D*, contains unsorted items which it passes to the computer. The computer performs an internal sort, distributing 13 unit strings to tape *A*, 11 to *B*, and 7 to *C* for the case illustrated. The subscript 1 indicates strings of unit length.

Unit Strings Passed	*A*	*B*	*C*	*D*	*Pass*	*Level*
—	13_1	11_1	7_1	0	dispersion	5
21	6_1	4_1	0	7_3	1	4
20	2_1	0	4_5	3_3	2	3
18	0	2_9	2_5	1_3	3	2
17	1_{17}	1_9	1_5	0	4	1
31	0	0	0	1_{31}	5	0
107						

Fig. 9.4.1 A polyphase merge sort for 31 US's.

FIRST PASS

A three-way merge is performed until drive *C*, which contains the least number of strings, namely 7, is exhausted. Tape *D* receives 7 strings of triple length. The number of unit strings passed is hence 21.

SECOND PASS

Now we perform another three-way merge onto the empty drive, *C*, until one of the other drives is exhausted. Drive *B* contains only four strings so that it will be exhausted first. Four strings are received by tape drive *C*, each of length 5. Strings of length 3 from *D* are merged with unit strings from both *A* and *B*.

THIRD PASS

Again a three-way merge is performed, this time onto drive *B*, which is now empty. Only two strings can be placed on drive *B* since that is all that drive *A* contains. Strings placed on drive *B* are of length 9: *A* contributes unit length strings; *C* contributes strings of length 5; *B* contributes strings of length 3.

PASS FOUR

One string of length 17 from drives *B*, *C*, and *D* is merged onto drive *A*. This leaves drive *D* empty and the other drives with one string each, but each of different unit lengths. These single strings are merged into one sorted output to pass five.

9.5 THE OSCILLATING SORT

Principle

For the oscillating sort, distribution and merging are performed at the same time; they are interspersed. Figure 9.5.1 shows the start of an oscillating sort using five tapes. Unsorted information is from a single input tape designated as *I*. A total of *T* (5, here) tapes are used, and $T - 1$ (4, here) of these are available for distribution.

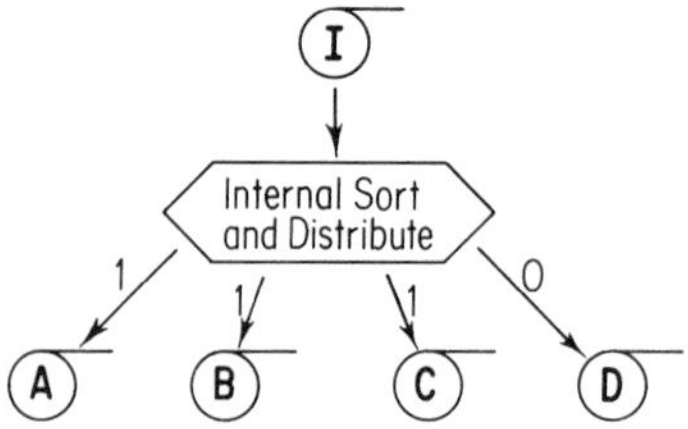

Fig. 9.5.1 Start of oscillating sort.

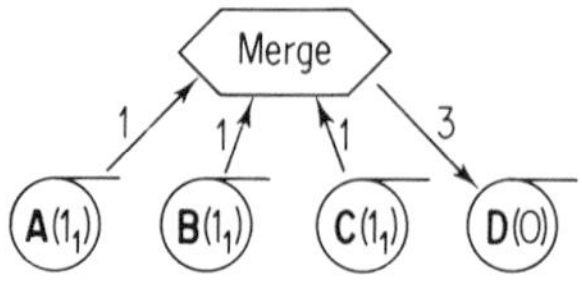

Fig. 9.5.2 First merge action.

INTERNAL SORT

Items from *I* are sorted by an internal sort which fabricates unit length strings. They are distributed, in turn, to each of $T - 2$ of the remaining $T - 1$ tapes.

In the figure, three unit strings of sorted items are fabricated ($T - 2 = 3$) and placed on *A*, *B*, and *C*, respectively.

Whenever a distribution is done, one unit string is passed to each of $T - 2$ tapes. However the $T - 2$ tape designated will differ from one distribution to the next.

FIRST MERGE

After the first distribution cycle we find:

- *I* with many more unsorted items for input;
- $T - 2$ tapes, each with one unit string;
- one tape which is empty.

A merge of order $T - 2$ combines the unit strings. *A*, *B*, and *C* are merged into a single sorted string on the remaining drive, *D*, in Fig. 9.5.2.

NEXT DISTRIBUTION

The operation of the first distribution cycle is repeated; $T - 2$ sorted strings are generated by an internal sort. However, the order in which these are distributed is different. One of the strings must be placed on the same drive (*D*) that received the merged string of the previous operation; the other two strings can go on any of the remaining units, A and B, in Fig. 9.5.3. We leave one of the other drives free so that it may receive a merged string of length $T - 2$.

In Fig. 9.5.4, the second merge operation takes the unit strings from A, B, and D and merges them into a triple string, placing this on C.

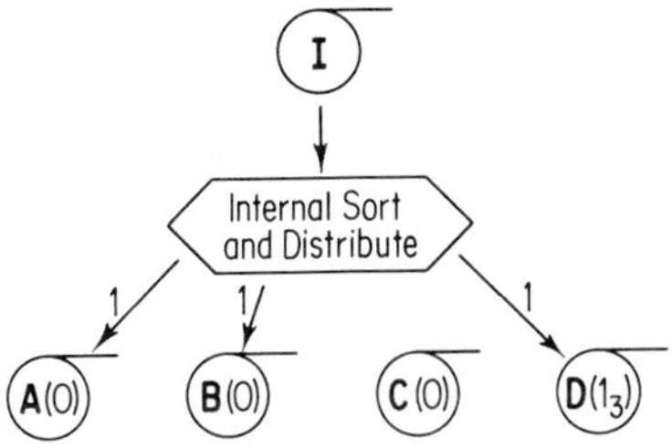

Fig. 9.5.3 Second distribution.

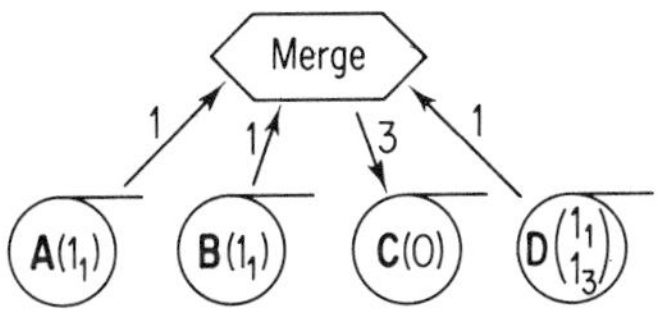

Fig. 9.5.4 Second merge.

Subsequent operations

Distribute and merge cycles continue thus until each of $T - 2$ units contains strings of length $T - 2$. This is illustrated in Fig. 9.5.5. The last first-order merge takes unit strings from A, C, and D and places a triple unit string on B. Another $(T - 2)$-way merge follows immediately, using $T - 2$ length strings and making one string of length $(T - 2)^2$. In the figure, three triple strings from A, B, and D are merged onto C.

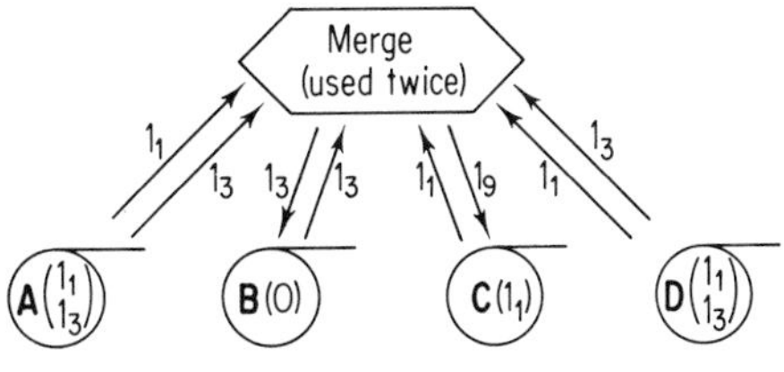

Fig. 9.5.5 Oscillating sort showing third merge of order 1 and first merge of order 2.

When we have fabricated $T - 2$ strings of unit length $(T - 2)^2$, another even larger merge is performed, making a string of length $(T - 2)^3$. Distribute and merge operations continue thus, going into higher and higher powers of lengths.

Tabulated example

Figure 9.5.6 tabulates some of the distributions (D) and merges (M) which occur with five drives. Passes are designated by two numbers. The first number indicates the length in unit strings in powers of the base, $T - 2$.

Line	*Unit Strings Passed* (*Merge Only*)	*Drives* A	B	C	D	*Pass*	*Tape* Read	Write
1	—	1_{1A}	1_{1A}	1_{1A}	0	*D*1		*F*
2	3	0	0	0	1_{3D}	*M*1-1	*R*	*F*
3	—	1_{1A}	1_{1A}	0	1_{1A} 1_{3D}	*D*2		*F*
4	3	0	0	1_{3D}	1_{3D}	*M*1-2	*R*	*F*
5	—	1_{1A}	0	1_{1A} 1_{3D}	1_{1A} 1_{3D}	*D*3		*F*
6	3	0	1_{3D}	1_{3D}	1_{3D}	*M*1-3	*R*	*F*
7	9	1_{9A}	0	0	0	*M*2-1	*R*	*F*
8	—	1_{9A}	1_{1A}	1_{1A}	1_{1A}	*D*4		*F*
9	3	1_{3D} 1_{9A}	0	0	0	*M*1-4	*R*	*F*
10	—	1_{1A} 1_{3D} 1_{9A}	1_{1A}	1_{1A}	0	*D*5		*F*
11	3	1_{3D} 1_{9A}	0	0	1_{3D}	*M*1-5	*R*	*F*
12		1_{1A} 1_{3D} 1_{9A}	1_{1A}	0	1_{1A} 1_{3D}	*D*6		*F*
13	3	1_{3D} 1_{9A}	0	1_{3D}	1_{3D}	*M*1-6	*R*	*F*
14	9	1_{9A}	1_{9A}	0	0	*M*2-2	*R*	*F*
- - -	- - -	- - -	- - -	- - -	- - -	- - -	- - -	
15	—	1_{1A} 1_{3D} 1_{9A}	1_{1A} 1_{3D} 1_{9A}	1_{1A}	0	*D*9		*F*
16	3	1_{3D} 1_{9A}	1_{3D} 1_{9A}	0	1_{3D}	*M*1-9	*R*	*F*
17	9	1_{9A}	1_{9A}	1_{9A}	0	*M*2-3	*R*	*F*
18	27	0	0	0	1_{27D}	*M*3-1	*R*	*F*
	81							

Fig. 9.5.6 Example of the oscillating sort (D = descending order; A = ascending order).

The second number (for merges) is a sequence number indicating the relative time in the sequence of merges in which the merge of this power has occurred. *M*1-3 is the third merge producing strings of length 3; *M*2-2 is the second merge producing strings of lengh $9(3^2)$; D5 is the fifth distribution or internal sort.

Strings

The number of strings on a drive at any point in the merge of a given length is indicated in Fig. 9.5.6. The subscript shows

1. the length of the string;
2. whether it is in ascending (*A*) or descending (*D*) order.

Thus in the figure on line 12, unit *A*, we interpret this listing as

1_{1A} means 1 string of length 1 in ascending order on top.
1_{3D} means 1 string of length 3 in descending order just below.
1_{9A} means 1 string of length 9 in ascending order on the bottom.

Forward and reverse operation

The effectiveness of the oscillating sort requires drives that can read either forward or reverse. Figure 9.5.6 shows how such drives are utilized. During distribution, strings are written forward. During merges, drives are read reverse and written forward. This eliminates rewind. For instance, in the figure, the first three strings produced by the internal sort are written forward on *A*, *B*, and *C*. After writing, we find the tape heads positioned at the end of each string. *A*, *B*, and *C* are now read in the reverse direction, merged, and written in the forward direction upon *D*. However, if the strings on *A*, *B*, and *C* were in ascending order, *D* will have its string in descending order.

To see this, note that each string is in ascending order of key. Records with highest keys are then at the end of blocks on *A*, *B*, and *C*. As tapes are read backwards, records with highest keys are read first. The merge routine takes this into account, doing a *descending* merge writing records with highest keys first onto *D*.

Hence, not only is a reverse read required, but the merge operation must be bidirectional. Original unit strings written forward in ascending order, when read backwards, appear in descending order. Merged strings written in descending order, when read backwards, appear in ascending order. The second string subscripts *A* and *D* in Fig. 9.5.6 indicate ascending or descending order.

The bidirectional merge requirement is emphasized in lines 6 and 7 of the figure. Here, for a merge of power 2, we have three strings of length 3, which we merge into a single string of length 9. The strings of length 3 are descending, producing an ascending string of length 9.

Another direction reversal is observed on lines 17 and 18, where strings of length 9 are merged into one of length 27.

Analysis

The oscillating sort is analyzed in Section 11.4. As a preview, we find that the oscillating sort becomes a most efficient sort when the number of tape units, *T*, becomes large. For about 10 or so drives, it seems to be more effective than any other known sort.

PROBLEMS

9.1 Why is a combination of internal sort and tape merge an effective tape sort procedure?

9.2 Why are two output tapes used during the input and internal sort?

9.3 How are read-backwards tapes used with a balanced merge? How much time does this save?

9.4 How do we know when the merge is complete for Problem 9.3? How do we make sure the tape is in the right order (ascending versus descending)?

9.5 Consider a two-reel file to be sorted with a balanced two-way merge. It may arise that at the end there are two strings left: one is more than one reel long. How will the computer handle this? How will it know when the sort is done?

9.6 A similar problem arises for multireel files with a multiway balanced sort. Describe the problem. Flowchart the solution.

9.7 (a) What are the advantages of the cascade sort over the balanced sort?
(b) Over the polyphase sort?
(c) Is there reason for the cascade sort to fall into disuse?

9.8 Is there a problem with multireel files for the polyphase sort? What precautions do you suggest?

9.9 As described in Section 9.4, would read-backwards drives help the polyphase sort? If so, outline or flowchart how.

9.10 (a) How can we do an oscillating sort without read-backward drives?
(b) What accounts for the efficiency of the oscillating sort?
(c) How does the string length produced by the internal sort affect efficiency?

10 POLYPHASE SORT

10.1 PERFECT NUMBERS

Definition

For polyphase, unit strings are distributed to tape drives in varying quantities. The more items to be sorted, the more unit strings are distributed to each drive. The first approach to determining the number of strings distributed assumes that we may fix the number of strings generated to a prescribed total.

Consider T **tape drives**. At any stage of our merge, one of these drives will receive merged strings; all the others will contribute strings. There are $T - 1$ active units; call this quantity t:

$$t = T - 1 \qquad (10.1.1)$$

The number of **stages** tells how many times we do merging. With a higher stage, we have more unit strings (we started with more items). We use S for the **stage number**.

The number of stages is equivalent to the number of passes. In the perfect number case which we examine first, an initial number of strings will require a calculatable number of stages or passes. Thus, for $N = 17$, where N is the **number of unit strings** and $T = 4$, 4 stages (passes) are necessary.

For larger N (N perfect), more stages are required. However, as passes proceed, the number of strings becomes smaller (though the length of each string becomes larger), and lower stages appear identical to the case where we began at that stage. For instance, when $N = 31$ and $T = 4$, 5 stages are required after the first pass. There are 17 strings distributed as in stage 4 when we started with $N = 17, T = 4$.

Stages

For a given stage S, call the **number of strings allocated to unit** U, $C_{S,U}$. Further, consider these numbers in order of descending size:

$$C_{S,1} > C_{S,2} > \ldots > C_{S,t} \tag{10.1.2}$$

One unit is always empty: It is the receiving unit for this stage and is designated as $C_{S,t+1}$. We have

$$C_{S,t+1} = 0, \quad \text{all S} \tag{10.1.3}$$

Hereafter (10.1.3) is assumed to prevail.

STAGE 0

Stage 0 is the lowest. Here all the strings have been merged into a single sorted string. This string appears on the lowest numbered unit, so that we have

$$C_{01} = 1 \tag{10.1.4}$$

There are no strings on any of the other units, so that we have

$$C_{0,U} = 0; \qquad 1 < U \leq t \tag{10.1.5}$$

STAGE 1

At this stage, each drive except one has exactly one string on it. The other drive receives the single merged string as we go to stage 0,

$$C_{1,U} = 1; \qquad 1 \leq U \leq t \tag{10.1.6}$$

GENERAL STAGE

If we know how to get from a stage to the next lower stage, then we can determine how to go from one level to the next higher level.

GOING DOWNHILL

Assume we are at stage $S+1$, and let us find the state of affairs at stage S. We proceed by merging strings from the t occupied units to one empty unit. We continue until *one* occupied unit becomes empty. This will be the one with the least number of strings. From (10.1.1), we know that the smallest number at stage $S+1$ is $C_{S+1,t}$. To find how many strings are left on each unit, we subtract $C_{S+1,t}$ from *each* of the $C_{S+1,i}$ thus

$$C_{S,j} = C_{S+1,i} - C_{S+1,t} \tag{10.1.7}$$

Notice that on the left we have $C_{S,j}$; the generation of numbers at stage S does not preserve their order. This is because (as may be demonstrated) $C_{S+1,t}$ is larger than any of the other numbers on stage S; and $C_{S+1,t}$ is also one of the numbers at stage S—we have just merged $C_{S+1,t}$ strings onto the empty unit. Then, since $C_{S+1,t}$ is also the largest number of units at stage S, we have,

$$C_{S,1} = C_{S+1,t} \tag{10.1.8}$$

The largest number on level $S + 1$ will form the next largest on level S,

$$C_{S,2} = C_{S+1,1} - C_{S+1,t} \tag{10.1.9}$$

In general, then,

$$C_{S,U+1} = C_{S+1,U} - C_{S+1,t}; \qquad U > 2 \tag{10.1.10}$$

GOING UPHILL

By an algebraic transposition of (10.1.10), we have

$$C_{S+1,U} = C_{S,U+1} + C_{S+1,t} \tag{10.1.11}$$

Substituting (10.1.8) into (10.1.11), we get

$$C_{S+1,U} = C_{S,U+1} + C_{S,1}; \qquad 1 \leq U \leq t \tag{10.1.12}$$

10.2 FIBONACCI NUMBERS

Definition

The simple Fibonacci number, f_j is defined as the sum of its two predecessors. This definition is incomplete unless we define

$$f_0 = 0, \qquad f_1 = 1 \tag{10.2.1}$$

Then we determine f_j by

$$f_j = f_{j-1} + f_{j-2}, \qquad j \geq 2 \tag{10.2.2}$$

GENERALIZED

The k-generalized Fibonacci number, ${}_kf_j$, is equal to the sum of its k predecessors; the first $k - 1$ numbers are 0, and the kth number is 1,

$${}_kf_j = 0; \qquad 0 \leq j \leq k - 2 \tag{10.2.3}$$

$${}_kf_{k-1} = 1 \tag{10.2.4}$$

$${}_kf_j = \sum_{i-1}^{k} {}_kf_{j-i} \tag{10.2.5}$$

Perfect numbers for three tape units

By manipulating (10.1.12), we may convert the perfect numbers into their Fibonacci equivalents. First, for $T = 3$

$$C_{S+1,1} = C_{S,2} + C_{S,1} \tag{10.2.6}$$
$$= C_{S,1} + C_{S-1,1} \tag{10.2.7}$$

Using (10.1.4) and (10.1.5) and substituting (10.2.1), we have

$$C_{0,1} = 1 = f_1; \qquad C_{0,2} = 0 = f_0 \tag{10.2.8}$$
$$C_{1,1} = 1 = f_2; \qquad C_{1,2} = 1 = f_1 \tag{10.2.9}$$

By iterative use of (10.1.12) and the definition of the Fibonacci numbers for $T = 3$, we have

$$C_{S,2} = f_S \tag{10.2.10}$$
$$C_{S,1} = f_S + f_{S-1} = f_{S+1} \tag{10.2.11}$$

Other perfect numbers

From the definition of the k-generalized perfect numbers, (10.2.3) through (10.2.5) and the relation of (10.1.12), these relationships are summarized thus

$$C_{0,1} = {}_t f_{t-1} = 1 \tag{10.2.12}$$
$$C_{0,i} = {}_t f_{i-1} = 0, \qquad i = t-1, t-2, \ldots, 3, 2, 1, 0 \tag{10.2.13}$$
$$C_{1,t} = {}_t f_t; \qquad C_{1,t-1} = 1 = {}_t f_t + {}_t f_{t-1}; \qquad \text{etc.} \tag{10.2.14}$$
$$C_{S,t} = {}_t f_{S+t-1} \tag{10.2.15}$$
$$C_{S,t-1} = {}_t f_{S+t-1} + {}_t f_{S+t-2} \tag{10.2.16}$$
$$C_{S,0} = \sum_{i=S+t-1}^{S} {}_t f_i \tag{10.2.17}$$

Notice that the minimum number is a single k-generalized Fibonacci number. The next-to-the-minimum number is the sum of two k-generalized Fibonacci numbers. The maximum perfect number is the sum of t k-generalized Fibonacci numbers.

Perfect number table

Since these numbers are useful in designing sorts, a table of them, generated by computer, is found in Appendix C.

10.3 GROUP PROPERTY OF SORT

As the polyphase sort proceeds, the empty unit precesses cyclically. To demonstrate mathematically which assignments lead to output on a desired unit, we examine alternate assignments and their permutations.

Basic assignment

Consider the set $\{C_{s,u}\}$ obtained for stage s. Allocate these, in order, to the T drives, T_1 through T_T. While for dispersion only $t = (T - 1)$ drives are available, the merge uses all T drives. Define the contents of drive u at stage s by $B_{s,u}$ thus,

$$\mathrm{B_s}: \quad \mathrm{B_{s,u}} = (\mathrm{T_u}) \quad \text{at stage } s \tag{10.3.1}$$

The basic assignment B_s assigns $C_{s,u}$ to T_u, leaving T_T empty; thus

$$\mathrm{B_s}: \quad \mathrm{B_{s,u}} = \mathrm{C_{s,u}}; \qquad \mathrm{B_{s,T}} = 0 \tag{10.3.2}$$

Stage operator

The stage operator, $\sum$, models the merge process. Given any assignment, A_s, at stage s; the stage operator, $\sum$, applied to A_s as $\sum A_s$, defines the contents of each drive after one merge operation is performed. In particular, when it is applied to the basic assignment B_s, we get $\sum B_s$. The contents of unit T_u after a merge is then $(\sum B_s)_u$.

It is interesting that, when $\sum$ is applied to B_s a permuted version of B_{s-1} results. We find that, if we start with a perfect number on each unit, there are perfect numbers present at all levels of our sort.

The level operator may be applied in multiple. Thus $\sum {}^iB_s$ is the result of i merge operations upon the basic assignment, B_s. We use the nimimum operator λ to define $\sum B_s$ thus

$$(\textstyle\sum \mathrm{B_s})_u = |\mathrm{B_{s,u}} - \lambda\, \mathrm{C_s}| \tag{10.3.3}$$

This yields

$$\begin{aligned}(\textstyle\sum \mathrm{B_s})_1 &= \mathrm{C_{s,1}} - \mathrm{C_{s,t}}; \qquad (\textstyle\sum \mathrm{B_s})_2 = \mathrm{C_{s,2}} - \mathrm{C_{s,t}}; \ \ldots\ ; \\ (\textstyle\sum \mathrm{B_s})_t &= 0; \qquad (\textstyle\sum \mathrm{B_s})_T = \mathrm{C_{s,t}}\end{aligned} \tag{10.3.3}$$

And, in general,

$$(\textstyle\sum {}^i\mathrm{B_s})_u = |(\textstyle\sum {}^{i-1}\mathrm{B_s})_u - \lambda\, \mathrm{C_{s-i+1}}| \tag{10.3.5}$$

Precession of B_s

As we apply $\sum$ to the basic assignment B_s, the number of the empty device moves leftward one place at a time. After ocupying the leftmost position, $(u = 1)$, it returns to the rightmost positon, $(u = T)$.

THEOREM 1

Given the basic assignment B_s with $B_{sT} = 0$, then

$$(\textstyle\sum {}^i\mathrm{B_s})_{T-i} = 0 \qquad \text{for} \quad s \geq T > i > 0$$

(For proofs, see Appendix C.)

But this is weak compared to what can be said about $\sum$. Consider the circular permutation operator of order T, Λ. It operates on an ordered set $X = \{X_i\}$, moving each item leftward one place. If $y = \{y_i\}$ and

$$\mathrm{Y} = \Lambda\,\mathrm{X} \qquad (10.3.6)$$

then

$$\mathrm{Y_i} = \mathrm{X_{i+1}} \qquad (10.3.7)$$

and

$$\mathrm{Y_T} = \mathrm{X_0} \qquad (10.3.8)$$

$$\Lambda\,^{\mathrm{m}}\mathrm{X_i} = \mathrm{X_{i+m(mod\ T)}} \qquad (10.3.9)$$

Then we can show that i applications of $\sum$ to B_s are equivalent to a leftward permutation of i places applied to B_{s-1}.

THEOREM 2

Given the basic assignment B_s, then $\sum{}^iB_s = \Lambda\,^{\mathrm{i}}B_{s-\mathrm{i}}$ for $s \geq T > i > 0$. This can be further generalized for $i > T$.

THEOREM 3

Given the basic assignment B_s, then $\sum{}^iB_s = \Lambda\,^mB_{s-1}$, where $m = i$ (mod K) and $s \geq T_i > 1$.

10.4 RECEIVING UNIT, STAGE $NT + 1$

Assuming perfect numbers of strings, how do we disperse them at a given level to require that the result end on a given device? First let us require output on unit T. To find the output on device T at stage 0, we require 1's on all but T on stage 1. The assignment B_1 of (10.3.2) assures this.

At stage $T + 1$, the assignment B_{T+1} works because, from Theorem 2, we have

$$\sum{}^{\mathrm{T}}\mathrm{B_{T+1}} = \Lambda^{\mathrm{T}}\mathrm{B_1} = \mathrm{B_1} \qquad (10.4.1)$$

At stage $NT + 1$ for N integral, the assignment B_{NT+1} also works because, from Theorem 3,

$$\sum{}^{\mathrm{NT}}\mathrm{B_{NT+1}} = \Lambda\,^{\mathrm{NT}}\mathrm{B_1} = \mathrm{B_1} \qquad (10.4.2)$$

Stage NT + 1

Obviously (10.4.2) is not the only choice at stage $NT + 1$ for $T_R = T_T$ (the receiving unit is T_R). All arrangements which leave T_T empty on stage $NT + 1$ do this.

Consider the class of permutations Π_b of order T which includes all permutations of T items which leave item b in its present position. Then the assignments $\Pi_T B_i$, at stage $i = NT + 1$ all have 0 in position T, but different values of the $C_{i,B}$ in the other positions.

THEOREM 4

$\Pi_T B_{NT+1}$ constitutes all assignments of the *perfect* numbers at stage $NT + 1$ for which device T receives.

Other output unit choices

To get the final output on device J, we just have to make sure that, on stage $NT + 1$, device J is empty. Consider a permutation δ_J which, when applied to $\{X_i\}$, sends into X_T/X_J and then rearranges the $T - 1$ items exclusive of T. Δ_J is the class of all possible permutations, δ_J. When δ_J is applied to the basic assignment B_s, we have $\delta_J B_s$.

THEOREM 5

The assignments $\Delta_J B_{NT+1}$ constitute all assignments of perfect numbers at stage $NT + 1$ for which $T_R = T_J$.

10.5 RECEIVING UNIT, ALL STAGES

Theorem 5 permits us to choose T_R at stage $NT + 1$. What about all the intermediate stages? The theorems in this section show that, at other stages, all the B_s's are even except one. If the B_s's are permuted by M_J, so that the odd B_s is assigned to T_J (using $M_J B_s$), then $T_R = T_J$.

Odd-even property

The odd-even property pertains to the *perfect* numbers regardless of their assignment.

THEOREM 6

The C_s's are all odd for $s = NT$; otherwise, for $s = NT + b$, only C_{T+1-b} is odd and the others are even.

$T_R = T_T$

For stage $NT + 1$, Theorem 5 holds. At other stages, we require a permutation μ_{YT} which, for $\{X_i\}$, interchanges X_Y and X_T and may have *any* effect on the other elements. The choice of X depends on the level s. For our purposes, for $s = NT + b$,

$$X = NT + 1 - b \tag{10.5.1}$$

Then, for a choice of s, μ_T is such that (10.5.1) applies. Let M_T be the class of all such μ_T's. Then we have the following theorem.

THEOREM 7

$M_T B_s$ comprises all assignments at stage s for which $T_R = T_T$ when $s \equiv 1 \pmod{T}$.

$T_R = T_J$

Finally, we wish a rule at any stage for any receiving device. In words, this is:

> For device J to receive: at any stage, one more than a multiple of T, T_J must be empty; for any other stage, T_J must have an odd number of strings.

We prove this as Theoem 8.

THEOREM 8

$T_R = T_J$ if and only if $M_J B_s$ for $s = NT + 1$ or $\Delta_J B_s$ for $s \neq NT + 1$.

10.6 NONPERFECT NUMBERS

Suppose we wish to sort twenty-five items on four tape units using the polyphase merge. How do we distribute these items so as to

- use the polyphase merge?
- have it work efficiently?

Fourth stage perfect numbers for $T = 4$ are 7, 6, and 4, which add up to 17; fifth stage perfect numbers 13, 11, and 7 add up to 31. The secret is to pretend to fill the tapes with null records as required. Null records are not actually placed on the tapes but are kept track of with a zero counter, Z_u, for each unit u.

Procedure

The procedure for the distribution of a nonperfect number of strings is

1. Having dispersed strings to fill tape units to stage s, we determine *perfect* numbers for stage $s + 1$.

2. We fill to stage $s+1$ if possible.
   (a). We distribute strings, in order, to all units.
   (b). If the number of strings on any unit reaches $C_{s+1,u}$, then we discontinue dispersing to this unit.
3. The computer monitors the dispersion and knows when the last string has been placed. If this does not take us to the next stage (of perfect numbers), we fill each zero counter, Z_u, so that the sum of its contents and the number of strings on u equals $C_{s+1,u}$.

Example

In Fig. 10.6.1, we find on line 4 the assignment after seventeen US's (unit strings) have been dispersed, respectively, to T_1 through T_4: 7, 6, 4, and 0. Twenty-five are to be dispersed. Two of those left go to T_1 and three each go to T_2 and T_3. After this, we find the actual distribution to the four tape T_1 through T_4 shown on line 3 of Fig. 10.6.1: 9, 9, 7, 0. The *perfect* numbers C_5 for stage five, shown on line 1, are 13, 11, 7, 0. The number of 0's to be filled into each zero counter is the difference between the C_5's and the number of strings *now* on each unit. As recorded on line 2, they are: 4, 2, 0, 0.

Line	*Item*	*Unit* 1	2	3	4	*Total*
1	C_5	13	11	7	0	31
2	$\mathfrak{z}$	4	2	0	0	6
3	d	9	9	7	0	25
4	C_4	7	6	4	0	17

Fig. 10.6.1 Dispersion of twenty-five items nonperfect, four tape by horizontal allotment (d), and zero counters ($\mathfrak{z}$) to fill up to next level (C_5).

Merge example

Merging the twenty-five items whose dispersion was shown in Fig. 10.6.1 is examined in Fig. 10.6.2.

At stage 5, there are nine strings and four blanks on tape 1. Actually, the fictitious four blank strings exist only by recording of the number 4 in the counter Z_1 corresponding to T_1. Similarly, on T_2 we find nine US's, and 2 is contained in Z_2. On T_3 there are seven US's, but Z_3 is empty.

The polyphase merge uses seven strings from each of T_1, T_2, and T_3, which are merged onto T_4. In general, strings are merged from all tapes for which the zero counters are empty. These are merged onto the receiving unit. Then all nonempty zero counters are tallied down. It is possible that the zero counters for all tapes are nonempty: This produces a trivial merge operation where no tape drive is activated; the only action is a tally down of the

Pass	*Stage*	T_1	T_2	T_3	T_4	*Items Passed*
0	5	9_1	9_1	7_1	0	
		4_0	2_0			
1	4				3_3	
					2_2	
		6_1	4_1	0	2_1	15
2	3			2_4		
		2_1	0	2_3	3_3	14
3	2	0	2_7	2_4	1_3	14
4	1	1_{14}	1_7	1_4	0	14
5	0	0	0	0	1_{25}	25
						83

Fig. 10.6.2 Polyphase merge of twenty-five items with four tapes using the dispersion of Fig. 10.6.1.

zero counters. However, a zero counter for the receiving drive must be tallied to record the "null" string.

In the example, Fig. 10.6.2, only Z_3 is 0. Hence a US is copied from T_3 to T_4, and Z_1 and Z_2 are tallied down. This is repeated once more so that Z_2 contains 0. Next, two strings are merged from T_2 and T_3 onto T_4, tallying down Z_1. This brings Z_1 to 0. Three full three-way merges now proceed from T_1, T_2, and T_3 onto T_4. After this, T_3 is empty.

The state of affairs is reflected in Fig. 10.6.2 on the line labelled "pass 1" where, as before, the subscripts indicate the number of US's per ordered string. The passes which follow are indistinguishable from the normal passes of the polyphase merge which has been started with perfect numbers on each tape unit. The only difference is the number of US's per ordered string, which may be different for strings on the same tape unit. Apart from making the production of the number of US's a bit more complicated, the merge after pass 1 is procedurally identical to one which starts with perfect numbers, as the reader may follow in the example.

10.7 REWIND

Forward only operation

In Fig. 10.7.1, we see how the polyphase may be done when read forward only tape drives are used. Strings of size 13, 11, and 7 are distributed to T_1, T_2, and T_3, respectively. Since all tapes read forward only, *all* of them are

Items Passed	T_1	T_2	T_3	T_4	*Pass*	*Stage*
	13_1	11_1	7_1	0	distribution	5
21	6_1	4_1	0	7_3	first	4
20	2_1	0	4_5	3_3	second	3
18	0	2_9	2_5	1_3	third	2
17	1_{17}	1_9	1_5	0	fourth	1
31	0	0	0	1_{31}	fifth	0
107						

Fig. 10.7.1 Polyphase sort/merge of 31 items using 4 tapes.

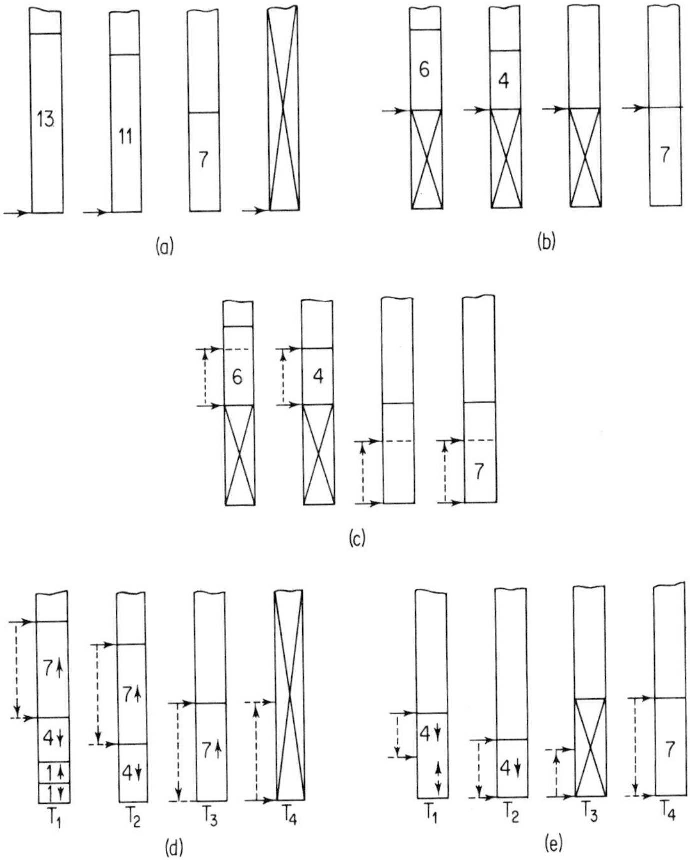

Fig. 10.7.2 (a) Polyphase read forward for 31 items, 4 tapes after distribution pass.
(b) As in (a) after first pass but before rewind.
(c) As in (b) after first pass rewind and showing second pass (dashed).
(d) An approach to elementary rewind.
(e) Same as (d) after first pass.

rewound. This includes T_4 which contained all the original information distributed to the other three units. Figure 10.7.2a shows the situation at the beginning of the first pass. Arrows indicate the positions of the read/write heads. *All* tape units have been rewound and are ready to read forward.

The first pass merges seven strings from each of the three tapes onto T_4. At the end of the first pass, the situation of Fig. 10.7.2b prevails. Now we wish to merge four strings from each of T_1, T_2, and T_4 onto T_3. If we had a read-reverse option, we could read T_1 and T_2 in the forward direction and T_4 in the reverse direction. But this would not work because, if the strings on the first units are in ascending sequence, say, so are the ones on T_4; but when T_4 is read backwards, these strings would be entered in descending order. It is not possible to merge a set of strings when strings from one unit are in one order and the strings from other units are in a different order.

Such being the case, we must rewind T_4 even though T_1 and T_2 are not rewound. Then we read the records in ascending order from T_1 and T_2 as well as from T_4. At the same time we rewind T_4, we might just as well rewind T_3 so that we are sure that there is enough room on it. The situation is then as found in Fig. 10.7.2c.

Read-reverse problem

The problem in eliminating rewind is to make the original distribution of the strings so that, however the tapes land from a given pass, they may be read properly without a rewind. This means that, as we start the next pass, we have either an ascending string or a descending string entering all tape units which are being read into the computer. However, all the substrings handled for a given pass need not be ordered in the same direction, ascending or descending. It is only necessary that all the input substrings for the fabrication of one output substring be ordered in the same direction. In fact, the solution we investigate alternates the direction in which strings are laid down.

Gilstad solution

The solution presented by Gilstad† is now discussed. Unit strings are originally distributed so that each tape unit contains successive strings which alternate in their order direction.

†R. L. Gilstad, "Read Backward Polyphase Sorting," *Comm. ACM*, Vol. 6, No. 5 (May, 1963), pp. 220–223.

Example

In Fig. 10.7.3, at the *bottom* of the tape is the first unit string that was placed on that tape. Information was read in from the tape, as shown in the figure, from the bottom towards the top. Thus the very first string put on T_1 is A† and it is in ascending order if that tape unit is read forward. The next string placed on T_1 is in descending order (if read forward). The last, or seventh, string placed on T_1 is in ascending order if read forward.

At the end of dispersion, tapes T_1, T_2, and T_3 have been written in the forward direction and contain, respectively, seven, six, and four strings in alter-

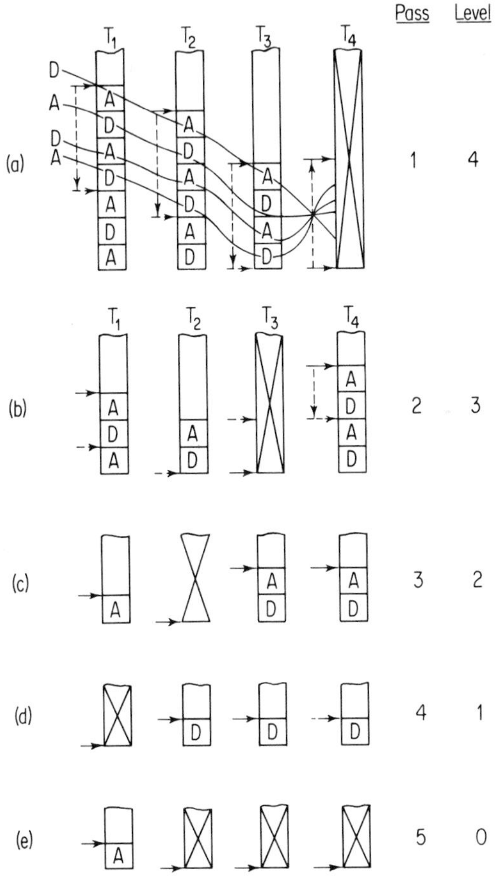

Fig. 10.7.3 Gilstad's method of alternating strings for for eliminating rewind where read backwards is available.

†A for ascending, D for descending, when the tape is read in the forward direction.

nating order. The first pass consists of reading information from T_1, T_2, and T_3 and writing it onto T_4. This is done, however, without a rewind. Let us see how.

All three strings, the ones which were most recently written, are in ascending order if read forward. However, we read them in reverse. Hence they appear in descending order to the computer. The computer merges them in this same order to produce a single merged string written forward onto tape T_4, in descending order. This is indicated by the bottom D for T_4 in the pass 2 of Fig. 10.7.3b. The D strings are read backward next from T_1, T_2, and T_3, and written forward as the next A on T_4. The condition of the tapes at the end of the first pass is shown in Fig. 10.7.3b. The position of each tape is indicated by the horizontal arrow.

Two strings from each of T_1, T_2, and T_4 are now to be merged and written on T_3. Notice that as these tape units are read backwards, they enter descending strings into the computer. These are written out onto T_3 and appear as the bottom D in Fig. 10.7.3c. At the end of pass 2, the situation is as shown in Fig. 10.7.3c.

The dashed arrows show the position where the tape stops. At the end of pass 3, Fig. 10.7.3, there is one string on each of T_1, T_3, and T_4. When these are merged, being read in reverse, they are written onto T_2 as an ascending series. The result is shown in Fig. 10.7.3e.

The dashed arrows show the direction in which the tape is to be read. At the end of pass 3, Fig. 10.7.3, there is one string on each of T_1, T_3, and T_4. When these are merged, being read in reverse, they are written onto T_2 as an ascending series. The result is shown at in Fig. 10.7.3e.

Rules

Rules can be developed which enable us to read reverse *and* determine T_R in *most* cases. A simplification of this rule is:

1. For T_R, start with an A string.
2. For all other T's, start with D strings.

Since, generally, T_R has an odd number of strings and the others have an even number, all have a final A string. This works when there are S stages and $S \neq NT + 1$. If we force this condition, using zero counters, we can achieve our double aim.

PROBLEMS

10.1 Make a list of k-generalized Fibonacci numbers for ${}_kf_j$ for $j = 0$ to $j = 15$ for (a) $R = 2$; (b) $R = 3$; (c) $R = 4$; (d) $R = 5$; (e) $R = 6$.

10.2 Make tables of perfect numbers, $C_{S,U}$, for seven stages ($S = 0$ to $S = 7$) for (a) $t = 2$; (b) $t = 3$; (c) $t = 4$; (d) $t = 5$; (e) $t = 6$.

10.3 Give the basic assignments for (a) $t = 2, S = 5$; (b) $t = 3, S = 8$; (c) $t = 4, S = 7$; (d) $t = 5, S = 6$; (e) $t = 6, S = 4$; (f) $t = 7, S = 3$.

10.4 For the t's and S's of Problem 10.3, find an assignment such that
(a) The result appears on unit 2.
(b) The result appears on unit 0.
(c) The result appears on unit 4.

10.5 For 50 unit strings to be sorted using zero counters show: (1) the initial basic assignment; (2) the number of strings; (3) the number of US's at each stage; (4) which is the receiving unit; (5) how many total US's are passed. Do this for $t =$ (a) 2; (b) 3; (c) 4; (d) 5; (e) 6.

10.6 For 50 US's and a balanced merge, find the total US's passed for $T =$ (a) 4; (b) 6; (c) 8.

10.7 Repeat Problems 10.5 and 10.6 for 196 US's.

10.8 What must be done in Problems 10.5 and 10.7 to get the output on unit 1?

10.9 Describe the distribution of 100 US's so that read backward drives can be used *and* $T_R = T_1$ *and* the result is in descending order. Do this for $t = 3, 4, 5,$ and 6.

11 MERGE SORT ANALYSIS (TAPE)

11.1 BALANCED MERGE

This chapter analyzes merge sorts and, in particular, those using tape drives. In this section, before we examine the balance merge, we take up some points that are common to all merge sorts.

Tape sort merges consist of a number of passes:

- Initially, we do an internal sort and distribute pass.
- Other merge and distribute passes follow.

Number of strings

For our analysis, let us consider a list of n records, **L**. Records are read in, a batch at a time. The size of the batch depends on the sorting program. The batch of records is then ordered, by an internal sort, into a string.

The length of the ordered string depends upon the technique used for the internal sort. Specifically, it usually depends upon whether a straight sort or a replacement sort is used. For a replacement sort, the exact number of items produced during an internal sort is indeterminate; only the average number is known.

On the other hand, if an internal sort such as quadratic selection is used, strings of fixed size are produced.

These symbols are used:

- n_r is the number of items produced by the internal sort when the ordered string is always of the same length.
- $n_{r,i}$ is the number of items produced by the internal sort for the ith string when the number of items per string is variable.

• *r* is the number of strings produced from the *n* items furnished.

We then have these relations

$$n = rn_r \qquad (n_r \text{ fixed}) \tag{11.1.1}$$

$$n = \sum_{i=1}^{r} n_{r,i} \qquad (n_r \text{ variable}) \tag{11.1.2}$$

The list **L** consists of records L_i. Records consist of a number of words, bytes, or characters. The length of a record may be fixed or variable from one record to the next. Many things should be specified about the record to produce a correct sort, such as:

- the number of keys
- their positions in the record
- whether the order should be ascending or descending
- and so forth

The discussion which follows ignores these factors.

The passes

The balanced merge using *T* drives requires that *T* be an even number.

INTERNAL SORT AND DISTRIBUTE

At the beginning of the internal sort, *L* is contained on one tape drive. **L** may be a multireel list, but this eventuality is ignored. The first pass produces *r* strings distributed to *T*/2 of the drives. For convenience, we use the following definition

$$t = t_B = \frac{T}{2} \tag{11.1.3}$$

After *r* strings are distributed to the *t* drives, approximately *r*/*t* ordered substrings appear on each of the output drives. These ordered substrings are called **unit strings** or simply **US**'s.

MERGE PASSES

The passes which follow in a balanced merge take one substring from each of the *t* drives and merge them into a single substring. This is placed on one of the remaining *t* drives designated as output drives for this pass. Subsequent substrings from input drives are used, one from each, in multiples of *t*, to form new substrings distributed to output drives. The number of passes, *p*, required to complete the sort will be investigated shortly.

Volume

A volume is defined for each pass (other than the first). The volume v_j for a given pass j is defined as the number of strings or the number of items which pass from an input device through the computer to an output device. Whether the volume v_j is determined in terms of unit strings or records depends on the reason for the calculation. In the general case, where the volume on each pass is different, the total volume V for the entire sort is given as

$$V = \sum_{1}^{p} v_j; \qquad (v_i \neq v_j, i \neq j) \tag{11.1.4}$$

In the case of the balanced sort, on any given pass, the entire list passes from the input devices, through the computer, to the output devices. Since the pass volume V for all passes is the same, we have for the balanced merge

$$V = pv \tag{11.1.5}$$

where v is the length of the list in number of items (n) or in unit strings (r).

NUMBER OF PASSES

To measure the effectiveness and efficiency of various sorts, we determine the total volume passed, V. As we see from (11.1.5), this depends upon the number of passes, p. Let us examine the length of string produced on each pass. We do this in terms of US's. The initial pass distributes r US's uniformly to the t drives. On the first pass, one US from each drive is merged into a substring of length t. These substrings are distributed uniformly to the output devices.

On the second pass, one substring of length t is provided by each device and merged into a new substring of length t^2. These substrings are distributed uniformly to the output devices. Passes continue thus until there is just one substring formed on the last pass. This *is* the ordered output. Then p is determined by the proper power of t which yields the following relation:

$$t^{p-1} < r \leq t^p \tag{11.1.6}$$

To make some sense out of this equation, we take logarithms to the base t, which yields

$$p - 1 < \log_t r \leq p \tag{11.1.7}$$

or

$$p = [\log_t r] \tag{11.1.8}$$

An exact formulation for p which makes (11.1.6) true is given as

$$p = [\log_t (r - 1) + 1] \tag{11.1.9}$$

If we take the result of (11.1.9) and substitute it into (11.1.5), we have this expression for total volume passed in the balanced merge

$$V = r[\log_{T/2}(r - 1)] + r \tag{11.1.10}$$

11.2 OSCILLATING SORT ANALYSIS

Definitions

As in the previous section, n is the total number of items to be sorted and r is the number of strings produced by the internal sort. n_r is the number of items produced in each string. This can vary if the internal sort used is the replacement sort. In general, we will be concerned only with the number of unit strings, r, produced by the internal sort.

For tape drive units, the oscillating sort uses t drives. We have

$$t = t_o = T - 2 \tag{11.2.1}$$

where we have elided the subscript o in this section. The oscillating sort described in Section 9.5 combines in a single ongoing process a number of different activities. To define a pass, we use the procedure of that section. We have the passes according to the length of the strings being built, which is evaluated in terms of US's.

Primary pass segment

The internal sort makes US's and these are distributed one at a time until there are t of these, one each on t drives. To best see what is happening, let us call g the number of US's created so far. A primary pass segment is performed whenever this condition exists

$$g \equiv 0 \pmod{t} \tag{11.2.2}$$

That is, whenever the number of US's created so far is exactly divisible by t, we perform a primary pass segment which creates a new string of length t^2.

Secondary pass segments

The internal sort continues to produce US's; primary pass segments continue to make primary strings; these alternate until we have t primary strings.

Whenever there are t primary strings, each consisting of t US's, we may describe this condition by

$$g \equiv 0 \pmod{t^2} \tag{11.2.3}$$

This dictates that we perform a secondary pass segment.

Whenever (11.2.3) prevails, (11.2.2) also prevails. This is because a primary pass segment always directly precedes a secondary pass segment.

General pass segment

A pass segment of order $k - 1$ makes strings which consist of t^k US's. To be ready to do this, there must already exist, on each of the t drives, strings of length t^{k-1}. This being the case, the condition for performing a pass segment of order $k - 1$ is

$$g \equiv 0 \pmod{t^k} \tag{11.2.4}$$

Notice that, whenever a pass segment of higher order is done, so are all pass segments of lower order. These *precede* the higher order pass segment.

Number of passes

We have spoken of primary pass segments, secondary pass segments, etc. The primary pass consists of all the primary pass segments which occur as defined in (11.2.2). Whenever that condition arises, a portion of a primary pass is performed. Similarly, whenever (11.2.3) arises, a secondary pass segment is performed; the secondary pass consists of all these segments.

What is the highest order of pass which will be performed? By the same reasoning through which we developed (11.1.6), we come out with

$$t^{p-1} < r < t^p \tag{11.2.5}$$

That is, we find a power, p, for which the t^p is just greater than r. Taking logarithms (11.2.5), we get

$$p - 1 < \log_t r < p \tag{11.2.6}$$

or

$$p = [\log_t (r - 1)] + 1 \tag{11.2.7}$$

Passed volume

A primary pass is performed on every US in order to form a primary string whose length is t. Therefore, the volume of US's passed during the primary pass is r.

Similarly, every primary string must be passed to form a secondary string. By induction, it can be seen that the number of US's passed for each pass is always r; hence we have

$$V = vp = rp \tag{11.2.8}$$

$$= r[\log_t (r - 1)] + r \tag{11.2.9}$$

where [(11.2.1)] $t = T - 2$.

11.3 VOLUME PASSED, POLYPHASE

To compare polyphase with other methods requires knowledge of the activity on each pass. Unlike the balanced sort, a different number of items is handled at each stage.

Unit strings

Our unit of measurement is the unit string. At the top stage, s, we assume *perfect numbers*. How these are assigned is not important. If we do our measurements using B_s, the variations will fall into place. The total US's (unit strings) we start with at stage s is N_s, given by

$$N_s = \sum_{S=1}^{t} C_s \tag{11.3.1}$$

Combining (10.2.13) and (11.3.1), we state N_s in terms of f

$$N_s = \sum_{\beta=1}^{t} \sum_{i=s+\beta-2}^{s+t-2} f_i \tag{11.3.2}$$

where the second subscript of f is elided. To simplify (11.3.2), note that for the right hand summation

- all the C's (t of them) contain f_{s+t-2};
- all the C's but the last ($t - 1$ of them) contain f_{s+t-3};

.

.

.

- only the last C contains f_{s-1}.

Then we have

$$N_s = tf_{s+t-2} + (t - 1)f_{s+t-3} + \cdots + f_{s-1} \tag{11.3.3}$$

or

$$\boxed{N_s = \sum_{i=0}^{t-1} (t - i)f_{s+t-i}} \tag{11.3.4}$$

Terms

Consider each pass: two examples are presented in Table 11.3.1. For each pass we have three parameters defined:

- Width, W, is the number of unit strings in the merged string being fabricated. It is the largest subscript on a given line in Table 11.3.1.
- Length, L, is the number of merged strings fabricated in this pass.
- Area, A, is the product of *length* and *width* and is the number of *unit strings* transported during the pass.

Table 11.3.1 ITEMS PASSED IN THE POLYPHASE SORT FOR $K = 4$ AT LEVEL 5 (ABOVE), AND $K = 6$ AT LEVEL 4 (BELOW).

Level, i	*Pass, p*	*C's*				*Length*	*Width*	*Area*
5	0	13_1	11_1	7_1	0			
4	1	6_1	4_1	0	7_3	7	3	21
3	2	2_1	0	4_5	3_3	4	5	20
2	3	0	2_9	2_5	1_3	2	9	18
1	4	1_{17}	1_7	1_5	0	1	17	17
0	5	0	0	0	1_{31}	1	31	31
								107 volume

Level, i	*Pass, p*	*C's*						*Length*	*Width*	*Area*
4	0	8_1	8_1	7_1	6_1	4_1	0			
3	1	4_1	4_1	3_1	2_1	0	4_5	4	5	20
2	2	2_1	2_1	1_1	0	2_9	2_5	2	9	18
1	3	1_1	1_1	0	1_{17}	1_9	1_5	1	17	17
0	4	0	0	1_{33}	0	0	0	1	33	33
										88 volume

Notice that the width is constant for a given stage: it is constant for the top stage; by induction it is seen to be constant for succeeding stages.

Finally, it is appropriate to continue our analogy:

- Volume, V, is the number of US's transported throughout the merge; it is the sum of the areas over all the passes.

Width

The width on the first W_1 pass is t. Each of the t devices contributes a unit string for merging.

On the second pass, the last receiver has strings of width t; the other $t - 1$ devices have unit width, so that we have

$$W_2 = t + (t - 1) \tag{11.3.5}$$

The generalized width is derived by the following theorem,

THEOREM 11

The width at pass p, W_p, is given by

$$W_p = \sum_{i=0}^{t-1} (t - i) f_{p-t+1} = N_p \tag{11.3.6}$$

Area

The length at pass p is the least C on stage $s - p + 1$. Hence we have

$$L_p = C_{s-p+1,\, t} \tag{11.3.7}$$

From (10.2.11) we have

$$C_{s,\,t} = f_{s+t-2,\,t} \tag{11.3.8}$$

$$C_{s-p+1,\,t} = f_{s-p+1+t-2,\,t} \tag{11.3.9}$$

$$= f_{s-p+t-1} \tag{11.3.10}$$

From the definition for area, we have

$$\boxed{\begin{aligned} A_p &= L_p W_p && (11.3.11)\\ &= f_{s-p+t-1} N_p && (11.3.12)\end{aligned}}$$

Volume

The volume, V, is the sum over p of the areas given in (11.3.12)

$$V = \sum_{p=1}^{s} A_p \tag{11.3.13}$$

By algebraic manipulation, we may prove the next theorem.

THEOREM 12

The volume of units strings passed on a polyphase sort is given by

$$V = \sum_{i=0}^{s-1} f_{t+i-1} N_{s-1} \tag{11.3.14}$$

This important result indicates that the volume is the cross product of two series:

- a set of t-generalized Fibonacci numbers
- the set of perfect number totals

This is demonstrated in Table 11.3.2.

Table 11.3.2 FINDING THE VOLUME PASSED ON A POLYPHASE SORT FOR $K = 5$ AND TWO VALUES OF a.

Width series	94	49	25	15	7	4		
Length series		1	1	2	4	8	15	29
Area series		49	25	26	28	32		
Width series	94	49	25	13	7	4		
Length series	1	1	2	4	8	15	29	
Area series	94	49	50	52	56	60		

11.4 VOLUME EQUIVALENTS

Let us reduce (11.3.4) using the Fibonacci equivalent. First, eliding t from q_t, we have

$$f_{S-t-i-2} \doteq q^{S+t-2-i-t} = q^{S-i-2} \tag{11.4.1}$$

where q is the Fibonacci root—see Appendix C.

Then

$$N_{S-1} \doteq \sum_{i=0}^{t-1} (t-i)q^{S-i-2} \tag{11.4.2}$$

$$= \sum (t-i)q^{t-i}q^{S-t-2} \tag{11.4.3}$$

$$\doteq q^{s-t-2} \sum_{i=0}^{t-1} (t-i)q^{t-i} \tag{11.4.4}$$

$$= q^{s-t-2} \sum_{i=1}^{t} iq^{i} \tag{11.4.5}$$

$$= Qq^{s-t-2} \tag{11.4.6}$$

where Q is a constant given by

$$Q = \sum_{i=1}^{t} iq^{i} \tag{11.4.7}$$

Passes

Consider, now, that r is given and we wish to find the number of passes required. This is the same as the number of stages, s. Omitting the subscript from (11.4.6), we have

$$r = Qq^{s-t-2} \tag{11.4.8}$$

But we are interested in s. Dividing by Q we have

$$q^{s-t-2} = \frac{r}{Q} \tag{11.4.9}$$

Taking logarithms, we obtain

$$s - t - 2 = \log_q\left(\frac{n}{Q}\right) \tag{11.4.10}$$

and

$$\boxed{s = \log_q n - \log_q Q + t + 2} \tag{11.4.11}$$

Volume passed

We now require an analytic expression for number of US's passed, V, as given in (11.3.14). We have, from (11.4.6),

$$V = \sum_{i=0}^{s-1} q^{s-t-i-2} f_{t+i-1} \tag{11.4.12}$$

but

$$f_{t+i-1} = q^{t+i-1-t} = q^{i-1} \tag{11.4.13}$$

However, (11.4.13) does not hold for $i = 0; f_{t+1}$ is 1, nor q^{-1}. Hence V is given as

$$V = \sum_{i=0}^{s-1} N_{s-1} f_{t+i-1} \tag{11.4.14}$$

$$= N_s f_{t-1} + \sum_{i=1}^{s-1} N_{s-1} f_{t+i-1} \tag{11.4.15}$$

$$= Qq^{s-t-2} + \sum_{1}^{s-1} Qq^{s-t-i-2} q^{i-1} \tag{11.4.16}$$

$$= Qq^{s-t-2} + Q \sum q^{s-t-3} \tag{11.4.17}$$

$$= Qq^{s-t-2} + (s-1)Qq^{s-t-3} \tag{11.4.18}$$

$$= Qq^{s-t-2}\left(1 + \frac{s-1}{q}\right) \tag{11.4.19}$$

But from (11.4.8), the left-hand factor is the number of items furnished, so that (11.4.19) becomes

$$V = r\left(1 + \frac{s-1}{q}\right) \tag{11.4.20}$$

This says that, for all but one of the passes, r/q US's are passed, as opposed to r for all passes of the balanced sort. Herein is where the advantage lies.

11.5 A CONTRAST OF TAPE SORT MERGES

We have derived formulas for volume for each of the sort merges. To contrast these methods it remains only to find the volume passed for each. We have

BALANCED

$$V = r[\log_{T/2}(r-1)] + r \tag{11.5.1}$$

OSC

$$V = r[\log_{T-2}(r-1)] + r \tag{11.5.2}$$

POLYPHASE

$$V = r\left(1 + \frac{s-1}{q}\right) \tag{11.5.3}$$

$$s = \log_q r - \log_q Q + t - 2 \tag{11.5.4}$$

$$Q' = t - 2 - \log_q A \tag{11.5.5}$$

$$s = \log_q r - Q' \tag{11.5.6}$$

$$V = \frac{r + r(\log_q r - Q' - 1)}{q} \tag{11.5.7}$$

$$Q'' = \frac{(Q' - 1)}{q} \tag{11.5.8}$$

$$V = \frac{r \log_q r}{q} + r - Q'' \tag{11.5.9}$$

First contrast (11.5.1) with (11.5.2). Notice in the former we find $T/2$, and in the latter $T-2$, as the base for *log*. For $T=4$, the least number of units for a sort, they are equivalent. As T gets larger, the base for the *balanced* sort is *always* smaller than for the *oscillating*. For a *larger* base the *log* of the same number is smaller than for a smaller base. Hence the volume passed for the *oscillating* sort is *always* smaller than for the *balanced* for $T > 4$.

In (11.5.9) we encounter q. This is the Fibonacci root derived in Appendix C. Its size depends on T but it is *always* less than 2. For large T, it is about 2. For small T, it is about 1.7.

When (11.5.9) is evaluated it is found smaller than (11.5.1) for T up to about 10. This leads to the following generalizations:

- *oscillating* is *always* faster than *balanced*
- *polyphase* is faster than *balanced* for T up to 10
- *polyphase* is faster than *oscillating* for small $T < 6$
- in increasing complexity of programming design we have
  * *balanced* * *polyphase* * *oscillating*
- *oscillating* can be used only with *reverse read*

PROBLEMS

11.1 For the two-way balanced merge, calculate the number of passes and volume of unit strings passed for (a) 100 US's; (b) 500 US's; (c) 1,000 US's; (d) 10,000 US's.

11.2 Repeat for the 3-way balanced merge.

11.3 Repeat for the 4-way balanced merge.

11.4 Repeat for the 5-way balanced merge.

11.5 Do Problem 11.1 for a 3-tape polyphase sort.

11.6 Do Problem 11.1 for a 4-tape polyphase sort.

11.7 Do Problem 11.1 for a 6-tape polyphase sort.

11.8 Do Problem 11.1 for an 8-tape polyphase sort.

11.9 Do Problem 11.1 for a 9-tape polyphase sort.

11.10 Do Problem 11.1 for a 4-tape cascade sort.

11.11 Do Problem 11.1 for a 5-tape cascade sort.

11.12 Do Problem 11.1 for a 6-tape cascade sort.

11.13 Do Problem 11.1 for a 7-tape cascade sort.

11.14 Do Problem 11.1 for an 8-tape cascade sort.

11.15 Which sort is most efficient in terms of volume passed for the following numbers of types: (a) 3; (b) 4; (c) 5; (d) 6; (e) 7; (f) 8; (g) 9; (h) 10. Justify.

11.16 Flowchart a polyphase sort program using read backward drive and zero counters. Show *all* important routines.

11.17 Flowchart a cascade sort for Problem 11.16.

11.18 Contrast the three kinds of sorts for programming complexity.

12 DISK AND DRUM SORTS

12.1 CYCLIC STORAGE

Properties and definitions, disk

The basic component of disk storage is the disk itself—the disk is the physical medium for magentic storage. This is discussed in detail in *Computer Programming*. A number of disks are assembled together to form a module, the smallest package a customer can buy. A drive consists of a number of modules in a large package.

Each disk consists of two surfaces on opposite sides of the disk. Heads are generally placed on both sides of the disk since information may be written or read from either surface, according to which is addressed. A track is the area addressed by a single set of heads as the disk rotates. Information is exchanged between a track and main memory via a channel, or the channel controller. Track organization is discussed in *Computer Programming*. The most popular organization is where information is stored bit-serially on the track. One bit at a time is transmitted from (or to) the disk to (or from) an assembly register.

A track is divided into **blocks.** Often manufacturers call a block a **physical record.** Block size may be prescribed by the manufacturer, or it may be left to the user to define block size for his particular application. If the user does this, the block size usually remains fixed for that application.

A block may be further subdivided into characters, each consisting of bits, or the block may be defined in terms of bytes of a fixed number of bits.

We define a **cylinder** as of those tracks which are addressable with no arm movement, only by electronic switching. If we consider the disks to be concentric, as they generally are, then cylinder as defined above is truly the cylinder formed by the present location of the head stations.

Two statements of the definition hierarchy for the disk may be helpful to the reader.

$$\text{bit} \subset \text{character} \subset \text{block} \subset \text{track} \subset \text{surface} \subset \text{disk} \subset \text{module} \subset \text{drive} \qquad (12.1.1)$$

$$\text{bit} \subset \text{character} \subset \text{block} \subset \text{track} \subset \text{cylinder} \subset \text{module} \subset \text{drive} \qquad (12.1.2)$$

Time problems

To analyze the use of the disk for sorting, we should be aware of the times involved in various activities associated with the disk. First, there is the **select time** to choose a module and a drive. Then there is the **seek time** to choose a cylinder within the module. Depending upon the manufacturer's hardware, this may or may not vary with the intercylinder distance. That is, to get from one cylinder to its neighbor may take less time than to seek a cylinder which is further away.

Then there is the **switch time** to choose another track within the *cylinder*. Finally, there is **latency.** This is the time required, after selecting, seeking, and switching, to get to the desired block on the given track. A precise definition of latency depends on the manufacturer's design. If the disk control hardware is always aware of the block above which the heads are currently lying, then it can immediately choose the next block if the desired one is coming up.

Some systems require that the disk reach a **home position** for adequate identification by the hardware. A block choice can take place only after this home position has been reached. Notice in the first case that the latency is approximately half a revolution, and maximum latency is a full revolution. For the second case, these figures are doubled.

Drums and head-per-track disks

We have discussed the disk for which there is only **one set of heads per surface.** It is possible for every track on every surface to have its own set of heads. This, of course, makes the equipment much more expensive. But it almost completely eliminates seek time. It is up to the customer to determine if the cost is worth the time saving.

When disk equipment is provided with one head for each track, it is identical, at least in theory, to a drum device for which one **head per track** is generally supplied. Then we may consider the head-per-track disk and the head-per-track drum identical. The three times of importance to these devices are hence:

- select time to choose a module and a drive
- switch time to choose the desired track
- latency

Magnetic card systems

The **magnetic card memory** device provides a very large amount of mass storage at a relatively low price and with a relatively high access time. Each device provides a number of cards coated with magnetic material. Information is stored on the cards in binary form as in most other dynamic magnetic storage media.

The hardware supplied with the equipment, upon command, chooses the proper card, transports it to a rotating drum, and makes sure that the card is securely fastened to the drum until another card is designed. The card must be accurately aligned on the drum so that it will pass beneath the proper set of reading heads. Once the drum has the magentic card attached to it, it appears to the user as any small magnetic drum device might. It has one head per track. The track is chosen by switching, and the block is chosen after the latency period.

DEFINITIONS

As with the disk drive, the **magnetic card drive** or **data cell** may consist of several modules. Each module contains a number of **cells** and **subcells.** The subcells contain a number of **magnetic cards** or simply **cards.**

Before a card can be chosen, a subcell is pointed to by the control subsystem, and the mechanical hardware causes the proper subcell to position so that the cards are accessible. When this is done, further actuation is required to choose the card and place it on the drum. Of course, before repositioning the module, it is necessary to put away the old card.

Once the card is on the drum, track and block selection begins.

TIME

Select time is required to select the desired drive and module. Next **position time** is required to mechanically acquire the proper subcell. This time may be variable depending on whether the new subcell is close to or far from *this* subcell.

The seek time in card memory is the time to acquire a new card and place it on the drum. Unlike the disk system, seek time does not depend on the card position within the subcell.

Switch time and latency are the same as for the disk.

Similiarities and differences

There are several alternatives for how devices can be constructed.

HEAD PER TRACK

We have examined the most expensive alternative where every track has its own set of heads, as in the magnetic drum.

HEAD PER MODULE

At the other extreme is the kind of device such as the IBM RAMAC and similar drum devices. Only one head is supplied in the RAMAC. This head is on a movable arm which can also reposition to other disks. The mechanics for a single head to access all tracks are quite complicated, expensive, and vulnerable to failure. The addition of lower overall device cost is offest by the unreliability of the device.

HEAD PER SURFACE

The most popular mode of operation provides one head for each surface. Generally these heads position simultaneously. That is the reason we make a special term, namely, **cylinder,** for all the tracks under the entire set of heads at a given moment.

MULTIPLE HEADS PER SURFACE

This concept is self-explanatory. We can extend the definition of a cylinder to apply to all the tracks addressed by the device heads in this case too.

Disc as a model system

The most general model that we could set up is a head-per-surface model. It will answer questions about most of the systems we have discussed earlier. The quantity of information which is of most interest is the cylinder. When the less expensive, head-per-module system is examined, the cylinder degenerates into a single track. When the head-per-track case is considered, the cylinder expands so that it becomes the complete module.

The times of most interest to us, then, are: those for changing from one cylinder to another—the seek time; the time to switch from one track to another within the cyliner—switch time; the time to find the desired block—latency.

Latency as a hardware problem

Of the three times discussed in the last paragraph, the latter two, latency and switching time, are intimately interrelated. They are interrelated so inextricably because it is the intent of the hardware designer to make a completely protected system.

TRACK IDENTIFICATION CONVENTION

Mass storage devices are produced by many manufacturers. To attain compatibility, they have adopted a convention which uses an index character to indicate home position. Following this, at home position, there is an address sector which identifies the cylinder and the head assignment for the track being read. This is preceeded by a flag which indicates the status of this track—whether it is readable. If the track is not readable, an alternative track address is furnished next (otherwise, *this* track address is *repeated*). This system, hence, provides for defects which might arise in tracks during use. The alternate or original address is detected by the hardware and mediated by the software. This obviates short term difficulties.

POSITIVE IDENTIFICATION

Whenever we switch from one track to another within the same cylinder, we must pass *through* home position to determine if the track selected is in working order. If not, hardware and software intervene the alternate track. This increases latency time tremendously. Suppose we have read a block on track 3 of the cylinder; the block we wish to read next, allowing for switching time, is coming up immediately on track 8. After switching to track 8, we cannot use the next block because we have not properly identified the track. We must wait for another complete revolution. This will take us through home position, properly identify the track, and bring us back to the correct block.

The hardware designers have made the tradeoff which we now live with: longer latency time for a protected system which can more easily overcome disk defects.

12.2 DATA ORGANIZATION

Item versus record sort

When we deal with large records, the question arises whether to move the entire record during the sort or to make a smaller item. After sorting (by moving) the item list, we can properly order the records at a later point in the procedure.

ITEM

Preceding the item sort is the item fabrication. Each item is made as small as possible usually, but contains at least:

- a compound key
- the record address
- tags

USE OF ITEM SORT

We have seen how the item sort can be used with techniques such as the tournament sort, where much item manipulation goes on. Note these facts:

* The item sort is generally employed to improve efficiency with most internal sorts.
* The item sort is very inefficient for disk type sorts, as we shall soon see.

Disk item sort

To perform item sort with a disk drive, we proceed as follows. We fabricate an item, using as a record address the location of the record in an input area of the disk. An internal item sort is performed upon these items. As each item string is produced, it is distributed. This is a multitrack distribution where each string is cyclically distributed to a different track.

After internal sort and distribution, a *K*-way merge is performed. The order of the merge is determined by techniques described later. The merge, of course, involves a distribution phase. As many merges as required are performed to get a final ordered item string.

The next operation depends upon the goal of the sort. We now have an ordered directory which lists the location of each record in our file. With the directory, any record can be found in three steps:

- Acquire the proper directory page.
- Look up the key in the directory, and get the record location.
- Get the record.

If an actual ordered string of records is required, it might pay to strip the key from the item during the last merge operation. The next operation is to retrieve the items and place them in the order of an output area. Since the items are in the same order as the records *should* be, we merely obtain the records from the address contained in the item and in the sequence in which the items have been placed.

Disk record sort

As each batch of records is brought into the input area, an internal sort is performed and a string of records produced in the output area. The way the output record list is ordered is determined by the designer of the internal sort. If he chooses a sort such as the tournament sort, he may extract the keys and fabricate an item. It is emphasized that this item is used only for the *internal sort;* the output of this phase is a string of ordered *records.*

Records are distributed to different tracks in blocks after each internal sort.

When the internal sort is completed, a K-way merge is performed. The output from this phase is, in turn, distributed. When the final merge is performed, the result is an ordered string of records. There is no retrieval problem with the record sort!

Record retrieval problem

How do we obtain records to place on the ordered output list using the ordered item list? Consider the three lists:

- **R** is the record input list contained on the disk and in random order.
- **K** is the item list, one entry per record.
- **S** is the output list which will contain the same records as in **R**, but in the same order as their keys.

There is no problem if **R**, **S**, and **K** can all be contained in the same cylinder. There are no seek times to worry about. Similiarly, if **R**, **S**, and **K** each consist of one cylinder or less, and if these are located in *separate modules*, there is no problem since each can be sought separately.

The problem *does* exist when the number of cylinders required for the various lists exceeds the number of modules.

To simplify matters, assume that there is a separate module available for input and for output. Also assume that there are c cylinders required for **R**. If the organization of **R** is truly random, then the probability is $1/c$ that the next input record is in the same cylinder. In other words, the probability is $(c - 1)/c$ that it will be in the wrong cylinder.

Improving record retrieval

Allocate area B_k to store the item list or part thereof. Suppose that the restrictions placed on the input and output areas are such that we bring in only a portion of the item list, say $\mathbf{K}^i$, where

$$\mathrm{K} = \bigcup \mathrm{K}^i, \qquad \nu\,\mathrm{K}^i = \nu\,\mathrm{K}^j \quad \text{all i, j} \tag{12.2.1}$$

An item in this item sublist is given as K^i_j, and it contains an address of a record in R so that

$$\mathrm{R}_{i_j} = (\mathrm{K}^i_j), \qquad \mathrm{R}_{i_j} \in \mathbf{R} \tag{12.2.2}$$

where

$$\mathrm{R} = \bigcup_i \bigcup_j \mathrm{R}_{i_j} \tag{12.2.3}$$

Now the order of the items in **K** corresponds exactly to the desired order of the records in **S**, thus

$$\mathrm{K}^i_j \longleftrightarrow \mathrm{S}^i_j \tag{12.2.4}$$

where $\longleftrightarrow$ means *corresponds to*.

Next define the buffer area B_S which will store a set of records for output. We have a procedure which will speed up the retrieval process.

Procedure

1. Bring the next block of items, $\mathbf{K}^i$, into B_K.
2. Make up a command for each item which:
   - gets from the disk the record specified in the record address portion of the item.
   - places the record so obtained in an output list area, B_S, at a position corresponding to the position of this item in the item list.
3. These commands are sorted by an internal sort according to *record address*. After sorting, these commands will be in order of cylinder; addresses within a cylinder will be in order of track; addresses within a track will be in order of block number.
4. Now these commands are given. Since they have been arranged for optimum accessing of the disks, they should take least time to perform.
5. After all the commands have been given, the area B_S has a sublist $\mathbf{S}^i$ of **S**, and $\mathbf{S}^i$ is in order.
6. $\mathbf{S}^i$ is now written from B_S onto the proper disk output area of **S**.
7. We continue thus, getting new blocks of items and outputting successive blocks of **S**.

Contrast of the techniques

Table 12.2.1 provides a contrast of the three techniques for two typical file lengths: record sort, item sort; modified item sort. The last method is the one described directly above.

The table shows that retrieval is the most significant portion of the item sort; for larger file size, it becomes even more significant. The modified item sort uses the address sort which reduces the total time for retrieval and, hence, causes a great reduction in total time.

The lower half of the table shows how effective this modification is in reducing the seek time.

Table 12.2.1 SORTING TIME IN SECONDS FOR A DISK SORT ON IBM 1301 DISK FILE (COURTESY OF IBM CORPORATION).

File Size	*5000 Records*			*10,000 Records*		
Sort Type	*Record*	*Item*	*Mod Item*	*Record*	*Item*	*Mod Item*
Operators						
Sort-Oriented						
Internal Sort	35	13	17	69	35	35
Merge	11	—	—	25	12	12
Retrieve	—	308	81	—	940	207
Total	46	321	98	94	987	249
Mechanism-Oriented						
Seek	3	215	3	7	750	12
Latency	14	89	32	29	187	187
Transfer	29	17	63	48	50	50
Total	46	321	98	94	987	249

Total characters/record = 100; Key character/record = 10; Core size = 100,000 characters.

12.3 MERGE TIME CONTRIBUTIONS

Disk merge operation

The internal sort produces ordered strings which may contain either records or items. These are assembled in a buffer area to be written out in blocks. There is a choice of how many strings comprise a block. We may have:

* multistring blocks
* unistring blocks
* multiblock strings

These terms describe, respectively, whether there are several, one, or a fraction of one string per block. This choice depends on many factors considered by the sort designer.

Blocks are assembled and distributed to tracks. The block is the amount of information read at one access to a track of a disk. A block may be a fraction of a track, a whole track, or several tracks.

One of the perplexing aspects of the sort is the number of strings per block versus the number of blocks per track, which, in turn, determines the number of strings per track.

STRATEGY

Regardless of the quantities concerned, the merge phase of the sort begins by reading one block from each of K lists. Here K is the order of the merge. Of course, K buffer areas must be supplied, one for each input block. It is preferable to have $2K$ such areas supplied as swinging buffers.

Merging takes records for each of the blocks and produces an ordered string larger than any of the input strings. Records for this string are assembled into blocks in an output area. When the area is full, a block may be written out. If it is a block for the final output string, it is written right after the preceding block. Generally, however, blocks are distributed according to some strategy, so it will be easy to pick them up for the input of the next merge operation.

As each input area becomes exhausted, new information is read into it. For swinging buffers, we direct the attachment of the alternate buffer and then request a read into it. The sequence of reading blocks into new areas is unpredictable since we do not know which records will be picked up from which blocks for output.

Merge proper

Three activities go on during the merge operation: read, merge, and write. The amount of a concurrency depends upon the computer system. For the larger computers which have two modules of disk storage, three-way concurrency is possible: read, merge, and write may all go on at the same time. Where only one disk module is present and processor overlap takes place, two-way concurrency is possible.

The time for merging, principally done in the processor, is small compared to the time required for reading or writing. Therefore, for the analysis which follows, processor time is neglected.

Reading and writing, in turn, consists of two operations: finding and transferring. Since the time it takes to get to a piece of information depends upon where the information is, the time to **find** depends upon the location of the information. On the other hand, the time to get the information from auxiliary memory to main memory, the **transfer** time, is independent of the location of the information and is generally fixed for a given block size.

Order of merge

Increasing the order of merge produces advantages and disadvantages.

FEWER PASSES

For higher order merges, fewer passes are required to complete the sort. Since information (records or items) is transferred once for each pass, fewer passes mean smaller total information transfer. Transfer time is hence reduced.

SMALLER BLOCK SIZE

In practical sorting situations, the internal core memory of the computer is limited. For higher order merges, a larger number of buffer areas is required. We provide at least one area for each input string and one area for the output string. Better results are obtained when double buffer areas are provided as swinging buffers. Buffer area size is determined by block size. Generally, this can be adjusted by programmed directions to the auxiliary memory subsystem.

Assuming that main memory size is fixed, we break it up into smaller chunks when the merge order increases. This constrains us to smaller block size. When block size becomes such that we have multiblock tracks, several accesses are required for each track. This increases total latency time for a given track of information (since we go to it several times). In all but the head-per-track case, extra seeks will undoubtedly be required.

OPTIMUM

An optimum merge order is difficult to determine and requires weighing the number of passes against the block size for all possible merge orders. It is a question of *find* time versus *transfer* time. A typical graph of these variables and total time versus merge order appears later in Fig. 12.6.3.

Subsystem strategies

The strategy to be used in performing the merge is determined by the subsystem composition. It, in turn, determines the optimum merge order.

We discuss three situations in sections which follow. Only latency need be considered when we deal with head-per-track devices such as drums. Again, if only a half cylinder of information is to be sorted, or if a full cylinder of information is sorted using two disk modules, only latency is considered.

The seek-dominated case arises when we have many cylinders of information and few modules to sort them. The mixed case arises for multicylinder, multimodule conditions with a similar number of cylinders and modules.

12.4 HEAD-PER-TRACK SORTS

No seek required

Since we assume head-per-track organization, all blocks are addressable with latency only. If the system permits read and write simultaneously, sort time will be reduced; but this is not necessary to the discussion nor is it common to unimodule subsystems.

Merge order

It is generally true here that the highest possible merge order will make for the shortest sort time. If it is feasible to do the merge in only one pass, this will generally be the shortest sort. Certainly, the least number of records will be passed during the sort. Further, there is no increase in transfer time per pass as the order of the merge increases: Since the same amount of information is transcribed, the same transfer time is required. Reducing passes hence reduces total transfer time.

A further factor should be considered. As pointed out in Section 12.3, for small block size, there are a greater number of latencies per track. Thus for four blocks per track, four latency periods are required to bring that track into memory and also to write on the output track of four blocks.

Thus, total latency depends on block size which, in turn, depends upon the total memory available for buffering. The ideal system would provide plenty of memory so that uniblock tracks are possible and latency is at a minimum; yet, the highest merge order is performed.

All other factors being equal, one more factor enters the picture, and that is the length of string produced by the internal sort. This, in turn, is determined by the total number of records contained in the input list and by the size of each. If the amount of internal memory is not seriously limited, it should be simple to prepare unitrack blocks or even multitrack blocks by a satisfactory internal sort.

The multitrack block is even more effective than the uniblock track for reducing latency. Once we have read in one track from a multitrack block, only electronic switching is required to get to the next track immediately. In most systems, this can be done during the terminal and/or initial reading phase of track acquisition. Hence, the electronic switching time can be masked: we go without any latency from one track to another in the same block.

Block and track factors

Quantities of information dealt with are of utmost importance in designing a merge sort. We are already familiar with these:

- A *record* is user-oriented and has been designated sometime earlier by the file designer.
- The *track* is of a fixed size determined by the manufacturer.
- A *block* of cuts across both areas; it is the information read at one access of the drum or disk.
- A *string* is a set of records or items which have been placed in key order (by an internal sort).

The sort designer determines proper string and block size from (given) record and track size. Obviously, we have multirecord strings. We probably have multirecord blocks, but unirecord blocks are also feasible. The important considerations are therefore:

- the number of strings per block
- the number of blocks per track

Unitrack blocks and multitrack blocks reduce latency, the latter being preferable. In either case, the merge order depends on the amount of memory available: The K-way merge requires at least $K + 1$ areas and, preferably, $2K + 2$ areas.

Multiblock tracks require multiple latency. In this case, the highest order of merge may no longer be best even with unlimited memory. We must weigh the total time for a given design against the design alternatives.

A set of plots similar to those in Fig. 12.6.3 may be made of *find*, *transfer*, and *total* time against order of merge for different block size. From this an optimum block size may be chosen.

12.5 MULTICYLINDER, SINGLE-MODULE DISK MERGE

Problem

No matter how many tracks comprise a cylinder, eventually the merge process can get us to the point where each cylinder contains a single string. Of course, we can manipulate unitrack strings from different cylinders, but the intracylinder merge is the most efficient. When unitrack strings are handled among cylinders, it is impossible to regain the time advantage obtained by an intracylinder merge.

Now let us oversimplify the condition to the one-disk merge where a cylinder consists of two tracks, one on the upper surface and one on the lower surface. Only two tracks are availble for reading or writing, without giving a seek command. At least two tracks are better than one!

To improve internal sorting, we need as much of each string available as possible, preferably the entire string. If a complete track is read, we need not refer to that track again during this merge. Suppose buffer areas for two full tracks of input and one track of output are available. Multiway merges would require additional buffering; we postpone this possibility.

Sequential distribution

A simple sequential string distribution for the one-disk merge is illustrated in Fig. 12.5.1. Starting on surface *A*, we have ordered strings, one string per track, indicated by the arrow which also shows the direction of order (from top to bottom of page).

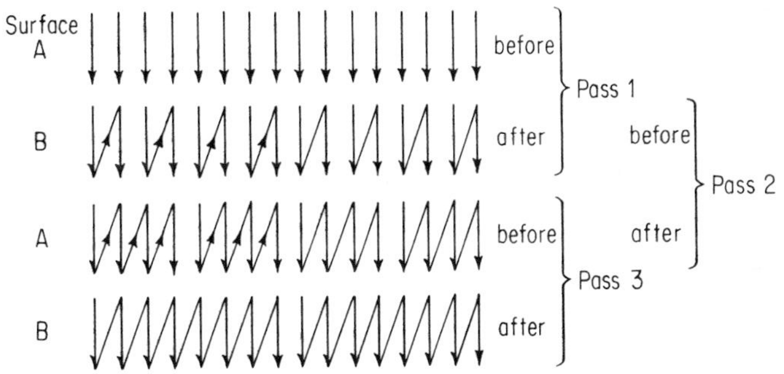

Fig. 12.5.1 The sequentially distributed one-disk merge.

Pass 1 brings in two strings from surface *A* and produces a single merged string two tracks long on surface *B*. This is indicated by the two vertical arrows connected by another arrow from the head of the left track to the tail of the right track. The next two strings from surface *A* are merged to make a two-track string on surface *B*, the next triple of arrows only (two vertical and one horizontal), and so on.

On the second pass, two 2-track strings from surface *B* are merged to form one 4-track string on surface *A*. This is indicated by the quadruple of vertical arrows connected together by three transverse arrows. This merging continues until all the strings are used up or until there is just one 2-track string which is unmatched and left over.

On the next pass, two 4-track strings are merged to make one 8-track string, and so forth.

Data arrangement, two-way merge

Are there distributions of information to tracks which provide fewer seeks? The most time consuming aspect of the merge is the seek. If the number of seeks can be reduced, or if the average length of seek in terms of the number of tracks over which a seek is made can be shortened, then merge time can be reduced. The literature is sparse concerning this topic, probably because one arm sorts are not common.

Analysis

Two input strings, X and Y, are arranged on adjacent groups of tracks (also called X and Y) on one side of the disk, say, A. Each string is up to P tracks long, where usually $P = 2^{p-1}$ tracks for the pth pass. Z is the output string which receives the merged string and is on side B. It comprises $2P = 2^p$ tracks. The xth track of X and the yth track of Y have just been read, and the zth track of Z is being written as shown in Fig. 12.5.2.

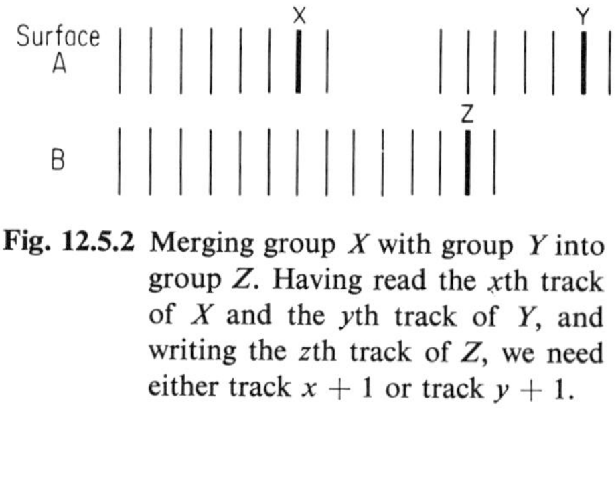

Fig. 12.5.2 Merging group X with group Y into group Z. Having read the xth track of X and the yth track of Y, and writing the zth track of Z, we need either track $x + 1$ or track $y + 1$.

We find that

$$z = x + y - 1 \tag{12.5.1}$$

What distance d_x or d_y must we travel to reach the new X or Y record, respectively, at $x + 1$ and $P + y + 1$?

$$d_x = z - (x + 1) = x + y - x - 1 = y - 1 \tag{12.5.2}$$

and

$$d_y = P + y + 1 - (x + y) = P - x + 1 \tag{12.5.3}$$

Call D_x the total distance covered for all seeks required to get the tracks in X when the head is positioned within Z; define D_y similarly. Then D_x

and D_y can be found by summing the distances d_x and d_y, assuming successively larger integers.

$$D_x = \sum_{x=1}^{P} d_x; \qquad D_y = \sum_{y=1}^{P} d_y \tag{12.5.4}$$

It happens that D_x is in terms of y, and vice versa, but we have

$$D_x = \sum_{y=1}^{P} (y - 1) = \sum y - \sum 1 \tag{12.5.5}$$

$$= \sum y - P \tag{12.5.6}$$

$$= \frac{P^2 + P}{2} - P = \frac{P^2 - P}{2} \tag{12.5.7}$$

$$D_y = \sum_{x=1}^{P^2} (P + 1 - x) \tag{12.5.8}$$

Substitute V for $P + 1 - x$, and we get

$$D_y = \sum_{V=P}^{1} V = \frac{P^2 + P}{2} \tag{12.5.9}$$

The total seek distance, D, from Z to X or V is then

$$D = D_x + D_y = \frac{P^2 + P}{2} + \frac{P^2 - P}{2} = P^2 \tag{12.5.10}$$

There are $2P$ items to be sought; hence the average seek distance, D, is

$$\bar{D} = \frac{D}{2P} = \frac{P^2}{2P} = \frac{P}{2} \tag{12.5.11}$$

When an input is required, two seeks of average distance $\bar{D}$ are required. The first gets the track in X or Y; the second returns to the present output track in Z. Hence, for the entire merge of 2P tracks, we do $4P$ input seeks of average length $P/2$.

When an output track is written, a seek is made to the next adjacent track. The pass requires $2P$ seeks of length 1 for output. The time, T_{ps}, for producing one output string on pass p is thus

$$T_{ps} = 4Pt_{P/2} + 2Pt_2 \tag{12.5.12}$$

For N input strings, there are s output strings produced, where

$$s = \frac{N}{2P} \tag{12.5.13}$$

and where t_i is the average time for a seek of i tracks when seek time is a function of seek distance. Otherwise, $t + t_i$ for all i. Also, p tells us what merge is being done in a multimerge sort.

The total time for this pass, T_p, in terms of seek times, is the time to produce all the output strings and is

$$T_p = sT_{ps} \tag{12.5.14}$$

$$T_p = \frac{N}{2P}(4Pt_{P/2} + 2Pt_1) \tag{12.5.15}$$

$$= N(2t_{P/2} + t_1) \tag{12.5.16}$$

The total time, T, for the sort is then

$$T = \sum_{i=1}^{n} N(2t_{2i-1} + t_1) \tag{12.5.17}$$

$$T = Nnt_1 + 2N \sum_{i=1}^{n} t_{2i-1} \tag{12.5.18}$$

When there are the same number of *full* strings, Eqs. (12.5.14) through (12.5.18) hold. When s of (12.5.13) is not an integer because N/P is odd, we get a similar result.

Interlaced two-way merge

Here input strings are interlaced so that X uses tracks 1, 3, 5, 7, etc., and Y uses tracks 2, 4, 6, 8, etc. Z is also interlaced as shown in Fig. 12.5.3.

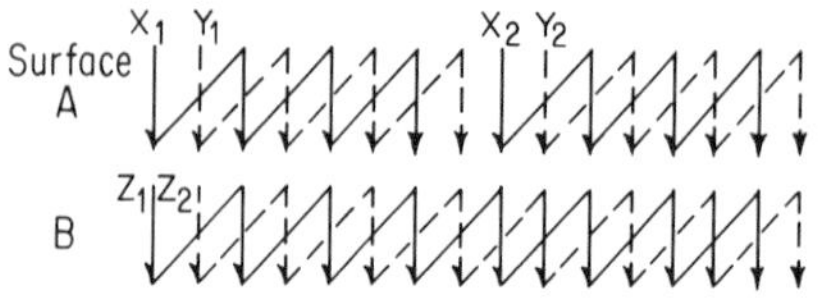

Fig. 12.5.3 Interlaced merging of X_1 and Y_1 into Z_1 and of X_2 and Y_2 into Z_2.

The input X and Y occupy $2P$ tracks. Z also occupies $2P$ tracks but, since it is interlaced too, it is spread over $4P$ alternate tracks. The seek distance calculation must be done for two sets of X and Y to get a complete result.

FIRST PAIR

For the left hand pass, we use the strings X_1 and Y_1 in Fig. 12.5.3. We have that the track number t_{x1} for X_1 is

$$t_{x1} = 2x - 1 \tag{12.5.19}$$

and for Y_1 it is t_{y1}, given as

$$t_{y1} = 2y \tag{12.5.20}$$

For Z_1, the output track t_{z1} is given as

$$t_{z1} = 2(x + y) - 1 \tag{12.5.21}$$

The seek distance for X_1 last using x is hence

$$d_{x1} = t_{z1} - (t_{x1} + 2) \tag{12.5.22}$$

$$= 2x + 2y - 1 - (2x - 1 + 2) \tag{12.5.23}$$

$$= 2y - 2 \tag{12.5.24}$$

and for Y_1, d_{y1} is

$$d_{y1} = t_{z1} - (t_{y1} + 2) \tag{12.5.25}$$

$$= 2x + 2y - 1 - (2y + 2) \tag{12.5.26}$$

$$= 2x - 3 \tag{12.5.27}$$

Then

$$D_{y1} = \sum_{y=1}^{P} (2y - 3) = 2\frac{(P^2 + P)}{2} - 3P \qquad (12.5.28)$$

$$= P^2 - 2P \qquad (12.5.29)$$

Similarly, $D_{x1} = P^2 - P$.

SECOND PAIR

As before, we show

$$t_{x2} = 2P + 2x - 1 \qquad (12.5.30)$$

$$t_{y2} = 2P + 2y \qquad (12.5.31)$$

$$t_{z2} = 2x + 2y \qquad (12.5.32)$$

$$d_{x2} = 2P - 2x - 1 + 2 = (2x + 2y) \qquad (12.5.33)$$

$$= 2P - 2y + 1 \qquad (12.5.34)$$

$$d_{y2} = 2P + 2y + 2 - (2x + 2y) \qquad (12.5.35)$$

$$= 2P - 2x + 2 \qquad (12.5.36)$$

$$D_{x2} = \sum_{y=1}^{P} (2P - 2y + 1) \qquad (12.5.37)$$

$$= 2\sum_{1}^{P} y = P^2 + P \qquad (12.5.38)$$

$$D_{y2} = \sum (2P - 2x + 2) \qquad (12.5.39)$$

$$= P^2 + 2P$$

The average distance for $4P$ items is hence

$$D = D_{x1} + D_{x2} + D_{y1} + D_{y2} \qquad (12.5.40)$$

$$= (P^2 - 2P) + (P^2 + P) + (P^2 - P) + (P^2 + 2P) \qquad (12.5.41)$$

$$= 4P^2 \qquad (12.5.42)$$

$$D = \frac{4P^2}{4P} = P \qquad (12.5.43)$$

We stop here; this is just twice as bad as (12.5.11). No use bothering with T.

Larger memory, one module

For larger memory, more buffer space is available. Four input tracks and one output sector, or three input tracks and one output track, could be provided. How would this work out?

FOUR-WAY MERGE

There are now four strings each of P input tracks, X_1 through X_4. The first starts at 0 and goes to $P - 1$; the second starts at P and goes to $2P - 1$; etc. This is shown in Fig. 12.5.3. Assume that track X of each string is being read. Output is then being made on $4x$ of the other surface. Table 12.5.1 gives the input setting and the seek distance for each string. The total distance is the summation shown for each set. Adding those totals, we get the total expected distance, $4P^2$. For the $4P$ tracks handled, we get

Table 12.5.1 FOUR-WAY BLOCKED MERGE SEEK DISTANCES.

Set	*Track Number*	*Seek Distance*	*Total Distance*
X_1	x	$3x$	$(3P^2 + 3P)/2 \quad = 3P^2 + 3P/2$
X_2	$P + x$	$3x - P$	$(3P^2 + 3P - 2P^2)/2 = P^2 + 3P/2$
X_3	$2P + x$	$3x - 2P$	$(3P^2 + 3P - 4P^2)/2 = P^2 - 3P/2$
X_4	$3P + x$	$3x - 3P$	$(3P^2 + 3P - 6P^2)/2 = 3P^2 - 3P/2$
			$4P^2$

@ $4P$ track/pass
$\bar{D} = 4P^2/4P = P$

$$\bar{D}_4 = \frac{4P^2}{4P} = P \tag{12.5.44}$$

The seek time for one string of tracks on pass p is

$$T_{4,ps} = 8Pt_p + 4Pt_1 \tag{12.5.45}$$

and the total seek time for pass p is then

$$T_{4,p} = \frac{N}{4P}(8Pt_p + 4Pt_1) \tag{12.5.46}$$

$$= N(2t_p + t_1) \tag{12.5.47}$$

There should be just half as many passes ($n/2$) as for the two-way merge (n). The total time, T_4, is hence

$$T_4 = N\sum_{i=1}^{n/2}(2t_{4i} + t_1) \tag{12.5.48}$$

$$= \frac{Nnt_1}{2} + 2N\sum_{1}^{n/2} t_{4i} \tag{12.5.49}$$

Comparison of (12.5.49) with (12.5.18) shows that there are twice as many unit output seeks and (since the limit is n, not $n/2$) that there are about twice as many comparable input seeks for the two-way merge as for the four-way merge.

Larger cylinder

So far we have examined the case where the cylinder consisted of just two tracks. It is a simple matter to extend the analysis to a multitrack cylinder. For instance, suppose the cylinder consists of ten tracks. If each is a unistring uniblock track, a five-way merge will produce a five-track string. Now the cylinder contains a single string of five tracks and an area of five tracks which is empty.

Viewing the cylinder as consisting of two semicylinders each of five tracks, we reach the conclusions presented in the earlier portion of this section. That is, as long as there is only one module, interlacing is a disadvantage rather than an advantage.

The blocked two-way merge is most efficient for small memory. As memory increases, the order of the merge may also increase, but the trade-offs must be examined.

12.6 MULTIMODULE SORTS

Separate read/write modules

The distinct advantage obtained by adding just one more module is immediately obvious when a separation of function is proposed. Input and output functions become independent. Since the time when one function occurs is dependent on the previous function performed, and since they tend to alternate, many seeks can be avoided with a multimodule system.

With two modules, when we do an input seek, the output head remains stationary. In fact, input and output seeks can be overlapped, producing an even greater saving.

Interlacing several modules

Although interlacing degrades merging for a single module, it helps when several independent seek heads are provided. This is the same as postulating several modules. The gain is intuitively evident if one (or more) modules is assigned to input while the other one (or more modules) is assigned to output. A format where concurrent tracks are neighbors is hence advantageous.

INPUT

In Fig. 12.5.3, we merge X_1 and Y_1 to form Z_1. For interlaced inputs, input tracks are adjacent when $x = y$. For randomized strings, we expect x

to differ from y during the merge by very little, perhaps, on the average, one and a half tracks. With this association, most of the time we go to the track just ahead or just behind this one. The other times, when we go further, when averaged it yields an average input distance $\bar{D}_I$ of 2,

$$\bar{D}_I = 2 \tag{12.6.1}$$

OUTPUT

Since output is also interlaced, the output head advances steadily to the next string, skipping one track each time, except during transition. Output seek distance, $\bar{D}_o$, is hence,

$$\bar{D}_o = 2 \tag{12.6.2}$$

Transition between the odd and even strings causes a long seek, D_T, which is given by

$$D_T = 4P - 1 \tag{12.6.3}$$

Transition between even and odd strings causes a seek of unit length which can be ignored in the calculations.

There are $2P$ inputs and $2P$ outputs per merge group, and there are $N/2P$ groups. Hence, for the T_p for pass p, we have

$$T_p = \frac{N}{2P}\left(2Pt_2 + \left(2P - \frac{1}{2}\right)t_2 + \frac{1}{2}t_{4P-1}\right) \tag{12.6.4}$$

or

$$T_p = N\left(2t_2 + \frac{t_{4p}}{4P}\right) \tag{12.6.5}$$

The total time, T, is hence

$$T = \sum_{p=1}^{n} N\left(2t_2 + \frac{t_{4p}}{4P}\right) \tag{12.6.5}$$

where

$$n = \log_2 N + 1 \tag{12.6.7}$$

The two-module two-way merge, regardless of data arrangement, first makes strings of two tracks out of the one-track data—this may be ignored in a comparison.

Adjacent arrangement

We contrast the segmented distribution of Fig. 12.5.1 with interlacing. Output seeks are still of unit length. But only one seek per input track is required. The derivation of (12.5.11) holds, and the average seek length is $P/2$ when the input tracks are assumed to be usually in step. Strings are

P tracks apart, and half the seeks are to adjacent tracks. Therefore, for two-way blocked merge, we have that the time for one blocked string, T_{Bs}, is

$$T_{Bs} = 2Pt_1 + 2Pt_{p/2} \tag{12.6.8}$$

For the whole pass, the time, T_{Bp}, is

$$T_{Bp} = \frac{N}{2P}(2Pt_1 + 2Pt_{p/2}) \tag{12.6.9}$$

$$= N(t_1 + t_{p/2}) \tag{12.6.10}$$

The time for the blocked merge sort, T_B, is hence

$$T_B = \sum_{i=1}^{n} N(t_1 + t_{2i-1}) \tag{12.6.11}$$

$$= Nnt_1 + N \sum t_{2i-1} \tag{12.6.12}$$

where n is the number of two-track strings.

Comparing (12.6.11) with (12.6.6), we see that the *number* of seeks is almost the same. But for the interlaced case, most are for one or two track lengths, while for the blocked case, *half* are of size $P/2$.

Interlacing for higher order merges

For merges of order 3 (or K), interlacing of order 3 (or K) accrues an advantage. Again the input device can stay near the adjacent input tracks which, in all likelihood, should keep in step. The output device goes through 2 (or K) transitions which require long seeks; but otherwise, it advances by 3 (or K) tracks each time.

Large memory, several modules

Larger memory provides buffer areas, making higher order merges feasible. This proves faster since fewer passes are required. Further, when input and output are independent, interlacing improves operation because, then, if the inputs are in step, all input tracks are in the same neighborhood. But what are the tradeoffs?

FOUR-MODULE CASE

Two of the alternatives for the four-module case are examined. In Fig. 12.6.1, we use the four modules in a two-way blocked merge. There is apparently a big advantage here. Only movement forward to an adjacent track is required on all four modules. In the figure, we have read track 6 of module 1 (the solid arrow); the next to be read is track 7 (the dashed arrow). Track 8 of module 2 (dashed arrow) is read next since track 7 (solid arrow) has just been read. Module 3 has just written a block for the last string. Though idle, it is in position to write the first track for the next output string.

Now look at Fig. 12.6.2. Here a four-way merge is in progress. Two input modules each contain pairs of interlaced strings. The output modules must

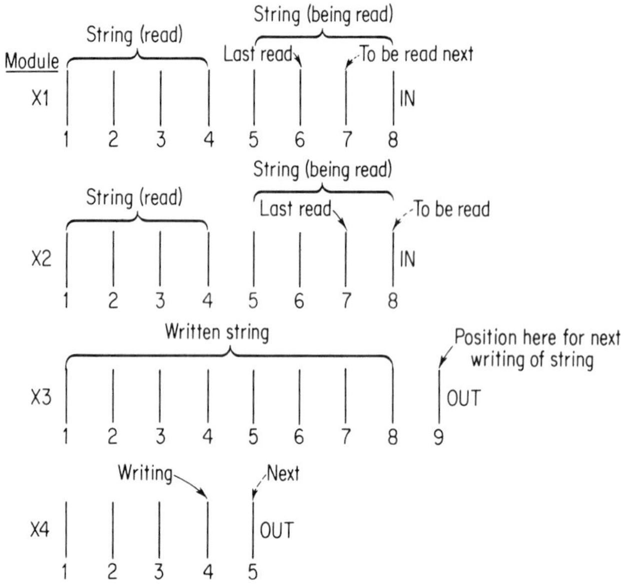

Fig. 12.6.1 Four modules ($X1$–$X4$) used for two-way blocked merge.

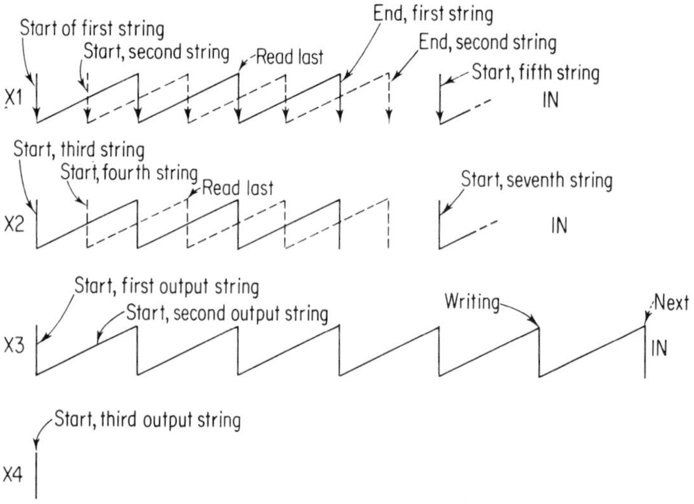

Fig. 12.6.2 Four modules ($X1$–$X4$) in a four-way interlaced merge.

be similarly set up. The next track for output is, except for transition, always the second track from *this* one. But the next input track is not immediately determinable. Interlacing guarantees that it is at least in the general neighborhood. Certainly, the four-way merge will need more seek time per pass. But since fewer passes are performed, the total sort time will be less.

Optimization, large memory

We have examined two alternatives for organization of information on the disk. Suppose internal memory is unlimited. As we increase the merge order, the seek time increases. But the number of passses decreases, thus reducing the total transfer time. Only the total merge design can determine which order of merge is best.

A typical plot of time versus merge order appears in Fig. 12.6.3 portraying the relations just described. Since, after a while, seek time increases faster than transfer time decreases, an optimum point exists.

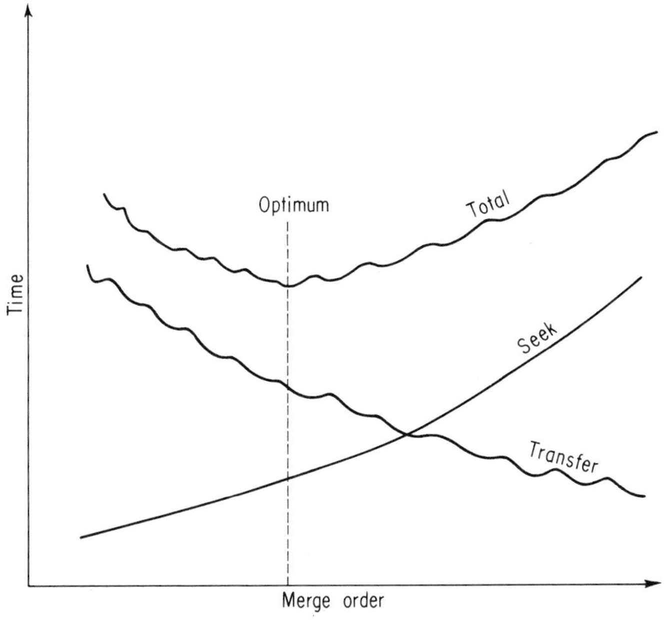

Fig. 12.6.3 Relation of merge, seek, and transfer time to merge order.

PROBLEMS

12.1 Why is polyphase unsuitable for disk sort?

12.2 Why is cascade unsuitable for disk sort?

12.3 Distinguish (a) block; (b) record; (c) blocking; (d) surface; (e) head; (f) track; (g) module; (h) drive; (i) latency.

12.4 What are the advantages and disadvantages of (a) *head per track* device? (b) *head per surface* device? (c) *single head* device?

12.5 What is the item? The item sort? Why might we use it? When?

12.6 For large files a record sort seems superior. Give all the reasons.

12.7 What is the modified item sort? What are its advantages and disadvantages?

12.8 Flowchart a record sort.

12.9 Flowchart an item sort.

12.10 Flowchart a modified item sort.

12.11 Tell when and why one might choose each of these blocking schemes: (a) multistring blocks; (b) unistrung blocks; (c) multiblock strings.

12.12 How is optimum merge order determined? What factors should be considered? Outline a procedure.

12.13 Contrast adjacent and interleaved cylinder two-way merge sorts. Which is better and why?

12.14 How would this be affected by providing more buffer in core—say for four input tracks and one output track?

12.15 Examine a three-way sort as in Problem 12.13.

12.16 What effect does more tracks per cylinder have on the analysis above? Explain.

12.17 Why do multiple modules improve disk sort performance? Perform the contrast of Problem 12.13 for this case.

12.18 Do Problem 12.15 for (a) 2 modules; (b) 4 modules.

12.19 Discuss optimization for disk sorts.

12.20 Flowchart a two module, two-way interleaved multicylinder merge right from the beginning of distribution, assuming an interval sort which produces a string of track length (use block track).

13 PROGRAMS FOR THE IBM 360

The IBM Series 360 provides several assembly languages. The one used here is generally called *basic assembly language*. To follow the programming examples, the reader should be acquainted with the applicable manuals.†

Transfer operators

The transfer operators were presented in FLAP in Section 2.2. They are now presented in 360/AL in Fig. 13.1.1. The first one illustrated in Fig.

```
         MVC    S(N*L'REC), R
```

(a) $\mathbf{R} \longrightarrow \mathbf{S}$

```
         MVC    R-L'REC(N*L'REC), R
```

(b) $\rho\mathbf{R}$

```
         L      NUM, N
         L      OFF, (N-1)*L'REC
         MVC    R+L'REC(L'REC, OFF), R(OFF)
         SR     OFF, L'REC
         BCT    NUM, *-2
```

(c) $\alpha\mathbf{R}$

```
TEMP     DS     N*L'REC
         MVC    TEMP(N*L'REC), S
         MVC    S(N*L, REC), R
         MVC    R(N*L'REC), TEMP
```

(d) $\mathbf{R}\chi\mathbf{S}$

Fig. 13.1.1 Four operators defined in 360/AL.

†IBM System/360 Principles of Operation, Form A22–6821. IBM System/360 Basic Programming Support Assembler with Input/Output Macros (Tape) Specifications, Form C24–3355–4.

13.1.1a is a transfer from one list to another. This can be done with a single move character command, MVC. The first field of such a command is the destination, in this case, S. The length of the area to be moved, listed in number of bytes, is included in parentheses. This is the product of the number of bytes per record, L'REC, and the number of records N. The * is an AL multiplication sign. Hence the total area to be moved is N*L'REC.

RETARD

The retard operator can be provided by a simple MVC command as shown in Fig. 13.1.1b. Here we are going to move the entire area of N records, R, backwards. The number of bytes contained in a record is L'REC. Then the destination address of the first byte is R−L'REC; again the number of bytes moved is N*L'REC.

ADVANCE

Now we wish to move an area of information forward. However, if we request an MVC of the information as a single unit, we find that the computer transfers information in terms of a byte. The first byte from the source area goes to the first byte of the destination area; the second byte from the source area goes to the second byte in the destination area; etc. However, the destination area overlaps the source area. Hence, to advance a record a distance of one byte, for instance, the first byte is copied over the rest of the destination area.

To get around this problem, we advance the last record, leaving its area open. Then we go back and advance the next-to-the-last record, and so forth.

The advance operator is programmed in Fig. 13.1.1c, using two base registers. The first base register NUM is loaded with the number of records. It is used for counting during our loop operation. The second general register, OFF, is loaded with length in bytes of the total area which precedes the last record. (In program terms, (N−1)*L'REC.) When this quantity is added to the starting address of the record area, R, it yields the location of the last record.

The destination of the move command is the record just following the total record area (or R+N*L'REC). We obtain this address by adding together the starting position of the original record area, R, the single record length L'REC, and the offset OFF. The length of each record is L'REC (first field within the parentheses). The starting address of the last record is obtained by the addition of R (last field) to the offset, OFF (in the last field parentheses).

We should repeat this set of operations after reducing the offset, OFF, by the record length, L'REC. This will move the next-to-the-last record one record position forward, etc. The offset is reduced by use of the *subtract register* command, SR. Before returning to the MVC command, we check to see if all the records have been advanced. We do this by using the count and branch on count command, BCT. This reduces the contents of the base register NUM and jumps if that base is nonzero.

EXCHANGE

The exchange operator is programmed in Fig. 13.1.1d using a temporary search area TEMP of the same size as the total area to be exchanged. This is reserved using the pseudo DS. Next S is placed in this temporary area; then R is placed in S. Finally, the contents of TEMP is placed in R.

Least

Figure 13.1.2 shows a routine for finding the least item in the list. Begin by defining the area MIN of record length. We set the offest, OFF, into the GPR, and make it equal to the record length; NUM is then set to the number of records. The first record in the list which starts at R is placed in MIN.

```
MIN     DS      L'REC
        L       OFF, L'REC
        L       NUM, N
        MVC     MIN(L'REC), L
        CLC     MIN(L'KEY, O), L(OFF)
        BL      *+2
        MVC     MIN(L'REC, O), L(OFF)
        AR      OFF, L'REC
        BCT     NUM, *-4
```

Fig. 13.1.2 A routine for finding the least of a list of records and place it at MIN.

At MIN+4, we begin the loop with a comarison. The key of the record in MIN is compared to the next record in the list which is at R+OFF. If the record in MIN is the lesser, the *branch low* command, BL, causes us to skip the next *move*. This move places in MIN the record with which MIN was just compared and which was found to be lesser. When we reach the command AR, either from BL or MVC, the least record so far is in MIN.

The *add register* command, AR, increases the offset OFF by the record length L'REC so that we are ready to get the next record. Finally, the *branch on count* command, BCT, checks if there are further records to be examined and, if so, returns us to the *compare* command, CLC.

LEAST subroutine

The routine in Fig. 13.1.2 can be rewritten as a subroutine to be called by other routines. When this is done, the calling sequence takes the form

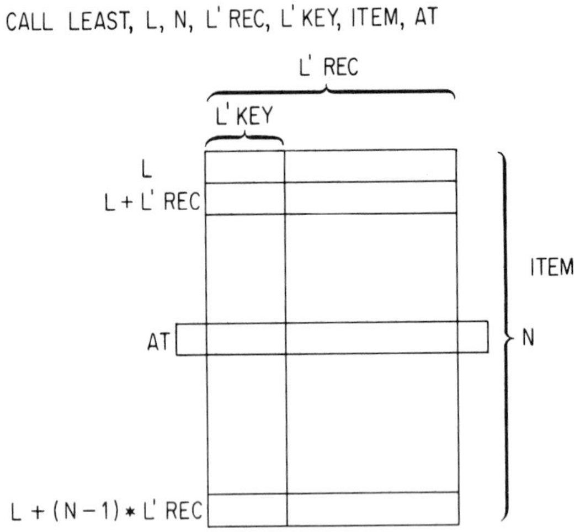

Fig. 13.1.3 The subroutine LEAST for 360/AL is referred to as a *library call.* In the call sequence LEAST is followed by: the list start address; the number of records; the record length; the key length (it's always at the beginning); the item found; the location where the item is found. The data layout appears at the bottom of the figure.

shown at the top of Fig. 13.1.3. To understand each of the fields in the call, refer to the data area in the diagram in the lower part of Fig. 13.1.3:

- LEAST is the name of the subroutine.
- R is the starting address of the record area.
- N is the number of records.
- L'REC is the record length—these are fixed size records.
- L'KEY is the length of the key—only one key is provided. It is of a fixed length and is always at the start of a word.
- ITEM—at the address ITEM, we store the least item.
- AT is the location at which the least item is found.

Selection sorting

The routine SELECT written in 360/AL is shown in Fig. 13.1.4. After placing the number of items, N, in the GPR, NUM, and setting the offset GPR, OFF,

```
SELECT   L      NUM, N
         L      OFF, =0
         CALL   LEAST, R, N, L'REC, L'KEY, ITEM, AT
         MVC    S(L'REC, OFF), ITEM(0)
         MVC    AT(L'KEY, 0), ZEE
         AR     OFF, =L'
         BCT    NUM, *-4
```

Fig. 13.1.4 The 360/AL SELECT routine.

equal to zero, we call the subroutine LEAST to determine the least item in our list for output. The first MVC takes the item from ITEM and places it in the output list S at S+OFF. The second MVC places ⋧ in the key portion of the record just removed. LEAST has determined where this record is, noting its position at AT. Next, the output list is advanced by the AR command. The BTC command sees if there are further items left.

The select and exchange routine appears in Fig. 13.1.5.

```
         L      REC, R
SLCTEX   L      NUM, N
         ST     NUM, LNGTH(0)
         ST     REC, START(0)
         CALL   LEAST, START, LNGTH, L'REC, L'KEY, ITEM, AT
         MVC    AT(L'REC, 0), START(0)
         MVC    START(L'REC, 0), ITEM(0)
         AR     REC, =L'REC
         BCT    NUM, *-6
```

Fig. 13.1.5 The sort by select and exchange 360/AL routine, SLCTEX.

SEARCH

Another important routine is BISRCH used for binary search. The call sequence for it, presented in Fig. 13.1.6a, is the same as that for LEAST, with

```
         CALL   BISRCH, L, N, L'REC, L'KEY, ITEM, AT, RRTRN, ARTRN
```

(a) Calling sequence

```
BISRCH   L      TWO, =2
         L      BETA, N
         L      BETA+1, =0            For division,
         AR     BETA, =1              apply beta
         DR     BETA, TWO             operator.
         ST     BETA, HALF            Use for halfway mark
         LR     FENCE, BETA           and for fence.
CMPR     CLC    ITEM(L'KEY, 0), L(FENCE)
         BE     HIT
         BL     *+3
         MVC    CMND(1, 0), =X'1A     Insert code for AR.
         B      *+2
         MVC    CMND(1, 0), =X'1B     Insert code for SR.
         C      BETA, =1
         BE     OUT                   Last item examined.
         DP     BETA, TWO             Apply beta.
CMND     NOP    FENCE, BETA           Add or subtract for fence.
         B      *-10
OUT      C      FENCE, HALF           Top or bottom?
         BH     TOP
                    etc.
```

(b) Part of routine

Fig. 13.1.6 Calling sequence and part of routine for BISRCH in 360/AL.

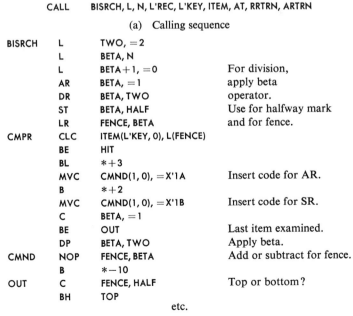

the addition of two fields: RRTRN is the return when the sublist should be retarded; ARTRN is the return when the sublist should be advanced.

Much of the subroutine BISRCH is presented in Fig. 13.1.6b; the calculation of data and the determination of the fence item FENCE should be clear.

One interesting aspect of this subroutine is the entering of a new command code at CMND. This is done at CMPR+3 for CMPR+5, where the hexadecimal code for AR (or SR) is moved to CMND. The compare command at CMPR determines whether the next fence is ahead or behind this particular fence. When the new fence is ahead, we replace the present command code at CMND by the amount code for the *add register* command, AR. This appears in the MVC command as a hexadecimal literal. This literal is indicated to the assembler by the presence in the second field of =. This is followed by X', indicating that the literal is hexadecimal. A similar method is used for entering a subtract register command, SR, when we wish to move backward.

PROBLEMS

13.1 The student can adapt any of the sorting techniques to be programmed in BAL. He should remember that the following must be specified:

- the length of record R;
- the length of key K;
- the position of the key(s) in the record.

The instructor may assign for reprogramming in BAL any of the excercises in the preceding chapters.

A INTERNAL SORT TIMING AND CONTRAST

A.1 INTRODUCTION

To compare and contrast methods for internal sorting, we must determine how long each method takes. One way is to program on a single machine each kind of sort and then theoretically, or with an empirical problem, find the time each sort takes. A second way is to examine flow charts to fix the number of basic machine orders per record sorted, using elementary commands such as transfers, address modifications, additions, comparisons, etc. A third way is to find the number of elementary manipulations of the key and record such as comparisons, transfers, etc., required for each method, by scrutinizing the philosophy of each sorting method. This last course of action is used here because

1. it is simpler to do;
2. it is independent of the computer used;
3. it produces an adequate assessment of each method.

The relative simplicity of the flow charts is evidence that the number of commands required to do most of these sorts is small compared to the record storage required. This number should be on the order of a few hundred.

The characteristic quantities calculated for each sorting method are:

- C number of comparisons
- E number of exchanges
- T number of transfers ($=2E$)
- S number of storage space in words required in the computer
- P number of passes (the number of times the file is examined)
- A number of additions to a counter(s)

Other symbols used to this end are:

N	number of items
i	number of items used so far
c_i	number of comparisons made in placing the $(i + i)$th item
t_i	number of transfers needed to place the $(i + i)$th item, etc.
C_M	maximum number of comparisons required to arrange any file
C_L	least number of comparisons required to arrange any file
$\bar{C}$	average number of comparisons required to arrange any file, etc.

As the formulas for finding the desired quantities are evolved, a numerical example consisting of a file of 100 one-word items will be sorted. The results of the sample problem with $N = 100$ appear at the end of the section in which the formulas are derived.

A.2 DISCUSSION OF TERMS

PASS (P)

Each time all or part of the file is reviewed is called a pass. A pass may refer to review of the new (sorted file) or the old (unsorted file). A pass of a partial file is almost always one of three cases: a review of the new file being assembled; a review, from the begining, of a file to some intermediate variable point; a review from some intermediate variable point to the end of file.

TRANSFER (T)

When information is moved from one location, A, to another, B, it is indicated as

$$(A) \longrightarrow B \tag{A.2.1}$$

If (A) is already in a register, as might be the case if it has just been used for a comparison, only one access time to the memory is required; otherwise, access to both A and B is required. These cases are not distinguished in the calculation.

EXCHANGE (E)

An exchange is characterized by two sets of transfers:

$$(A) \longrightarrow B; \qquad (B) \longrightarrow A \tag{A.2.2}$$

The number of access times required, using the above reasoning, might be two, three, or four. These cases are not distinguished.

COMPARE (C)

Two quantities compared must both be procured before comparison and replaced after comparison. When a comparison is preceded or followed by a transfer or exchange, the disposition of the comparands might be included in the transfer or in the comparison. *C* is the number of comparisons made during a sort without regard to transfers or exchanges.

ADDITION (A)

Sorting by counting requires that 1 be added to a number of counters. Addition is considered independent of the procuring and replacement of the augend.

SPACE (S)

During sorting, a minimum space is required by the computer to manipulate the item keys and addresses. *S* is the number of *additional* word spaces for this (unless otherwise stated), assuming that the item key and address can both be stored in one word.

AVERAGE VALUES

Items to be sorted are *randomly* selected from the present universe. In a method like insertion, it is necessary to insert *this* item into the file-so-far. It may be inserted near either end; on the average it will be inserted in the middle of the file.

A.3 DERIVATIONS

The computer time using the symbols of Section A.1 and the definitions of Section A.2 are now derived.

Insertion

With *i* items in the new file, the average number of comparisons required to place the next item is given by

$$\mathrm{e_i} = \frac{\mathrm{i}}{2} \qquad \text{(A.3.1)}$$

and

$$\bar{\mathrm{c}}_\mathrm{i} = \frac{\mathrm{i}}{2} \qquad \text{(A.3.2)}$$

and

$$C = \sum_{i=0}^{N=1} c_i \tag{A.3.3}$$

$$= \frac{(N^2 - N)}{4} \tag{A.3.4}$$

$$E = \frac{(N^2 - N)}{4} \tag{A.3.5}$$

$$P = N - 1 \tag{A.3.6}$$

$$S = N$$

Then

Sample	$N = 100$	$S = 100$
	$P = 99$	$C = E = 2500$

Centered insertions

After the initial comparison is made to determine which half-file to examine, only half the number of comparisons and half the exchanges in the preceding sample are required; so

$$C = \frac{(N^2 - N)}{8} \tag{A.3.7}$$

$$E = \frac{(N^2 - N)}{8} \tag{A.3.8}$$

$$P = N - 1 \tag{A.3.9}$$

$$S = N \tag{A.3.10}$$

Then

Sample	$N = 100$	$S = 100$
	$P = 99$	$C = E = 1250$

Binary insertion

$$c_i = \log_2 i \tag{A.3.11}$$

or

$$= \log_2 e \ln i \tag{A.3.12}$$

so that

$$C = \sum_{0}^{N-1} \log_2 e \ln i \tag{A.3.13}$$

Apporoximately, by integration,

$$\doteq \log_2 e \int_0^{N-1} \ln i \, di \tag{A.3.14}$$

$$\doteq \log_2 e[i \ln i - i]_0^{N-1} \tag{A.3.15}$$

and

$$C \doteq \log_2 e(N \log_e N - N) \tag{A.3.16}$$

As before in the centered case,

$$E = \frac{(N^2 - N)}{8} \tag{A.3.17}$$

$$P = N - 1 \tag{A.3.18}$$

$$S = N \tag{A.3.19}$$

Equation (A.3.16) may also be written as

$$C = N(\log_2 e \log_2 N - \log_2 e) \tag{A.3.20}$$

$$= N \log_2 \left(\frac{N}{e}\right) \tag{A.3.21}$$

Sample	$C = 100 \log_2 (100/e) = 100 \log_2 (36.8)$			
	$= 100(5.2) = 520$			
	$N = 100$	$E = 1250$	$P = 99$	$S = 100$

Counting

A comparison is made with every new item so that

$$c_i = i \tag{A.3.22}$$

and

$$C = \frac{(N^2 - N)}{2} \tag{A.3.23}$$

For each item in the new file, one of two counters is added to

$$a_i = i \tag{A.3.24}$$

so that

$$A = \frac{(N^2 - N)}{2} \tag{A.3.25}$$

$$P = N - 1 \tag{A.3.26}$$

$$S \text{ (including counters)} = 2N \quad \text{(or } 3N) \tag{A.3.27}$$

Sample	$C = 5000$	$A = 5000$
	$P = 99$	$S = 200$

Exchanging

When the old file is in order, then

$$C_L = N - 1 \tag{A.3.28}$$

$$E_L = 0 \tag{A.3.29}$$

$$P_L = 1 \tag{A.3.30}$$

When the old file is in reverse order,

$$C_M = \frac{N(N-1)}{2} \tag{A.3.31}$$

$$E_M = \frac{N(N-1)}{2} \tag{A.3.32}$$

$$P_M = N \tag{A.3.33}$$

On the average, the number of passes is

$$\bar{P} = \frac{N}{2} \tag{A.3.34}$$

$$\bar{C} = \frac{N(N-1)}{2} \tag{A.3.35}$$

$$\bar{E} = \frac{N(N-1)}{4} \tag{A.3.36}$$

$$S = 100 \tag{A.3.37}$$

Sample	C = 5000	E = 5000	S = 100

Digital

For a base *B*, there are *B* areas required. Each one must accommodate a full file since this is a possibility. If each item key contains *D* digits, then *D* passes are made. Each pass completely reviewed the file. Then:

$$P = D + 1 \tag{A.3.38}$$

$$C \text{ (number of examinations)} = DN \tag{A.3.39}$$

$$T = N(D + 1) \tag{A.3.40}$$

$$S = BN \tag{A.3.41}$$

Sample	C = 200	T = 300	P = 3
	S = 1000		

Linear selection

The entire old file, including substitutes for the items already sorted, must be reviewed on each pass. Hence

$$c_i = N - 1 \tag{A.3.42}$$

This is a pass made for each item

$$P = N \tag{A.3.43}$$

Then

$$C = Pc_i = N^2 - N \tag{A.3.44}$$

$$T = N \tag{A.3.45}$$

and

$$S = N \tag{A.3.46}$$

Sample	C = 9801	P = 100	T = 100	S = 100

Linear selection with exchanging

Here

$$P = N - 1 \tag{A.3.47}$$

$$c_i = N - i - 1 \tag{A.3.48}$$

$$C = \frac{(N^2 - N)}{2} \tag{A.3.49}$$

$$E = N - 1 \tag{A.3.50}$$

$$S = N \tag{A.3.51}$$

Sample	C = 4550	P = 99	E = 99	S = 100

Quadratic selection

To fill the $\sqrt{N}$ control registers from groups of $\sqrt{N}$ items requires $\sqrt{N} - 1$ comparisons each. This is a total of preliminary comparisons of $\sqrt{N}(\sqrt{N} - 1)$. To fill the master register also requires $\sqrt{N} - 1$ comparisons. The total preliminary comparisons, c_p, is then given by

$$\begin{aligned} c_p &= \sqrt{N}(\sqrt{N} - 1) + \sqrt{N} - 1 \\ &= N - 1 \end{aligned} \tag{A.3.52}$$

After the preliminary comparisons are done and the control registers are filled, it is necessary to perform a number of operating comparisons,

c_o. For each item filed, the control registers are completely examined once, requiring $\sqrt{N} - 1$ comparisons; the empty control register must be filled from the group of item keys, requiring $\sqrt{N} - 1$ comparisons. There are $N - 1$ items left to be sorted, so that

$$c_o = (N - 1)(\sqrt{N} - 1 + \sqrt{N} - 1) \quad \text{(A.3.53)}$$

$$= (N - 1)(2\sqrt{N} - 2) \quad \text{(A.3.54)}$$

But

$$C = c_p + c_o \quad \text{(A.3.55)}$$

$$= N - 1 + (N - 1)(2\sqrt{N} - 2) \quad \text{(A.3.56)}$$

$$= (N - 1)(2\sqrt{N} - 1) \quad \text{(A.3.57)}$$

There is one preliminary pass and $N - 1$ filing passes, so that with each pass covering $\sqrt{N}$ items,

$$P = N \quad \text{(A.3.58)}$$

Each item file is transferred first into a control register and then to the master (which might be the proper position in the new file). Also, a code word must be substituted for each withdrawn item. Then,

$$T = 3N \quad \text{(A.3.59)}$$

Space for the new file (N) and control registers ($\sqrt{N}$) is needed.

$$S = N + \sqrt{N} \quad \text{(A.3.60)}$$

Sample	C = 1881	P = 100	T = 300	S = 110

Quadratic selection preceded by group sorting using linear selection and exchanging

To arrange in order each group of $\sqrt{N}$ items requires, using Eq. (A.3.44), $(N - \sqrt{N})/2$ comparisons. There are $\sqrt{N}$ groups, so that

$$c_p = \frac{\sqrt{N}(N - \sqrt{N})}{2} = \frac{N(\sqrt{N} - 1)}{2} \quad \text{(A.3.61)}$$

where c_p is the number of comparisons to arrange the $\sqrt{N}$ items in each of the $\sqrt{N}$ groups.

Each of the control registers can be filled directly from the groups now. Each time the control register is reviewed for each new item to be sorted, $\sqrt{N} - 1$ comparisons are made.

Then, for the N items to be filed,

$$c_o = N(\sqrt{N} - 1) \quad \text{(A.3.62)}$$

Then

$$C = c_p + c_o$$
$$= \frac{N(\sqrt{N} - 1)}{2} + N(\sqrt{N} - 1) \qquad (A.3.63)$$

and

$$C = \frac{3N(\sqrt{N} - 1)}{2} \qquad (A.3.64)$$

The number of exchanges to sort each group using Eq. (A.3.50) are $\sqrt{N} - 1$; for the $\sqrt{N}$ groups there are then $N - \sqrt{N}$ exchanges, so that

$$E_p = N - \sqrt{N} \qquad (A.3.65)$$

and

$$T_p = 2(N - \sqrt{N}) \qquad (A.3.66)$$

There are N transfers to fill the control registers and N transfers to fill the file, so that

$$T = N + N + 2N - 2\sqrt{N}$$
$$= 4N - 2\sqrt{N} \qquad (A.3.67)$$

The formula for space given by (A.3.60) is applied here and is

$$S = N + \sqrt{N} \qquad (A.3.68)$$

There are $\sqrt{N} - 1$ passes for $\sqrt{N}$ groups of $\sqrt{N}$ items each, and there are N passes of $\sqrt{N} + 1$ items, so that

$$P = 2N - \sqrt{N} \qquad (A.3.69)$$

But fewer items are covered in each pass than are covered in a pass for quadratic selection.

Sample	C = 1350	T = 380	P = 190	S = 110

Straight two-way merge

The first pass forms groups of twos; the second pass, groups of fours; the kth pass, groups of 2^K. When $N \leq 2^K$, sorting is completed. Hence

$$P = [\log_2 N] \qquad (A.3.70)$$

where the square brackets, [ ], indicate the next *larger* integer. For each item, one comparison and one transfer is made during each pass. Hence

$$C = NP = N[\log_2 N] \qquad (A.3.71)$$

and

$$T = NP = N[\log_2 N] \qquad (A.3.72)$$

For the straight sort, the receiving areas never need to be larger than $N/2$ except on the last run; for the last run, two areas can be combined. Four areas of size $N/2$ are needed—two sending and two receiving.†

$$S = 2N \tag{A.3.73}$$

Sample $[\log_2 100] = 7$	$P = 7$	$C = 700$	
$T = 700$	$S = 200$		

Natural two-way merge

It can be shown that the number of passes is reduced by about one if the first merging pass combines the items using natural groups instead of arbitrarily taking two at a time. Then

$$P = [\log_2 N] - 1 \tag{A.3.74}$$

But now for each item, during each pass, two comparisons and one transfer are required. The extra comparison determines whether a single or double stepdown condition exists. Then

$$C = 2NP = 2N([\log_2 N] - 1) \tag{A.3.75}$$

and

$$T = NP = N([\log_2 N] - 1) \tag{A.3.76}$$

Since it is possible in passes before the last to have more than $N/2$ items in a receiving area, four areas of N words must be provided, so that

$$S = 4N \tag{A.3.77}$$

Sample $[\log_2 100] - 1 = 6$	$P = 6$	
$C = 1200$	$T = 600$	$S = 400$

Straight three-way merge

These formulas are comparble to those for the straight two-way merge with 3 (the number of ways) used for the logartithmic base instead of 2. Each item must be compared with two other items before filing, except when one or more groups are exhausted. If these are neglected, then

$$P = [\log_3 N] \tag{A.3.78}$$

$$C = 2NP = 2N[\log_3 N] \tag{A.3.79}$$

†Equation (A.3.73) may be reduced to $S = 1.5N$ if we resort to a more complicated program which feeds the output string into the space left by the withdrawal of items from the input area, as suggested by D.A. Bell in "The Principles of Sorting," *British Computer J. 1* (July, 1958), pp. 71–77.

$$T = NP = N[\log_3 N] \tag{A.3.80}$$

$$S = 2 \times 3 \times \left(\frac{N}{3}\right) = 2N \tag{A.3.81}$$

Sample	$[\log_3 100] = 5$	$P = 5$	
	$C = 100$	$T = 500$	$S = 200$

Straight K-way merge

Extending the formulas for the straight three-way merge, we have

$$P = [\log_k N] \tag{A.3.82}$$

$$C = (k - 1)NP = (k - 1)N[\log_k N] \tag{A.3.83}$$

$$T = NP = N[\log_k N] \tag{A.3.84}$$

$$S = 2N \tag{A.3.85}$$

Sample	$k = 5$	$[\log_5 100] = 3$		
	$P = 3$	$C = 1200$	$T = 300$	$D = 200$

Straight K-way merge with K-way comparison box

The formulas for the straight *k*-way merge prevail, except that only one comparison per item per pass is necessary; hence

$$P = [\log_k N] \tag{A.3.86}$$

$$C = NP = N[\log_k N] \tag{A.3.87}$$

$$T = NP = N[\log_k N] \tag{A.3.88}$$

$$S = 2N \tag{A.3.89}$$

Sample	$k = 5$	$[\log_5 100] = 3$		
	$P = 3$	$C = 300$	$T = 300$	$S = 200$

Address calculation

As determined elsewhere† for a space ratio of 2.5:1, the following approximations hold:

$$P = 1 \tag{A.3.90}$$

$$C = 1.33N \tag{A.3.91}$$

†See Ivan Flores, "Computing time for address calculation sorting," *J. Assoc. Comput. Mach.* 7 (1960), pp. 389–409.

$$T = 1.66N \tag{A.3.92}$$

$$S = 2.5N \tag{A.3.93}$$

Sample	P = 1	C = 133	T = 166	S = 250

A.4 COMPARISON AND EVALUATION

In this section, we will evaluate the available methods for internal sorting in terms of the reasons for sorting and the characteristics of the computer being used.

Reason for sorting

The usual reason for sorting records is to transfer of "post" information from one record to another. The records correspond with respect to their keys, which might represent the employee number or item number. The record into which information is placed or where it is altered is called the *master;* the record from which the altering information is taken is called the *source*; simply stated, the source is posted to the master.

One way to do this is to search the master file for each record to be posted. This becomes excessively long for long master files. If the sources are ordered in the same sequence in the masters, before posting is done, the master file need be reviewed only once.

The question arises whether the sources are *ordered and then posted* within the computer or whether they are *ordered and then written out and later posted.*

Several other points must be considered before a sorting method for a given internal sorting job can be chosen.

Considerations

MEMORY SIZE

Since sorting takes place wholly within the computer, the size of its memory is of importance. Current computers use a fixed addressing structure which usually necessitates a fixed word length computer. The memory is therefore described in terms of word lengths.

Very small describes the memory of the very smallest computers, less than 2000 words.

Small describes the memory of some current small computers, 2000–10,000 words.

Medium is used for memories from 25,000 to 100,000 words.

Large is applied to memories storing more than 150,000 words, often running into the millions.

RECORD SIZE

The record consists of the *key* upon which ordering is based and the *fact* containing the information variable from record to record. The size of the record dictates the amount of manipulation which is economical in sorting the record.

Small records are one word long.

Medium records are between two and ten words long.

Large records exceed ten words but are usually less than one hundred.

INPUT/OUTPUT

All information must be entered into the computer from the outside and transmitted from the computer to the outside. This operation is a constant for a given problem, computer, and input/output equipment; hence, it has been eliminated from this comparison. It is assumed that the information is in the computer and stays there during the sorting operation.

The question of sorting from IO media arises, especially when the source file exceeds the capacity of internal storage. This is beyond the scope of this appendix but should provide some avid researcher with a juicy morsel, and with meaty applications too.

BUFFERS

The amount of information which can be accumulated before processing and after processing is determined by the buffer size. This capacity may be rated in terms of the record size.

A small buffer holds less than a record (but at least one word).

A single record buffer holds one record.

A large buffer holds at least two or more records.

RECORD MANIPULATION

This applies to the phases of the sorting procedure, if any, during which the key and the fact are separated.

Full record sort does not ever separate key and fact.

Key-separated internal sort sorts the key first but then orders the full record.

Key-separated output sort separates the keys and sorts them only; the records appear in order only when written into the output medium. The records are not in order in storage.

POSTING RATIO

This is the ratio of source records to master records.

A high posting ratio exists in such jobs as labor distribution, where there are several labor charges for each account.

A unity posting ratio applies to the payroll, where there is one time card for each employee.

A low posting ratio occurs in inventory operations, where only a few items are active during the posting period.

POSTING PROCEDURE

Several methods are available to get information from the source record.

Random Posting. If the computer memory is large enough to store all the master records, it is very effective to store them in order in the machine permanently. Posting can be done on a random basis: Source records are entered singly into a work area; the proper master record is found using a suitable address scheme; the master is updated; the proper output write-outs are made through the buffer. Sorting is not necessary here except in the original setup of the file and for making additions and deletions to the file. The latter is often best done by specialized methods such as double selection discussed later.

Ordered Input Posting. The system often encountered for posting requires that both the master file and the source file be in order. The first source record is read into the computer; master records are read and transcribed to the new master output medium until the record corresponding to the source record is found; posting is done and the new updated record transcribed when fully updated. Since the master records are produced in order at each posting period, it is never necessary to sort them (except initially). It is necessary to sort the source record, and this may be done by one of the internal methods described earlier or by external means such as tabulating card sorters.

Posting From Memory. If the sorting of the source records is done in the memory, an advantage is found in posting directly from the memory. This saves a writing-out process and a reading-in process. The source records are read in only once and then sorted by one of the methods discussed earlier; sorting of only keys may be done. The master records are then read one at a time and transcribed until one with a key corresponding to the first source key is found. It is entered into working storage. If *keys-only* sorting is used, the key has with it the address of the source record. The latter is looked up and posted. The master record is written out together with any other report documents. This method has not been sufficiently exploited in commercial computer applications.

Analysis of available methods and procedures

This section discusses the overall procedure for sorting within the computer with regard to the applicable methods and the characteristics of both the computer and the data.

IMMEDIATE SORTING—FROM BUFFER TO DESTINATION

After the record is entered into the input buffer, its place in the file in storage is determined by the computer, and the whole record is transferred there. Since the record must be moved from the buffer to some storage location, it is a saving if it can be put immediately into the proper place. Naturally, this procedure cannot be used if the buffer does not hold at least a full record. The only two methods previously considered, which are usable for immediate sorting, are insertion and address calculation.

Insertion requires the frequent moving of many complete records; this is not satisfactory when the record is medium or large and is inefficient even for small records.

Address calculation requires knowledge of the distribution of the keys and advance warning of the number of items to be sorted. Optimum speed is obtained when the file area is about 2.4 times the number of records.

TEMPORARY STORAGE, FULL RECORD SORT

This procedure has all the disadvantages of the above, and, in addition, requires an extra transfer and storage cycle. It might be useful only for machines with less than one word of buffer storage.

RECORD STORED, KEYS SORTED

If the keys only are to be sorted, they must all be available before the sort starts. The address of the fact associated with the key is stored in the "key" word and transported along with the key during sorting.

Full record transfer into the proper order is not necessary whether the records are posted before write-out or written directly into the output medium.

No record transfer is then the most economical procedure for sorting if separation of keys from facts is allowed.

KEY SORT ONLY, NO RECORD TRANSFER

All of the methods discussed and flow-charted earlier could now be used. It is then possible to choose one for either least time or least space. It is assumed that the key and the record address together occupy only one word. This word must be composed and then sorted in a separate work area. The minimum space required for the work is N words—one for each record.

Insertion requires only N words of working storage and is the most efficient method meeting this space requirement. Binary insertion is most efficient, with central insertion being more efficient than straight insertion.

Address calculation, as in other cases, requires the least amount of word manipulations and is recommedned provided knowledge is available about the distribution and number of source records.

Internal merge sorting is an alternate to address calculation when sufficient distribution or quantity information is not available. Space is conserved if extreme distribution is used.

Presorted quadratic selection is sometimes more efficient than merging, especially for small values of N. Depending upon the computer, either one may turn out to be simpler to program.

Conclusions

The following statements may be made about internal computer sorting:

1. The size of the input/output buffer does not affect the choice of a sorting method.
2. The posting ratio does not affect the choice of an internal sorting method.
3. There are no advantages to sorting the complete record after the key alone has been sorted, unless the information is going to be permanently stored in the memory; extra time and space is required for such a manipulation. A record may be posted by first finding the sorted key and, using the address (listed there), then finding the record to be posted from or to be posted to. Sequential readout is done by writing into the output medium from the addresses associated with the sorted keys.
4. The immediate transfer of a record from the buffer to the proper place in the file is practical in only two cases: (a) for address calculation for records that are small or medium and where a space of abut $2.4N$ is available, and for large records when even more space is available;

Table A.4.1 PARAMETERS FOR VARIOUS KINDS OF SORTING WHERE THE KEY OF THE RECORD ONLY IS SORTED. $N = 100$ FOR SAMPLE CALCULATION.

Kind of Sort	*Space*		*Passes*		*Comparisons*		*Transfers*		*Remarks*
	Formula	*Sample*	*Formula*	*Sample*	*Formula*	*Sample*	*Formula*	*Sample*	
Insertion, straight	N	100	$N - 1$	99	$(N^2 - N)/4$	2500	$(N^2 - N)/2$	5000	
Insertion, centered	N	100	$N - 1$	99	$(N^2 - N)/8$	1250	$(N^2 - N)/4$	2500	
Insertion, binary	N	100	$N - 1$	99	$N \log_2 (N/e)$	520	$(N^2 - N)/4$	2500	Program complicated
Counting	$2N$	200	$N - 1$	99	$(N^2 - N)/2$	5000	$(N^2 - N)/2$	5000	Additions, not compares given
Digital	BN	1000	$D + 1$	3	DN	200	$(D + 1)N$	300	
Selection, linear	N	100	N	100	$N^2 - N$	9801	N	100	
Selection, linear with exchange	N	100	$N - 1$	99	$(N^2 - N)/2$	4550	$2N - 2$	148	
Selection, quadratic	$N + \sqrt{N}$	110	N	100	$(N - 1) \times (2\sqrt{N} - 1)$	1881	$3N$	300	
Selection, quadratic with group sorting	$N + \sqrt{N}$	110	$2N - \sqrt{N}$	190	$3N(\sqrt{N} - 1)/2$	1350	$4N - 2\sqrt{N}$	380	
Merge, straight 2-way	$2N$	200	$[\log_2 N]$	7	$N[\log_2 N]$	700	$N[\log_2 N]$	700	
Merge, natural 2-way	$2N$	200	$[\log_2 N] - 1$	6	$2N[\log_2 N] - 1$	1200	$N[\log_2 N] - N$	600	
Merge, straight 3-way	$2N$	200	$[\log_3 N]$	5	$2N[\log_3 N]$	1000	$N[\log_3 N]$	500	
Merge, straight k-way	$2N$	200	$[\log_k N]$	3	$\{(k - 1)N\} \times [\log_k N]$	1200	$N[\log_k N]$	300	$k = 5$ for sample
Merge, straight k-way with k compare box	$2N$	200	$[\log_k N]$	3	$N[\log_k N]$	300	$N[\log_k N]$	300	$k = 5$ for sample
Address calculation	$2.5N$	250	1	1	$1.33N$	133	$1.66N$	166	

and (b) for insertion where space is at a premium (only N spaces of working storage available) and where inefficient manipulation can be tolerated.

5. The memory must be able to hold all the records to be sorted, must have the working storage required by the method chosen, and must have space for the internally stored program.
6. The method of storing the record randomly as received and then sorting the key only may use any of the sorting procedures described. Some of these may offer advantages, depending upon the parameters that are most important for the problem under consideration. In Table A.4.1, the formulas and a sample problem with $N = 100$ are presented so that an assessment of the methods can be made quickly.

A.5 SUMMARY

1. The majority of internal computer sorting procedures have been described and flow-charted.
2. Time calculations have been made for each sorting procedure.
3. A chart and sample calculations have been made for time and space calculations for each key-separate sorting method; see Table A.4.1.
4. Each of the computer characteristics that affects the choice of a sorting method has been discussed.
5. Posting procedures have been examined.

B POLYPHASE SORT THEOREM PROOFS†

Theorem 1

Given the basic assignment B_a with $B_{aK} = 0$, then $(L^i B_a)_{K-i} = 0$ for $a \geq K > i > 0$.

It is true for $i = 1$ since, by definition,

$$B_{a,K-1} = C_{a,K-1} = \lambda B_a \tag{B.1.1}$$

Hence

$$(L\,B_a)_{K-1} = |B_{a,K-1} - \lambda B_a| = |B_{a,K-1} - B_{a,K-1}| = 0 \tag{B.1.2}$$

The minimum of $L\,B_a$ is in the position of the next-to-the-minimum of B_a; hence

$$\lambda L'\,B_a = (L\,B_a)_{K-2} \tag{B.1.3}$$

and

$$(L^2\,B_a)_{K-2} = |(L\,B_a)_{K-2} - \lambda L\,B_a| = 0 \tag{B.1.4}$$

Generally, the minimum of $L^{i-1}\,B_a$ is in the $(i-1)$th minimum position of B_a for $i < K$. Hence

$$\lambda L^{i-1}\,B_a = (L^{i-1}\,B_a)_{K-i} \tag{B.1.5}$$

Therefore we have

$$(L^i\,B_a)_{K-1} = |(L^{i-1}\,B_a)_{K-i} - \lambda L^{i-1}\,B_a| \tag{B.1.6}$$

$$= 0 \tag{B.1.7}$$

†Theorems are numbered as they appear in Chapter 10 and in Appendix heretofore.

Theorem 2

Given the basic assignment B_a, then $L^i B_a = \Lambda^i B_{a-1}$ for $a \geq K > i > 0$. From (B.1.2) and (10.1.12) we have

$$(\mathrm{L\ B_a})_\beta = \mathrm{C}_{a-1,\beta-1} \quad \text{(B.2.1)}$$

From (10.3.1) we have

$$\mathrm{B}_{a-1}\text{:}\quad \mathrm{B}_{a-1,\beta} = \mathrm{C}_{a-1,\beta} \quad \text{(B.2.2)}$$

But from the property of Λ, we have

$$\Lambda\ \mathrm{B}_{a-1}\text{:}\quad \mathrm{B}_{a-1,\beta} = \mathrm{C}_{a-1,\beta-1} \quad \text{(B.2.3)}$$

Then from (B.2.1) and (B.2.3)

$$(\mathrm{L\ B_a})_\beta = (\Lambda\ \mathrm{B}_{a-1})_\beta \quad \text{(B.2.4)}$$

Hence

$$\mathrm{L\ B_a} = \Lambda\ \mathrm{B}_{a-1} \quad \text{(B.2.5)}$$

Repeating this reasoning, it is obvious that

$$\mathrm{L^i\ B_a} = \Lambda^{\mathrm{i}}\ \mathrm{B}_{a-\mathrm{i}}; \qquad \mathrm{i} < \mathrm{K} \quad \text{(B.2.6)}$$

Theorem 3

Given the basic assignment B_a, then $L^i B_a = \Lambda^m B_{a-i}$, where $m \equiv i \pmod{K}$ and $a \geq K > 1$.

From the method used in Theorem 2, it is easy to show that

$$\mathrm{L^K\ B_a} = \Lambda^{\mathrm{K}}\ \mathrm{B}_{a-\mathrm{K}} = \mathrm{B}_{a-\mathrm{K}} \quad \text{(B.3.1)}$$

because Λ is of order K; therefore

$$\Lambda^{\mathrm{K}} = \mathrm{I} = \Lambda^{\mathrm{rK}} \quad \text{(B.3.2)}$$

where I is the identity operator, and r is an integer.

Similarly, we may show that

$$\mathrm{L^{rK}\ B_a} = \Lambda^{\mathrm{rK}}\ \mathrm{B}_{a-\mathrm{rK}} = \mathrm{B}_{a-\mathrm{rK}} \quad \text{(B.3.3)}$$

Now suppose $i > K$ so that

$$\mathrm{i} = \mathrm{rK} + \mathrm{m} \quad \text{(B.3.4)}$$

Then

$$\mathrm{L^i\ B_a} = \mathrm{L^{rK+m}\ B_a} \quad \text{(B.3.5)}$$

$$= \mathrm{L^m\ L^{rK}\ B_a} \quad \text{(B.3.6)}$$

$$= \mathrm{L^m}\ (\Lambda^{\mathrm{rK}}\ \mathrm{B}_{a-\mathrm{rK}}) \quad \text{(B.3.7)}$$

$$= \mathrm{L^m}\ (\mathrm{I\ B}_{a-\mathrm{rK}}) \quad \text{(B.3.8)}$$

$$= \mathrm{L}^{\mathrm{m}}\, \mathrm{B}_{\mathrm{a-rK}} \tag{B.3.9}$$

$$= \Lambda^{\mathrm{m}}\, \mathrm{B}_{\mathrm{a-rK-m}} \tag{B.3.10}$$

$$= \Lambda^{\mathrm{m}}\, \mathrm{B}_{\mathrm{a-i}} \tag{B.3.11}$$

Theorem 4

$\prod K^B NK+1$ constitute all assignments of the *perfect* numbers at level $NK+1$ for which device K receives.

Consider some specific π of $\prod_K$ which reassigns $B_{a\beta}$, $\beta \neq K$, but leaves $B_{aK}=0$. This is called $\pi\, B_a$. On level $a-1$, we have $\mathrm{L}(\pi\, B_a)$. Here $a = NK+1$. At level 1 we have $L^{NK}(\pi\, B_a)$. But L^{NK} reduces to Λ^{NK} with B_a changed to B_{a-NK}. This is so regardless of the presence of π. Hence,

$$\mathrm{L}^{\mathrm{NK}}(\pi\, \mathrm{B_a}) = \Lambda^{\mathrm{NK}}\, \pi\, \mathrm{B}_{\mathrm{a-NK}} \tag{B.4.1}$$

But

$$\Lambda^{\mathrm{NK}} = \mathrm{I} \tag{B.4.2}$$

hence

$$\mathrm{L}^{\mathrm{NK}}\, \pi\, \mathrm{B_a} = \mathrm{I}\, \pi\, \mathrm{B_1} \tag{B.4.3}$$

$$= \pi\, \mathrm{B_1} \tag{B.4.4}$$

Since $(\pi\, B_1)_K = 0$, $T_R = T_K$.

Next, suppose we have $\rho \notin \prod_K$ where ρ alters (T_K). For $\rho\, B_a$ we have

$$\mathrm{L}^{\mathrm{NK}}(\rho\, \mathrm{B_a}) = \Lambda^{\mathrm{NK}}\, \rho\, \mathrm{B}_{\mathrm{a-NK}} \tag{B.4.5}$$

$$= \mathrm{I}\, \rho\, \mathrm{B_1} \tag{B.4.6}$$

$$= \rho\, \mathrm{B_1} \tag{B.4.7}$$

But ρ alters (T_K) and hence $(\rho\, B_1)_K \neq 0$ so that $T_R \neq T_K$.

Theorem 5

$\Delta J^B NK+1$ constitute all assignments of *perfect* numbers at level $NK+1$ for which $T_R = T_J$.

Consider a specific δ_J at level $NK+1$. We have

$$\mathrm{L}^{\mathrm{NK}}\, \delta_{\mathrm{J}}\, \mathrm{B_a} = \Lambda^{\mathrm{NK}}\, \delta_{\mathrm{J}}\, \mathrm{B}_{\mathrm{a-NK}} \tag{B.5.1}$$

But

$$\Lambda^{\mathrm{NK}} = \mathrm{I} \tag{B.5.2}$$

$$\mathrm{L}^{\mathrm{NK}}\, \delta_{\mathrm{J}}\, \mathrm{B_a} = \mathrm{I}\, \delta_{\mathrm{J}}\, \mathrm{B_1} = \delta_{\mathrm{J}}\, \mathrm{B_1} \tag{B.5.3}$$

Now $\delta_J\, B_1$ assigns 1 to all T's except T_J. When L is applied to $\delta_J\, B_1$, all T's (other than T_J) are merged onto T_J.

Next consider some $M \neq J$. For M we have

$$\mathrm{L}^{\mathrm{NK}}\, \delta_{\mathrm{M}}\, \mathrm{B}_{\mathrm{a}} = \Lambda^{\mathrm{NK}}\, \delta_{\mathrm{M}}\, \mathrm{B}_{\mathrm{a-NK}} \tag{B.5.4}$$

$$= \mathrm{I}\, \delta_{\mathrm{M}}\, \mathrm{B}_1 = \delta_{\mathrm{M}}\, \mathrm{B} \tag{B.5.5}$$

When L is applied to $\delta_M B_1$, T_M becomes the receiving unit. But

$$\Delta_{\mathrm{J}} \cup \Delta_1 \cup \Delta_2 \cup \cdots \cup \Delta_{\mathrm{K}} = \bigcup_{\mathrm{I}=1}^{\mathrm{K}} \Delta_{\mathrm{I}} \tag{B.5.6}$$

and (B.5.6) represents all the permutations possible upon B_a. Of these, only Δ_J satisfies the requirement of the theorem.

Theorem 6

The C_a's are all odd for $a = NK$; otherwise, for $a = NK + b$, only C_{K+1-b} is odd and the others are even.

The C's are all 1 at level 1, so we have

$$\mathrm{C}_{1\beta} = 1 \equiv 1 \pmod 2 \tag{B.6.1}$$

The upwards recursive expressions for $C_{1\beta}$ are

$$\mathrm{C}_{\mathrm{i,k}} = \mathrm{C}_{\mathrm{i-1,1}} \tag{B.6.2}$$

and

$$\mathrm{C}_{\mathrm{i},\beta} = \mathrm{C}_{\mathrm{i-1},\beta-1} + \mathrm{C}_{\mathrm{i-1,1}} \tag{B.6.3}$$

from which

$$\mathrm{C}_{2,\mathrm{k}} \equiv 1 \pmod 2 \tag{B.6.4}$$

and

$$\mathrm{C}_{2,\beta} = \mathrm{C}_{1,\beta-1} + \mathrm{C}_{1,1} = 1 + 1 \equiv 0 \pmod 2, \qquad \beta \neq \mathrm{k} \tag{B.6.5}$$

We continue by applying (B.6.2) and (B.6.3) to (B.6.4), and (B.6.5)

$$\mathrm{C}_{3,\mathrm{k}-1} \equiv 1 \pmod 2 \tag{B.6.6}$$

$$\mathrm{C}_{3,\beta} \equiv 0 \pmod 2; \qquad \beta \neq \mathrm{k} - 1 \tag{B.6.7}$$

and, in general,

$$\mathrm{C}_{\mathrm{j+1,k-j+1}} \equiv 1 \pmod 2; \qquad 1 \leq \mathrm{j} \leq \mathrm{k} \tag{B.6.8}$$

$$\mathrm{C}_{\mathrm{i+1},\beta} \equiv 0 \pmod 2; \qquad \beta \neq \mathrm{k} - \mathrm{j} + 1 \tag{B.6.9}$$

Examine, now, the case where j reaches $k + 1$; (B.6.8) becomes

$$\mathrm{C}_{\mathrm{k+1,1}} \equiv 1 \pmod 2 \tag{B.6.10}$$

so that, from applying (B.6.8) to (B.6.10) we have

$$\mathrm{C}_{\mathrm{k+2,k}} \equiv 1 \pmod 2 \tag{B.6.11}$$

And from (B.6.3)

$$\mathrm{C}_{\mathrm{k+2},\beta} = \mathrm{C}_{\mathrm{k+1},\beta-1} + \mathrm{C}_{\mathrm{k+1,1}} \equiv 0 + 1 \equiv 1 \pmod 2; \qquad \beta \neq \mathrm{k} \tag{B.6.12}$$

so that at level $k + 2$, all C's are odd.

The theorem is now proved by induction. Call

$$M = N(k+1) + 1 + b \tag{B.6.13}$$

We have shown it true for $N = 1$ and 2; assume it true for $N = a$. By the reasoning of (B.6.4) through (B.6.12), we find from (B.6.13)

$$C_{M, k-b+1} \equiv 1 \pmod 2, \quad b \neq 0 \tag{B.6.14}$$

$$C_{M,\beta} \equiv 0 \pmod 2, \quad b \neq 0; \quad \beta \neq k - b + 1 \tag{B.6.15}$$

$$C_{M,\beta} \equiv 1 \pmod 2, \quad b = 0; \quad 1 \leq \beta \leq k \tag{B.6.16}$$

Since (B.6.14), (B.6.15), and (B.6.16) restate the theorem, this is a proof thereof.

Theorem 7A

For B_a with $a = NK + 1$, $(L^j B_a)_K \equiv 1 \pmod 2$ for all $j \leq NK$, $j = nK$. We have

$$B_{aK} = 0 \tag{B.7.1}$$

and

$$L\, B_a = \Lambda\, B_{a-1} \tag{B.7.2}$$

for which we have, by Theorem 6,

$$(L\, B_a)_k = (\Lambda\, B_{a-1})_k = C_{a-1,1} \equiv 1 \pmod 2 \tag{B.7.3}$$

Similarly,

$$(L^2\, B_a)_k = (\Lambda^2\, B_{\alpha-2})_k = C_{a-2,2} \equiv 1 \pmod 2 \tag{B.7.4}$$

and, in general, for $j = nK$

$$(L^j\, B_a)_k = (\Lambda^j\, B_{\alpha-j})_k = C_{a-j,j} \equiv 1 \pmod 2 \tag{B.7.5}$$

Theorem 7B

An assignement $\mu_K B_a$ with $a \neq NK + 1$ results in $T_R = T_K$. Let $a = NK + 1 + b$. Then from Theorems 6 and 7A, we have

$$(L^b\, \mu_K\, B_a)_K = (\Lambda^b\, \mu_K\, B_{a-b})_K \tag{B.7.6}$$

$$= (\Lambda^b\, \mu_K\, B_{NK+1})_K \tag{B.7.7}$$

$$= B_{NK+1, K} = 0 \tag{B.7.8}$$

Hence

$$(L^{a-1}\, \mu_K\, B_a)_K = (L^{NK}\, L^b\, \mu_K\, B_a)_K \tag{B.7.9}$$

$$= L^{NK}\, B_{NK+1, K} \tag{B.7.10}$$

$$= B_{1, K} \tag{B.7.11}$$

$$= 0 \tag{B.7.12}$$

Theorem 8

$T_R = T_J$ if and only if $M_J B_a$ for $a \neq NK + 1$ or $\Delta_J\, B_a$ for $a = NK + 1$.

M_J consists of $p_{K-1}^{K-1} = (K-1)!$ permutation operators μ_J. Similarly, there are $(K-1)!$ operators δ_J in the class Δ_J. It is asserted that each δ_J corresponds to exactly one μ_J. Through the relation

$$\mu_J\, B_{i,\beta} = L^m\, \delta_J\, B_{i+m,\beta}; \qquad i + m \equiv 1 \pmod{k} \tag{B.8.1}$$

we have

$$L^m\, \delta_J\, B_{i+m} = \delta_J\, \Lambda^m B_i \tag{B.8.2}$$

Hence, given a μ_J, there corresponds a δ_J, such that (B.8.1) holds and is defined by

$$\delta_J = \Lambda^{-m}\, \mu_J \tag{B.8.3}$$

where Λ^{-1} is the unit rightwards circular permutation and

$$\Lambda^{-m} = (\Lambda^{-1})^m \tag{B.8.4}$$

Now, by Theorem 5, the assignment $\delta_J\, B_{i+m}$ leads to output on device J, and hence, so does the assignment $\mu_J\, B_i$ where μ_J is given by (B.8.3). Therefore, we state that $M_J B_a$, $a \neq NK + 1$ and $\Delta_J\, B_a$ for $a = NK + 1$ produce $T_R = T_J$.

Consider now any δ'_J with $J' \neq J$ for which

$$\delta'_J = \Lambda^{-m}\, \mu'_J \tag{B.8.5}$$

By the foregoing, $\mu'_J\, B_a$ for $a \neq NK + 1$ and δ'_J for $a = NK + 1$ produce $T_R = T'_J$. Call $\{\delta'_J\} = \Delta'_J$. Then $\Delta = \Delta_J \cup \Delta'_J$ comprise all permutations of order K; no $\delta'_J\, B_a$ with $\delta'_J \in \Delta'_J$ and $a = NK + 1$ produces $T_R = T_J$. It may be similarly argued that no $\mu'_J\, B_a$, $\mu'_J \in M_J$, and $a \neq NK + 1$ produces $T_R = T_J$, proving the theorem.

Theorem 9

The width at pass p, W_p, is given by

$$W_p = N_p \tag{B.9.1}$$

Consider the individual nonzero widths (subscripts) after pass p for device β, and call it $W_{p\beta}$. We have

$$W_{o\beta} = 1 \tag{B.9.2}$$

Define

$$W_p = \sum_{\beta=1}^{k} W_{p\beta} \tag{B.9.3}$$

Make the replacement

$$W_{p\beta}: \quad W_p \longrightarrow \lambda W_{p-1,\beta}$$
$$W: \quad W_{p-1,\beta} \longrightarrow W_{p-1,\beta}\,(W_{p-1,\beta} = \lambda W_{p-1,\beta}) \tag{B.9.4}$$

Then we have

$$W_1 = \sum_1^k 1 = k \tag{B.9.5}$$

$$W_2 = \sum_1^{k-1} 1 + W_1 = k + k - 1 \tag{B.9.6}$$

and, in general,

$$W_p = \sum_{i=0}^{k-1} (k-1) f_{p-k-i} \tag{B.9.7}$$

$$= N_p \tag{B.9.8}$$

Theorem 10

The volume of US's passed on a polyphase sort is given by

$$V = \sum f_{k+i-1} N_{a-i} \tag{B.10.1}$$

By making a substitution, we have

$$V = \sum_{p=1}^{a} f_{a-p+k-1} N_p \tag{B.10.2}$$

Make the substitution

$$p = a - i \tag{B.10.3}$$

with i the variable subscript. After changing the limits of summation, we have

$$V = \sum_{i=0}^{a-1} f_{k+i-1} N_{a-i} \tag{B.10.4}$$

Theorem 11

The jth k-generalized Fibonacci number is approximated by

$$f_{j,k} \doteq r_k^{j-k} \tag{B.11.1}$$

The definition of $f_{j,k}$ is given as

$$f_{j,k} = \sum_{i=1}^{k} f_{j-i,k} \tag{B.11.2}$$

Miles [7] and Flores [8] postulate that each f is a combination of k terms, each containing constant factors $r_{i,\kappa}$ raised to a power. It is further to be shown that $k - 1$ of these r's are negligible. First define

$$f_{j,k} = b_1 r^j_{1,k} + b_2 r^j_{2,k} + \cdots + b_k r^j_{k,k} \tag{B.11.3}$$

If this is so, then the *k* defining equation can be shown to reduce to

$$q^n = q^{n-1} + q^{n-2} + \cdots + q^{n-k} \tag{B.11.4}$$

which, in turn, reduces to

$$q^k - q^{k-1} - q^{k-2} - \cdots - 1 = 0 \tag{B.11.5}$$

or

$$q^k - \sum_{i=1}^{k} q^{k-i} = 0 \tag{B.11.6}$$

There are *k* roots for (B.11.6) which we label $r_{1,k} \cdots r_{k,k}$. For these roots, Miles [7] demonstrates

$$|r_{jk}| < 1 \qquad \text{for} \quad 1 \leq j < k \tag{B.11.7}$$

$$1 \leq r_{kk} < 2 \tag{B.11.8}$$

He sets up the boundary conditions for the *b*'s of (B.11.3),

$$\sum_{i=1}^{k} b_i r^m_{i,k} = 0; \qquad m = 1, 2, \ldots, k-2 \tag{B.11.9}$$

$$\sum_{i=1}^{k} b_i r^{m-1}_{i,k} = 1 \tag{B.11.10}$$

When the Vandermonde determinant to (B.11.9) and (B.11.10) is solved and the limit taken, we find,

$$\lim_{j\to\infty} \frac{f_{j+1,k}}{f_{j,k}} = r_{kk} \tag{B.11.11}$$

Eliding the final *k* of $r_{k,k}$ and substituting (B.11.11) into (B.11.2), we find

$$f_j \doteq r_k^{j-k} \tag{B.11.12}$$

which becomes an equality when *j* becomes indefinitely large.

C POLYPHASE SORT, MISCELLANEOUS ITEMS

C.1 TOTAL EFFICIENCY

Let us find the total efficiency E_T and the total limiting efficiency E_{Tlim} in terms of V and V_B, the number of items passed in the balanced merge. Here

$$V_B = Nn \tag{C.1.1}$$

where

$$n = \log_{k/2} N \tag{C.1.2}$$

and

$$E_T = \frac{V_B}{V} \tag{C.1.3}$$

and

$$E_{Tlim} = \lim_{N \to \infty} E_T \tag{C.1.4}$$

From (C.1.9), (C.1.1), and (C.1.2), we have,

$$E_T = \frac{Nn}{N(1 + (a - 1)/r)} \tag{C.1.5}$$

$$= \frac{n}{(1 + (a - 1)/r)} \tag{C.1.6}$$

Rearranging,

$$E_T = \frac{rn}{(r + a - 1)} \tag{C.1.7}$$

Since $r - 1$ is always less than 1, then as N becomes large, a also becomes large, and $r - 1$ may be ignored in the denominator; therefore

$$E_{Tlim} = \frac{rn}{a} \tag{C.1.8}$$

$$= rE_{lim} \tag{C.1.9}$$

or, from (C.1.2)

$$E_{Tlim} = \frac{r}{\log_r (K/2)} \tag{C.1.10}$$

Notice that, for K of 8 or more, r is about 2, and (C.1.10) becomes

$$E_{Tlim} \longrightarrow \frac{2}{\log_2 (k/2)} \tag{C.1.11}$$

C.2 RATIONALE FOR EFFICIENCY

Polyphase is more efficient for small K's because the pass inefficiency is more than compensated for by the smaller number of items handled in the $a - 1$ passes, namely, N/r instead of N for the balanced merge.

The pass inefficiency is due to the sequence of N_a. In going up one level, we have

$$\frac{N_{a+1}}{N_a} \doteq \frac{Rr^{a-k-1}}{Rr^{a-k-2}} = r \tag{C.2.1}$$

so that we can handle only r more items at level $a + 1$.

For the balanced merge we have,

$$\frac{N_{n+1}}{N_n} = \frac{k}{2} \tag{C.2.2}$$

Since r is always smaller than $K/2$, more passes are required by polyphase; this is made up for by the N/r items handled on $a - 1$ of the a passes for K less than 8.

For larger K, r approaches 2. The number of items on each higher level for polyphase doubles; for balanced merge, it increases by $K/2$. This is no longer made up for by the $N/2$ items handled at the $a - 1$ levels by polyphase.

C.3 DISCUSSION

Polyphase has a definite advantage for three to seven devices. It is about equivalent to the balanced merge for eight units. Since a balanced merge can't be done with nine units, there is some advantage if *exactly* nine units are available. For ten or more units, there is a *decided* advantage to the balanced merge.

A universal sort program for a variable number of device configurations would work well over a span of three to nine units with polyphase, since it is so close to the balanced merge for eight and, otherwise, is superior.

Nonperfect numbers

When we are dealing with a number of US's which is not the sum of a set of perfect numbers, the volume transported depends mostly upon the intermediate dispersion procedure. An optimum procedure has not been described in the literature. This is certainly an area for further investigation.

Two points should now be made:

- The methods of this appendix are applicable to a nonprfect number of strings when a dispersion procedure is furnished.
- In the limit, for a near optimum procedure, these results should hold.

Since the latter statement is procedure-dependent, it is somewhat intuitive. However, practical measurements seem to indicate that, *for useful dispersion procedures for nonperfect numbers of strings, the volume transported is a* **monotonic** *function of* **N**.

C.4 FIBONACCI ROOTS

k	r_k	k	r_k
2	1.61803	9	1.99803
3	1.83929	10	1.99902
4	1.92756	11	1.99951
5	1.96595	12	1.99976
6	1.98358	13	1.99988
7	1.99196	14	1.99994
8	1.99601	15	1.99997

C.5 BIBLIOGRAPHY

1. "Polyphase merge sorting—an advanced technique," R. L. Gilstad. *Proc Joint E Comp Conf*, December 1960.
2. "A generalized polyphase sort algorithm," S. W. Reynolds. *Comm ACM*, Vol. 4, No. 8, August 1961, pp. 347–9.
3. "String distribution for the polyphase sort," W. D. Malcolm Jr. *Comm ACM*, Vol. 6, No. 5, May 1963, pp. 217–20.
4. "Read backward polyphase sorting," R. L. Gilstad. *Comm ACM*, Vol. 6, No. 5, May 1963, pp. 220–223.

5. "Analysis of internal computer sorting," Ivan Flores. *JACM*, Vol. 8, No. 1, January 1961, pp. 41–81.
6. *Fibonacci Numbers*, N.N. Vorob'ev. New York: Blaisdell Pub. Co., 1961, pp. 66. (Vol. 2 in Popular Lectures in Mathematics Series.)
7. "Generalized Fibonacci numbers and associated matrices," E. P. Miles Jr. *American Mathematics Monthly*, Vol. 67, October 1960, pp. 745–57.
8. "Direct calculation of *k*-generalized Fibonacci numbers," Ivan Flores. *Fibonacci Q.*, Vol. 5, No. 4, November 1967.

INDEX